Higher Physics

Jim Lowrie
Telford C

Alasta
Wester H

Oxford University Press

Oxford University Press, Great Clarendon Street, Oxford OX2 6DP

Oxford New York
Athens Auckland Bangkok Bogota Bombay
Buenos Aires Calcutta Cape Town Dar es Salaam Delhi
Florence Hong Kong Istanbul Karachi
Kuala Lumpur Madras Madrid Melbourne
Mexico City Nairobi Paris Singapore
Taipei Tokyo Toronto Warsaw

and associated companies in
Berlin Ibadan

Oxford is a trade mark of Oxford University Press

© Oxford University Press 1992

First published 1993
Reprinted 1984, 1985, 1988, 1989

Second edition 1992
Reprinted 1992 (twice), 1993, 1997

ISBN 0 19 914324 2

Cover illustration by
Colin Rattray.

Phototypeset by Tradespools Limited,
Frome, Somerset

Printed in Hong Kong

Preface to the 1992 edition

This new edition of *Higher Core Physics* covers all the objectives of the Revised Higher Grade syllabus issued by the Scottish Examination Board in 1990. The text has been extensively revised both to take account of the changed content of Standard Grade Physics and to include the developments in the subject that are now required by the curriculum. The book forms the basis of a supported study pack produced nationally.

Amongst the major changes, new chapters have been included on analogue electronics and on measurement and uncertainty. The chapter on optoelectronics brings together consideration of light radiation, photoelectric emission, lasers and the effect of photons on semiconductors. The early chapters on kinematics, dynamics and properties of matter as well as that on radioactivity have been extended to give more detail and to describe topics previously encountered at an earlier stage.

The practical nature of the course continues to be emphasized by frequent reference to experiments, to sample results and to worked examples that reinforce understanding of the issues raised in the laboratory. Each chapter concludes with a summary and an extensive set of problems, many of which are from past Higher Grade papers. The numerical answers to problems are at the end of the book and are our sole responsibility.

We would again like to express our appreciation to the many people who have assisted in this work, in particular to Lis Unsworth and Anne Smith for their help and advice, and to Ellice, Eleanor and Sylvia for their support and encouragement. We gratefully acknowledge permission granted by the Scottish Examination Board for allowing us to include questions from past papers and by those listed on page 219 for use of diagrams and photographs.

Geoff Cackett, Jim Lowrie, Alastair Steven
Edinburgh 1991

Preface to the 1983 edition

This book is written specifically for students preparing for Scottish Higher Grade Physics and takes full account of the revised syllabus to be first examined in 1984. The text is designed to equip students with understanding, basic knowledge and problem-solving skills required at this level.

The Higher Grade syllabus is an extension of and includes the work of the Ordinary Grade syllabus. This book was written on this basis and follows the same style as Core Physics (for Ordinary Grade) in dealing with all the objectives in sections N, O, P, and Q of the revised syllabus: the remaining section R is dealt with in memoranda from the Scottish Curriculum Development Service in Dundee.

Each chapter covers a particular topic of the syllabus with a full explanation. The practical nature of the course is emphasized by reference to many experiments with diagrams and photographs. Sample results are used to derive relationships and to help with understanding. Each chapter ends with a summary and problems, many of the problems being from past Higher Grade papers. Numerical answers to all problems have been provided; SI units are used throughout, other units being referred to only when they are in common use. The negative index notation for units has been used (e.g. $m\ s^{-1}$ rather than m/s) in accordance with examination requirements. 'Electron flow' current convention is used and conventional current is not used at all.

We should like to express our appreciation to the various people and establishments listed on page 208 for permission to reproduce drawings and photographs, and to the Scottish Examination Board for allowing us to include questions from past Higher Grade examination papers.

Finally, we should like to thank Ellice, Eleanor and Sylvia for their support and encouragement.

Geoff Cackett, Jim Lowrie, Alastair Steven
Edinburgh 1983

Contents

1 Kinematics

1.1 Distance and displacement

Distance has magnitude only and can be described in terms of a number and unit; for example, 10 metres. Such a quantity defined by a number and a unit is called a **scalar** quantity.

Displacement has magnitude and direction; for example, 10 m due West. This is a **vector** quantity which is defined by a number, a unit and a direction.

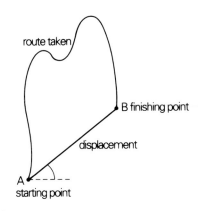

To illustrate the difference between distance and displacement, consider an object moving from point A taking an irregular route and ending up at point B, shown in Figure 1.1.

Figure 1.1

The displacement is the straight line path between the starting point A and the finishing point B.

The displacement can be represented by an arrow drawn in the direction of the displacement and of length proportional to the magnitude of the displacement. This arrow is called a **vector** and represents the vector quantity shown in Figure 1.2.

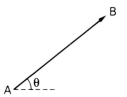

Figure 1.2

1.2 Resultant displacement

A person starts at A, crosses a pelican crossing to B and walks along the pavement to C.

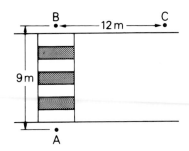

Figure 1.3

In going from A to C what is
a) the distance travelled
b) the resultant displacement?

a) distance travelled = (A to B) then (B to C)
$$= 9 + 12$$
$$= 21 \text{ m}$$
b) Drawing a scale diagram of the route allows the resultant displacement to be found.

If we choose 1 cm to represent 3 m the resultant displacement is found by measuring the length of AC and the angle BAC
AB = 9 m represented by 3 cm
BC = 12 m represented by 4 cm
by measurement length of AC = 5 cm
this represents 5 × 3 = 15 m
angle BAC = 53°
The resultant displacement is 15 m at an angle of 53° to direction AB

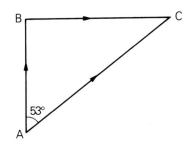

Figure 1.4

1

Example 1

A person starts walking into a maze, the direction of the first section being due North.

If the starting point is X, find the distance to point Y and also determine the displacement of Y from X.

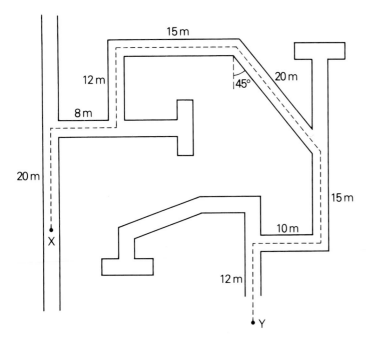

a) total distance walked = 20 + 8 + 12 + 15 + 20 + 15 + 10 + 12
$$= 112\,\text{m}$$

b) using a scale diagram with 1 cm to represent 10 m

length of XY = 2.8 cm

displacement of Y = 28 m

The displacement of Y from X is 28 metres at an angle of 20° South of East

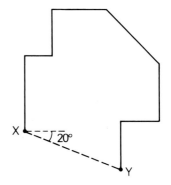

1.3 Velocity and speed

Speed is a scalar quantity with magnitude only: it tells only how fast an object is travelling.

Velocity is a vector quantity which provides the direction of travel as well as the speed.

Two cars approach a cross-roads at 70 mph.
They each have the same speed, 70 mph, but they have different velocities.

car A velocity is 70 mph due North

car B velocity is 70 mph due West.

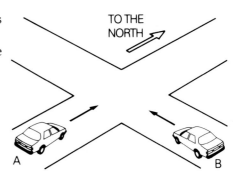

Figure 1.5

1.4 Resultant velocity

The velocity of an object can be the result of combining two separate velocities.

A swimmer attempts to swim due West across a river without allowing for the current.

The actual velocity of the swimmer is the resultant of his velocity through the water and the velocity of the current.

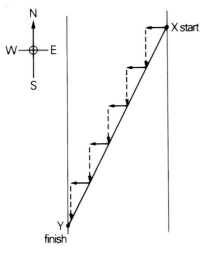

Figure 1.6

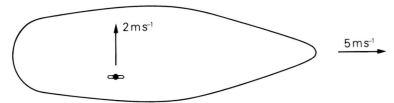

Figure 1.7

As the swimmer swims West (solid line) the current pulls him at a certain speed South (dotted line). This process takes place continuously so that the direction of motion is along XY.

The resultant velocity can be found by drawing a scale diagram, Figure 1.7.

Example 2

A ship is sailing due East at 5 m s^{-1}. A passenger walks due North at 2 m s^{-1}.
What is the resultant velocity of the passenger?

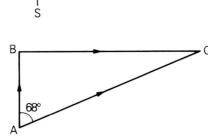

Using a scale diagram where 1 cm represents 1 m s^{-1}, the velocity of the passenger is represented by AB, a line 2 cm long, due North.

The velocity of the ship is represented by BC, a line 5 cm long, due East.

The resultant velocity is represented by line AC.

length AC = 5.4 cm. This represents 5.4 m s^{-1}.

angle BAC = 68°

The resultant velocity of the passenger is 5.4 m s^{-1} at 68° East of North.

1.5 Uniformly accelerated motion in a straight line

When an object moves with uniform acceleration in a straight line it is often necessary to predict some of the quantities involved such as displacement or the velocity attained after a given time. This is most usefully done by developing a set of equations usually known as the **equations of motion**. It is essential to remember that these are valid for **uniform** acceleration in a straight line only and cannot be used when the acceleration is variable.

The following symbols will be used:

u initial velocity s displacement t time interval
v final velocity a uniform acceleration

We shall consider motion in a straight line only, so that the vector quantities velocity and displacement will not have a direction quoted. When an object such as a car is moving, the changes in motion which take place over a given period of time can be displayed in the form of a graph. For example a car moving along a motorway at a steady velocity of $30\,\text{m s}^{-1}$ (70 mph) will have the velocity-time graph shown in Figure 1.8. Because the velocity is uniform, the displacement in each second will be the same, namely 30 metres, so that after one second the displacement will be 30 m and after two seconds 60 m. This is shown graphically in Figure 1.9. After t seconds the displacement will be $30 \times t$ metres.

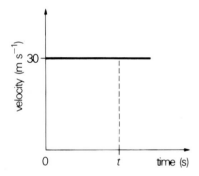

Figure 1.8

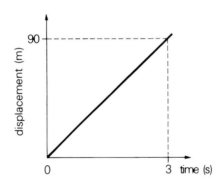

Figure 1.9

If however the car starts from rest and accelerates by $2\,\text{m s}^{-2}$, the velocity will be changing by $2\,\text{m s}^{-1}$ every second and the displacements in successive seconds will be continuously increasing.

A velocity-time graph of this motion, Figure 1.10, can be constructed as follows.

At the start the velocity will be zero

After 1 second the velocity will be $2\,\text{m s}^{-1}$

After 2 seconds the velocity will be $4\,\text{m s}^{-1}$

After 3 seconds the velocity will be $6\,\text{m s}^{-1}$

After 4 seconds the velocity will be $8\,\text{m s}^{-1}$

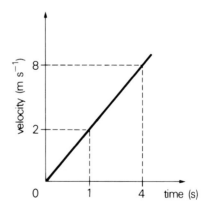

Figure 1.10

The acceleration can be found by calculating the gradient of the velocity-time graph. In Figure 1.11 the velocity is u at time t_1 and v at time t_2.

$$\text{acceleration} = \frac{\text{change of velocity}}{\text{time interval}}$$

$$a = \frac{v - u}{t_2 - t_1} = \text{gradient of graph}$$

using values from Figure 1.10,

$v = 8\,\text{m s}^{-1}$ when $t_2 = 4\,\text{s}$

$u = 2\,\text{m s}^{-1}$ when $t_1 = 1\,\text{s}$

$$\Rightarrow \qquad a = \frac{8 - 2}{4 - 1} = \frac{6}{3} = 2$$

The acceleration is $2\,\text{m s}^{-2}$.

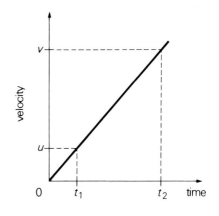

Figure 1.11

1.6 Displacement-time graph

The displacement-time graph associated with the motion represented in Figure 1.12 can be constructed in the following way.

For uniform acceleration

the average velocity is given by $\bar{v} = \dfrac{u + v}{2}$

and the displacement is given by $s = $ average velocity × time.
We can apply this to the data given in Figure 1.12.

displacement in first second

   initial velocity   = 0; final velocity = $2\,\text{m s}^{-1}$

   average velocity = $1\,\text{m s}^{-1}$

   displacement   = 1 m

displacement in second second

   initial velocity   = $2\,\text{m s}^{-1}$; final velocity = $4\,\text{m s}^{-1}$

   average velocity = $3\,\text{m s}^{-1}$

   displacement   = 3 m

   the total displacement after 2 seconds = 1 + 3 = 4 m

displacement in third second

   initial velocity   = $4\,\text{m s}^{-1}$; final velocity = $6\,\text{m s}^{-1}$

   average velocity = $5\,\text{m s}^{-1}$

   displacement   = 5 m

   the total displacement after 3 seconds = 4 + 5 = 9 m

displacement in fourth second

   initial velocity   = $6\,\text{m s}^{-1}$; final velocity = $8\,\text{m s}^{-1}$

   average velocity = $7\,\text{m s}^{-1}$

   displacement   = 7 m

   the total displacement from the start = 9 + 7 = 16 m

The displacement-time graph is shown in Figure 1.13.

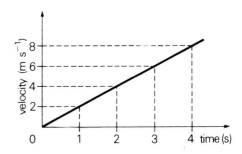

Figure 1.12

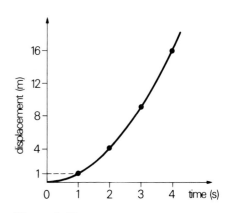

Figure 1.13

1.7   Velocity-time graph from displacement-time graph (constant velocity)

We can use the data from a displacement-time graph to draw the corresponding velocity-time graph.

The displacement-time graph for an object moving in a straight line is shown in Figure 1.14.

$$\text{average velocity} = \frac{\text{displacement}}{\text{time}}$$

$$= \text{gradient of line}$$

over first second   gradient $= \dfrac{3-0}{1-0} = 3$

over second second   gradient $= \dfrac{6-3}{2-1} = 3$

over third second   gradient $= \dfrac{9-6}{3-2} = 3$

The velocity is constant at $3\,\text{m s}^{-1}$

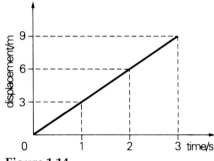

Figure 1.14

The graph of velocity against time is shown in Figure 1.15

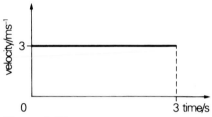

Figure 1.15

1.8   Velocity-time graph from displacement-time graph (constant acceleration)

A car starts from rest and the displacement varies with time as shown. The slope of this graph is continuously changing so that the gradient is not constant.

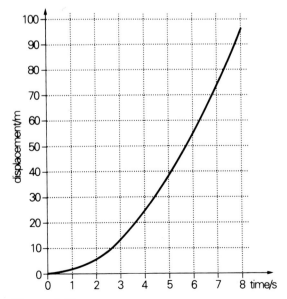

Figure 1.16

The instantaneous velocity is the gradient of the graph at any point. An estimate of the velocity at any instant can be obtained by calculating the average velocity over a short time interval.

In this case a one second interval is used, Figure 1.17.

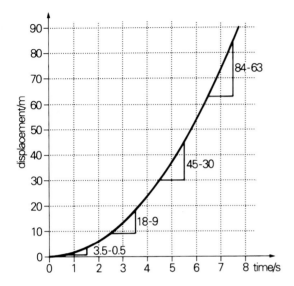

Figure 1.17

for $t = 1\,\text{s}$ average velocity $= \dfrac{3.5 - 0.5}{1.5 - 0.5} = 3$

for $t = 3\,\text{s}$ average velocity $= \dfrac{18 - 9}{3.5 - 2.5} = 9$

for $t = 5\,\text{s}$ average velocity $= \dfrac{45 - 30}{5.5 - 4.5} = 15$

for $t = 7\,\text{s}$ average velocity $= \dfrac{84 - 63}{7.5 - 6.5} = 21$

When these velocities are plotted, a straight line graph is obtained

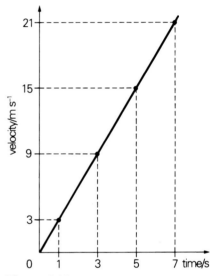

Figure 1.18

1.9 Acceleration-time graph from a velocity-time graph

Using the data from the velocity-time graph for the motion of the car, Figure 1.18, an acceleration-time graph can be constructed.

Acceleration = gradient of the velocity-time graph: $a = \dfrac{v - u}{t_2 - t_1}$

from 1 s to 3 s   acceleration $= \dfrac{9 - 3}{3 - 1} = 3$

from 3 s to 5 s   acceleration $= \dfrac{15 - 9}{5 - 3} = 3$

from 5 s to 7 s   acceleration $= \dfrac{21 - 15}{7 - 5} = 3$

In this case the acceleration is constant at $3\,\text{m s}^{-2}$. The acceleration-time graph is as shown in Figure 1.19.

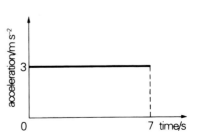

Figure 1.19

1 Kinematics

Starting from the displacement-time graph, the corresponding velocity-time graph was constructed. It is therefore possible, starting from the displacement-time graph, to construct the corresponding velocity-time and acceleration-time graphs for the motion of the car. These are given in Figure 1.20.

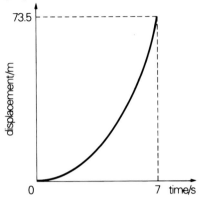 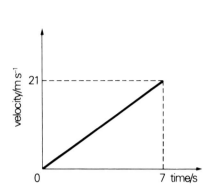 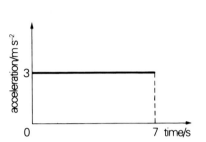

Figure 1.20

Example 3

The velocity of a train varies as shown.
Plot an acceleration-time graph for the motion.

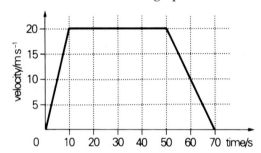

from 0–10 s $\quad a = \dfrac{20-0}{10-0} = +2$

from 10–50 s $\quad a = \dfrac{20-20}{50-10} = 0$

from 50–70 s $\quad a = \dfrac{0-20}{70-50} = -1$

The resulting acceleration-time graph is shown below.

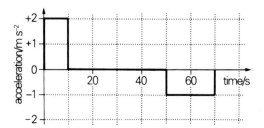

1.10 Equations of motion

Using graphical methods, we can now develop equations which can be used to analyse uniformly accelerated motion.

Figure 1.21 shows the velocity-time graph for a body which, initially moving at velocity u accelerates at a for time t until the final velocity is v.

final velocity = initial velocity + increase in velocity but after a time t the increase will be at. The equation will be

$v = u + at$ ...[1]

If the same graph is redrawn as in Figure 1.22 it can be seen that the area under the graph can be divided into a rectangle and a triangle. The total area gives the displacement.

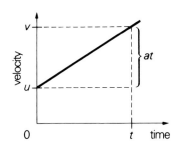

Figure 1.21

For the rectangle: base = $t - 0 = t$;   height = $u - 0 = u$

$\Rightarrow$ area = base × height = ut

For the triangle: base = $t - 0 = t$;   height = $v - u$,

but from equation [1], $v - u = at$

$\Rightarrow$ area = $\frac{1}{2}$ × base × height

$= \frac{1}{2} \times t \times at$

$= \frac{1}{2}at^2$

$\therefore$ total displacement = area of rectangle + area of triangle

$\Rightarrow$ $s = ut + \frac{1}{2}at^2$ ...[2]

By combining equations [1] and [2], a third equation can be developed which does not involve time.

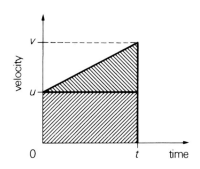

Figure 1.22

From equation [1], $t = \dfrac{v - u}{a}$

and substituting for t in equation [2]

$$s = u\left(\frac{v - u}{a}\right) + \frac{1}{2}a\left(\frac{v - u}{a}\right)^2$$

$$= \frac{uv - u^2}{a} + \frac{v^2 - 2uv + u^2}{2a}$$

$\Rightarrow$ $2as = 2uv - 2u^2 + v^2 - 2uv + u^2$

$$= v^2 - u^2$$

$\Rightarrow$ $v^2 = u^2 + 2as$ ...[3]

The acceleration term can be eliminated between equations [1] and [2] to give equation [4].

From equation [1], $a = \dfrac{v - u}{t}$

and substituting in equation [2]

$$s = ut + \frac{1}{2}at^2$$

$$= ut + \frac{1}{2}\left(\frac{v - u}{t}\right)t^2$$

$$= ut + \frac{1}{2}vt - \frac{1}{2}ut$$

$$= \frac{1}{2}ut + \frac{1}{2}vt$$

$\Rightarrow$ $s = \left(\dfrac{u + v}{2}\right)t$ ...[4]

The term $\left(\dfrac{u + v}{2}\right)$ is the average velocity $\bar{v}$ if acceleration is uniform.

Example 4

A ball is thrown vertically upwards at $30\,\mathrm{m\,s^{-1}}$.
The velocity-time graph is shown.
a) construct an acceleration-time graph
b) calculate the displacement at one second intervals and draw the displacement-time graph

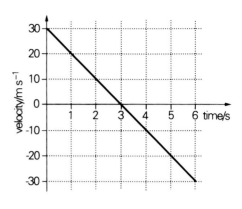

a) acceleration = gradient of velocity-time graph.

during first second $\qquad a = \dfrac{20 - 30}{1 - 0} = -10$

during third second $\qquad a = \dfrac{0 - 10}{3 - 2} = -10$

during fifth second $\qquad a = \dfrac{-20 - (-10)}{5 - 4} = -10$

The acceleration is constant at $-10\,\mathrm{m\,s^{-2}}$ and gives the graph shown.

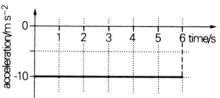

b) using $s = ut + \frac{1}{2}at^2$ this becomes

$$s = 30t + \tfrac{1}{2}(-10)t^2$$
$$s = 30t - 5t^2$$

at $t = 1$ second $\qquad s = 30 - 5 = 25$
at $t = 2$ seconds $\qquad s = 60 - 20 = 40$
at $t = 3$ seconds $\qquad s = 90 - 45 = 45$
at $t = 4$ seconds $\qquad s = 120 - 80 = 40$
at $t = 5$ seconds $\qquad s = 150 - 125 = 25$
at $t = 6$ seconds $\qquad s = 180 - 180 = 0$

The displacement-time graph is as shown.

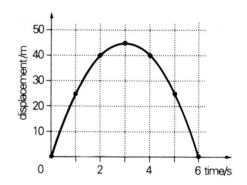

Example 5

A car starts from rest and accelerates uniformly at $3\,\mathrm{m\,s^{-2}}$
a) How long will it take to reach a velocity of $30\,\mathrm{m\,s^{-1}}$?
b) What distance will it have travelled in this time?

a) $u = 0$, $a = 3\,\mathrm{m\,s^{-2}}$, $v = 30\,\mathrm{m\,s^{-1}}$, $t = ?$
Using: $\qquad\qquad\qquad v = u + at$
$\Rightarrow \qquad\qquad\qquad 30 = 0 + 3t$
$\Rightarrow \qquad\qquad\qquad t = \frac{30}{3} = 10$

The car takes 10 seconds to reach a velocity of $30\,\mathrm{m\,s^{-1}}$.

b) $u = 0$, $v = 30\,\mathrm{m\,s^{-1}}$, $t = 10\,\mathrm{s}$, $s = ?$

Using $\qquad s = \left(\dfrac{u + v}{2}\right)t$

$\Rightarrow \qquad s = \left(\dfrac{0 + 30}{2}\right)10$

$\qquad\qquad = 15 \times 10 = 150$

The distance travelled is 150 m.

1.11 Acceleration produced by gravity

The acceleration 'g' produced by the gravitational field of the Earth is always directed towards the centre of the Earth.

It is usual to measure displacement in a direction away from the centre of the Earth so that all vectors upwards are positive and all vectors downwards are negative.

positive vectors	negative vectors
upward displacement	downward displacement
upward velocity	downward velocity
upward acceleration	downward acceleration

In this book, the approximate value of acceleration due to gravity is always taken to be $-10\,\mathrm{m\,s^{-2}}$.

Example 6

If a ball is dropped from a window, what is its velocity 3 seconds later?

$$u = 0, \quad a = -10\,\mathrm{m\,s^{-2}}, \quad t = 3\,\mathrm{s}, \quad v = ?$$

Using:
$$v = u + at$$
$$\Rightarrow \qquad v = 0 + (-10) \times 3 = -30$$

The velocity of the ball 3 seconds later is $30\,\mathrm{m\,s^{-1}}$ downwards.
(The negative sign shows that the velocity of the ball is downwards)

Example 7

An arrow is shot vertically upwards with a velocity of $20\,\mathrm{m\,s^{-1}}$.

a) How long will the arrow take to reach its maximum height?
b) What is the maximum height reached by the arrow?

a) The maximum height is reached when the velocity of the arrow is zero: the velocity then becomes negative as the arrow falls.

$$u = +20\,\mathrm{m\,s^{-1}}, \quad v = 0\,\mathrm{m\,s^{-1}}, \quad a = -10\,\mathrm{m\,s^{-2}}, \quad t = ?$$

Using:
$$v = u + at$$
$$\Rightarrow \qquad 0 = 20 - 10 \times t$$
$$\Rightarrow \qquad t = \frac{-20}{-10} = 2$$

The arrow takes 2 seconds to reach its maximum height.

b) $u = +20\,\mathrm{m\,s^{-1}}, \quad v = 0\,\mathrm{m\,s^{-1}}, \quad t = 2\,\mathrm{s}$

Using:
$$s = \left(\frac{u + v}{2}\right)t$$
$$\Rightarrow \qquad s = \left(\frac{20 + 0}{2}\right) \times 2$$
$$= 20$$

The maximum height reached is 20 metres.

1 Kinematics

Example 8

A helicopter is climbing vertically with a velocity of $15\,\mathrm{m\,s^{-1}}$ when an object is released from it. If the object hits the ground $4\,\mathrm{s}$ later, find

a) the velocity of the object just as it hits the ground
b) the original height of the object.

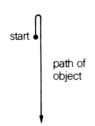

$15\,\mathrm{m\,s^{-1}}$

a) At the instant of release, the object has the same velocity as the helicopter, so that it is moving upwards at $15\,\mathrm{m\,s^{-1}}$. The path of the object is therefore as shown.
When the object is released: $u = +15\,\mathrm{m\,s^{-1}}$, $a = -10\,\mathrm{m\,s^{-2}}$, $t = 4\,\mathrm{s}$, $v = ?$

Using: $$v = u + at$$
$\Rightarrow$ $$v = +15 - 10 \times 4$$
$$= +15 - 40 = -25$$

The velocity of the object just as it hits the ground is $25\,\mathrm{m\,s^{-1}}$ downwards.

start

path of
object

b) To calculate the original height of the object, we must find the displacement of the object from the start.

Using: $$s = ut + \tfrac{1}{2}at^2$$
$\Rightarrow$ $$s = +15 \times 4 - \tfrac{1}{2} \times 10 \times 4^2$$
$$= +60 - 80 = -20$$

The displacement from the starting point is $20\,\mathrm{m}$ downwards so that the original height is $20\,\mathrm{m}$.

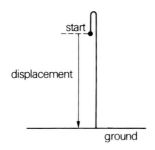

start

displacement

ground

Example 9

An object is projected vertically upwards with a velocity of $40\,\mathrm{m\,s^{-1}}$

a) Find the time taken to reach the maximum height.
b) Calculate the maximum height reached.
c) Find the time taken to fall back to the starting point.
d) Draw a graph showing the variation of velocity with time until the object hits the ground.

a) At the maximum height the object stops rising so that the velocity is zero.
$u = +40\,\mathrm{m\,s^{-1}}$, $v = 0$, $a = -10\,\mathrm{m\,s^{-2}}$.

Using: $$v = u + at$$
$\Rightarrow$ $$0 = +40 - 10 \times t$$
$\Rightarrow$ $$-40 = -10t$$
$\Rightarrow$ $$t = \frac{-40}{-10} = 4$$

The time taken to reach the maximum height is 4 seconds.

b) The maximum height is reached after $4\,\mathrm{s}$
$t = 4\,\mathrm{s}$, $u = +40\,\mathrm{m\,s^{-1}}$, $a = -10\,\mathrm{m\,s^{-2}}$, $s = ?$

using $s = ut + \tfrac{1}{2}at^2$
$$s = 40 \times 4 - \tfrac{1}{2} \times 10 \times 4^2$$
$\Rightarrow$ $$s = 160 - 80$$
$\Rightarrow$ $$s = 80$$

The maximum height is $80\,\mathrm{m}$.

c) When the object has returned to the ground the displacement is zero.

$$s = 0, \quad u = +40\,\mathrm{m\,s^{-1}}, \quad a = -10\,\mathrm{m\,s^{-2}}, \quad t = ?$$

using $s = ut + \frac{1}{2}at^2$

$$0 = +40 \times t - \frac{1}{2} \times 10 \times t^2$$

$$\Rightarrow \quad 0 = 40t - 5t^2$$

$$5t^2 - 40t = 0$$

$$\Rightarrow \quad t^2 - 8t = 0$$

$$\Rightarrow \quad t(t - 8) = 0$$

$$t = 0 \text{ or } 8$$

The time taken to return to the starting point is 8 s.

d) In order to construct the velocity-time graph, $v = u + at$ must be applied.

After 1 second, $v = 40 - 10 \times 1 = 40 - 10 = 30$

After 2 seconds, $v = 40 - 10 \times 2 = 40 - 20 = 20$

After 3 seconds, $v = 40 - 10 \times 3 = 40 - 30 = 10$

After 4 seconds, $v = 40 - 10 \times 4 = 40 - 40 = 0$

Similarly it is found that

After 6 seconds, $v = 40 - 10 \times 6 = 40 - 60 = -20$

After 8 seconds, $v = 40 - 10 \times 8 = 40 - 80 = -40$

The graph will therefore be as shown on the right.

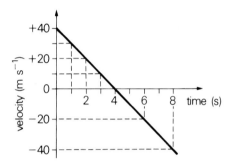

1.12 Measuring acceleration

Acceleration can be measured from a multiflash photograph of a moving object. Figure 1.23 shows a multiflash photograph of a white marker attached to an accelerating vehicle running on a sloping linear air track. A scale showing in centimetres the actual distance travelled is given underneath. The stroboscopic light flashes every 0.1 s. The vehicle started from rest.

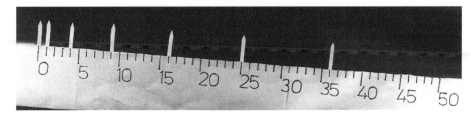

Figure 1.23

The spaces between each image are increasing, indicating that the velocity is also increasing. The average velocity during each time interval is given by

$$\text{average velocity} = \frac{\text{displacement during time interval}}{\text{time interval}}$$

In order to calculate the acceleration a table is drawn up.

The acceleration is thus uniform and equal to $2\,\mathrm{m\,s^{-2}}$

distance travelled in each 0.1 s interval (m)	0.01	0.03	0.05	0.07	0.09	0.11
average velocity in each 0.1 s interval (m s^{-1})	0.10	0.30	0.50	0.70	0.90	1.10
increase in velocity during each 0.1 s interval (m s^{-1})		0.20	0.20	0.20	0.20	0.20
increase in velocity during a 1 s interval (m s^{-1})		2.00	2.00	2.00	2.00	2.00

Table 1

If the acceleration is uniform, its value can be checked from:

$$s = ut + \tfrac{1}{2}at^2$$

where s = total displacement from the start.

From Figure 1.23 it can be seen that when $t = 0.6\,\text{s}$, $s = 0.36\,\text{m}$,

so that $s = 0.36$, $u = 0$, $t = 0.6\,\text{s}$, $a = ?$

$$0.36 = 0 \times 0.6 + \tfrac{1}{2}a \times 0.6^2 = 0 + \tfrac{1}{2} \times 0.36 \times a = 0.18a$$

$$\Rightarrow \quad a = \frac{0.36}{0.18} = 2$$

The acceleration is thus $2\,\text{m s}^{-2}$ confirming the result obtained from Table 1.

Example 10

A golf ball is dropped from rest and a multiflash photograph of the motion is taken at 12 flashes per second.
A reproduction of the photograph is shown.
A metre stick is set up vertically and also photographed to provide the scale factor (i.e. to indicate how lengths on the photograph are related to actual distances fallen)

a)   What is the scale factor?
b)   Calculate the acceleration of the ball.

a)   In the photograph the metre stick measures 8 cm.
This means that 1 metre (100 cm) is represented by 8 cm.

The scale factor is $\dfrac{100}{8}$

b)   The time between images is $\dfrac{1}{12}$ second.
Drawing up a table allows the acceleration to be calculated. Distances between images are taken by direct measurement from the photograph.

distance cm	velocity v cm s^{-1}	change of velocity v cm s^{-1}
0.3	3.6	
0.8	9.6	6.0
1.4	16.8	7.2
1.9	22.8	6.0
2.5	30.0	7.2

$$\text{average change of velocity} = \frac{6.0 + 7.2 + 6.0 + 7.2}{4} = 6.6$$

$$\text{average acceleration} = \frac{6.6}{\frac{1}{12}} = 79\,\text{cm s}^{-2}$$

The 'real life' acceleration is given by

$$\text{calculated acceleration} \times \text{scale factor} = 79 \times \frac{100}{8} = 988\,\text{cm s}^{-2}$$

From the analysis of the photograph, the acceleration of the ball is $9.9\,\text{m s}^{-2}$.

1.13 Projectile motion

The equations of motion can be used to analyse the motion of a projectile. The simplest case involves a projectile which is fired or thrown horizontally, for example, a bomb leaving an aircraft which is flying in a horizontal direction, Figure 1.24. The path taken by the bomb is curved.

Figure 1.24

Figure 1.25 shows two steel balls released simultaneously, one allowed to fall, the other fired in a horizontal direction.

Notice that both balls fall through the same vertical distance for each time interval. Notice also that the horizontal distance for the ball following the curved path is the same for each time interval because each image is equally spaced horizontally.
   We can say that the velocity v of each ball has a vertical component v_y and a horizontal component v_x.
   Both balls have the same vertical velocity v_y but for the ball that is falling, the horizontal component v_x is zero.
   The ball that is fired horizontally has a constant horizontal velocity v_x because the images are equally spaced horizontally.

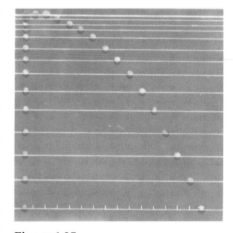

Example 11

A ball rolls along a horizontal bench and falls off the end. The figure shows the horizontal and vertical distance travelled at intervals of 0.1 s after it has left the bench.
a)   Calculate the horizontal component v_x of its velocity.
b)   Calculate the vertical component a_y of its acceleration.
c)   Find its true velocity v at a time 0.3 s after it has left the bench.

Figure 1.25

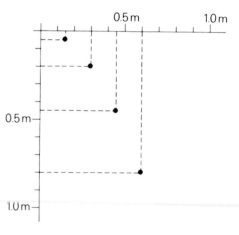

time (s)	0.1	0.2	0.3	0.4
horizontal distance (m)	0.15	0.30	0.45	0.60
vertical distance (m)	0.05	0.20	0.45	0.80

a)   For each time interval of 0.1 s the ball travels a constant horizontal distance of 0.15 m; the horizontal component v_x of its velocity is constant.

$$v_x = \frac{\text{horizontal distance}}{\text{time interval}} = \frac{0.15}{0.1} = 1.5$$

This is the velocity of projection from the horizontal bench.

The horizontal component of velocity (velocity of projection) is 1.5 m s⁻¹.

b)

time interval (s)	0.1	0.1	0.1	0.1
vertical distance interval (m)	0.05	0.15	0.25	0.35
average vertical velocity (m s⁻¹)	0.5	1.5	2.5	3.5

Between each image the average vertical velocity increases as follows:
$(1.5 - 0.5) = 1.0\,\text{m s}^{-1}$ in 0.1 s
$(2.5 - 1.5) = 1.0\,\text{m s}^{-1}$ in 0.1 s
$(3.5 - 2.5) = 1.0\,\text{m s}^{-1}$ in 0.1 s

So the acceleration a_y is constant: $a_y = \dfrac{\text{vertical velocity interval}}{\text{time interval}} = \dfrac{1.0}{0.1} = 10$

The vertical component of acceleration is 10 m s⁻² downwards.

c) The actual velocity at any instant is found by combining the horizontal velocity component v_x with the vertical velocity component v_y at that instant in a triangle of velocities.

v_x is constant and equals $1.5\,\text{m s}^{-1}$

The value of v_y when $t = 0.3$ is found from $v_y = u_y + a_y t$

where $a_y = -10\,\text{m s}^{-2}$ and $u_y = 0\,\text{m s}^{-1}$

$\Rightarrow \quad v_y = 0 - 10 \times 0.3$

$\qquad\qquad = -3$

The triangle of velocities shown is used to obtain the velocity v from v_x and v_y after $0.3\,\text{s}$.

By Pythagoras' theorem $v^2 = v_x^2 + v_y^2$

$\qquad\qquad\qquad = 1.5^2 + (-3)^2$

$\qquad\qquad\qquad = 11.25$

$\Rightarrow \qquad\qquad v = 3.35$

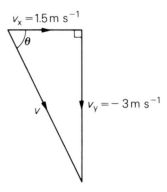

The angle θ that the actual velocity makes with the horizontal is given by

$\tan \theta = \dfrac{v_y}{v_x} = \dfrac{-3}{1.5} = -2.0$

$\Rightarrow \quad \theta = -63.4°$

The velocity after $0.3\,\text{s}$ is $3.35\,\text{m s}^{-1}$ at an angle of $63.4°$ below the horizontal.

Example 12

A ball is projected horizontally off the end of a bench. It hits the ground $3\,\text{m}$ from the base of the bench and a vertical distance $1.25\,\text{m}$ below the point of projection. Find **a)** the time of the flight and **b)** the velocity of projection.

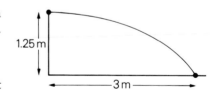

a) Consider the vertical motion. The displacement s_y is negative displacement it is downwards.

$s_y = -1.25\,\text{m}, \quad u_y = 0, \quad a_y = -10\,\text{m s}^{-2}$

Using the equation $s = ut + \frac{1}{2}at^2$

$\Rightarrow \qquad -1.25 = 0 + \frac{1}{2} \times -10 \times t^2$

$\Rightarrow \qquad t^2 = \dfrac{-1.25}{-5} = 0.25$

$\Rightarrow \qquad t = \pm 0.5 \text{ (the negative value has no meaning)}$

The time of flight is $0.5\,\text{s}$.

b) Consider the horizontal motion.

$\text{velocity } v_x = \dfrac{\text{horizontal displacement}}{\text{time interval}}$

$\qquad\qquad = \dfrac{3}{0.5} = 6$

The velocity of projection is $6\,\text{m s}^{-1}$.

1.14 Resolution of vectors

Two vectors can be replaced by a single vector which is the vector sum of these two vectors. In the same way a single vector can be replaced by two vectors. These two vectors are called components. The splitting up of a vector into two component vectors is called resolution. The vector sum of the two components is equal to the single vector that they replace.

To find the effect of a vector in one particular direction we resolve it into two components, one along the direction we are interested in, the other at right angles to this.

If the vector is v, the component at angle θ is v_1, and the other component at right angles to this is v_2. Then vector v = vector v_1 + vector v_2.

Figure 1.26

In the right-angled vector triangle

$$\cos \theta = \frac{\text{adjacent}}{\text{hypotenuse}}$$

$$= \frac{v_1}{v}$$

multiplying both sides by v

$$v \cos \theta = v_1$$

The component which makes an angle of θ with a vector v is given by $v \cos \theta$. If both components are required

$$v_y = v \cos \phi$$
$$v_x = v \cos \theta$$

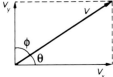

Figure 1.27

Figure 1.28

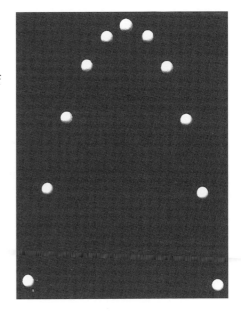

Figure 1.29

When a golfer drives the ball down the fairway, the ball is projected at an angle to the horizontal, Figure 1.28. We can see that the ball has both a horizontal component and an upwards (positive) vertical component when it is hit. So that u_y is not zero.

If air resistance is neglected, the path of the ball is symmetrical about the point of maximum height as shown in Figure 1.29. A similar motion is given in Figure 1.30. The range is the total horizontal distance travelled, AQ in Figure 1.30.

The maximum height is OP.

The time of flight is the time taken to return to the horizontal again, that is to go from point A to point Q.

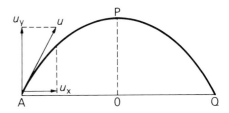

Figure 1.30

Example 13

A golfer hits a ball with a velocity of 48 m s^{-1} at an angle of 30° to the horizontal. If air resistance is neglected, find **a)** the time of flight, **b)** the range, **c)** the maximum height

a)   The time of flight is the time taken for the ball to return to the ground (assumed horizontal), i.e. $s_y = 0$

The vertical component u_y of the velocity is found from the triangle ADC.

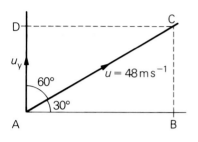

$$\frac{AD}{AC} = \frac{u_y}{u} = \cos 60°$$

$$\Rightarrow \quad u_y = u \cos 60°$$

$$= 48 \times 0.5 = 24$$

Using the equation $s_y = u_y t + \frac{1}{2} a_y t^2$
where $s_y = 0$, $u_y = +24$ m s^{-1}, $a_y = -10$ m s^{-2}, $t = ?$

$$\Rightarrow \quad 0 = 24t + \frac{1}{2} \times -10 \times t^2$$

$$\Rightarrow \quad 0 = t(24 - 5t)$$

$$\Rightarrow \quad t = 0 \text{ or } \frac{24}{5}$$

$$= 0 \text{ or } 4.8$$

The time of flight is 4.8 seconds.

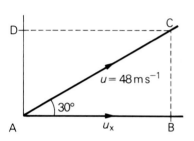

b)   The range is the total horizontal displacement s_x for the time of flight and is found from the horizontal component u_x of the velocity.

From the triangle ABC

$$\frac{AB}{AC} = \frac{u_x}{u} = \cos 30°$$

$$\Rightarrow \quad u_x = u \cos 30°$$

$$= 48 \times 0.87 = 41.8$$

$$\Rightarrow \quad s_x = u_x t = 41.8 \times 4.8 = 200$$

The range is 200 metres.

c)   The maximum height is gained when the vertical component v_y of the velocity is zero.

Using the equation $v_y^2 = u_y^2 + 2a_y s_y$

$$v_y = 0, \quad u_y = +24 \text{ m s}^{-1}, \quad a_y = -10 \text{ m s}^{-2}, \quad s_y = ?$$

$$\Rightarrow \qquad\qquad 0 = 24^2 + 2 \times -10 s_y$$

$$\Rightarrow \qquad\qquad s_y = \frac{576}{20} = 28.8$$

The maximum height is 28.8 metres.

Summary

Quantities that have magnitude only are called **scalars**. Quantities that have magnitude and direction are called **vectors**.

Distance and speed are scalars.

Displacement, velocity and acceleration are vectors.

The resultant of two vectors is found by drawing a vector triangle.

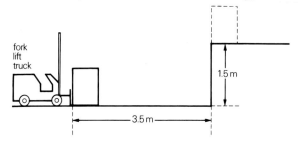

For vectors at right angles:
$$v^2 = v_1^2 + v_2^2$$

A vector can be resolved into two components at right angles:

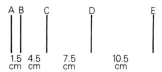

The distance travelled by a moving object is equal to the area under the velocity-time graph.

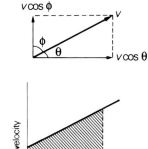

The equations of motion are:
$$v = u + at$$
$$s = ut + \tfrac{1}{2}at^2$$
$$v^2 = u^2 + 2as$$
$$s = \left(\frac{u + v}{2}\right)t$$

Acceleration is given by the gradient of the velocity-time graph:

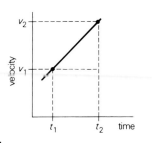

$$a = \frac{\text{change in velocity}}{\text{time}} = \frac{v_2 - v_1}{t_2 - t_1}.$$

The instantaneous velocity of a projectile is the vector sum of the horizontal and vertical components of velocity.

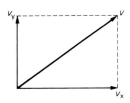

Problems

1 **a)** What is meant by a scalar quantity?
   b) Classify the following as either vector or scalar quantities: speed, displacement, velocity, acceleration, distance
   c) One of the equations of motion is $s = ut + \tfrac{1}{2}at^2$. Write down each symbol and state whether it is a vector or scalar.

2 A person walks due North at $1.5\,\mathrm{m\,s^{-1}}$ across the deck of a ship which is travelling due West at $2\,\mathrm{m\,s^{-1}}$. Determine the magnitude and direction of the velocity of the person relative to the water.

3 A fork-lift truck raises a box vertically, then moves 3.5 m across the floor of a warehouse and deposits the box on a platform 1.5 m high. Calculate the displacement of the box from the starting position.

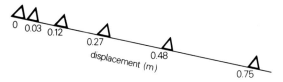

4 **a)** A train enters a tunnel which is 180 m long and emerges 6 s later. What is the average speed of the train as it goes through the tunnel?
   b) An electron takes 1.2 nanoseconds to travel a distance of 10 cm. Calculate the speed of the electron.
   c) A runner travels a distance of 1500 m in a time of 3 minutes 55 seconds. Calculate his average speed.

5 A reproduction of a multi-flash photograph is shown. The flash rate is 8 Hz.

```
A B      C         D            E
| |      |         |            |
| |      |         |            |

1.5 4.5  7.5       10.5
cm  cm   cm        cm
```

   a) Calculate the average speeds between AB and DE and hence find the acceleration.
   b) What is the average speed for the motion between A and E?

6 An object slides from rest down a slope and the positions at intervals of 0.2 s are shown.

   a) Calculate the acceleration.
   b) Determine the displacement of the object after a further 0.2 s.

7 a) Describe an experiment to find the acceleration of a moving trolley using a ticker-timer and tape. State what measurements would be taken and show how they would be used to calculate the acceleration.

b) Explain how you would check that the reading of 48 km/h on a car speedometer is correct.

c) How could the frequency of rotation of the shaft of an electric motor be determined using a multi-flash stroboscope?

d) You are asked to determine the acceleration of gravity g using a multi-flash photograph of a falling golf ball. Describe how you would do this, clearly explaining the measurements you would take and how you would calculate a value for g.

8 A ball is thrown vertically upwards with a velocity of $15\,\mathrm{m\,s^{-1}}$.

a) How long will it take to fall back to the starting position?

b) What distance has the ball travelled in this time?

9 A coin rests on a record-player turntable a distance of 10 cm from the spindle. When the turntable is revolving at 45 r.p.m., what is the average speed of the coin? Is the velocity of the coin changing?

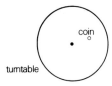

10 Describe three situations in which an object moves with varying acceleration.

11 A vehicle is catapulted along a horizontal linear air track. The friction force acting on the vehicle is negligible.

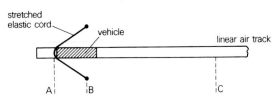

Describe the acceleration of the vehicle during sections AB and BC.

12 The speed-time graph shows how the speed of a trolley varies as it runs down a slope. How far did the trolley travel in the first 3 seconds?

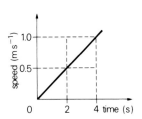

13 The speed-time graph for a runner is shown.

a) Construct an acceleration-time graph.

b) How far did she run in the first 10 s?

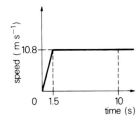

14 The velocity-time graph for a moving object is shown. What is the displacement after 6 s?

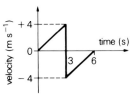

15 The total displacements of an object moving in a straight line at given times are listed in the table.

displacement s (m)	0	2	8	18	32	50
time t (s)	0	1	2	3	4	5

a) Is the object accelerating or decelerating?

b) Construct a speed-time graph for the motion.

16 The acceleration of an object varies with time as shown. If the initial speed is zero construct a speed-time graph.

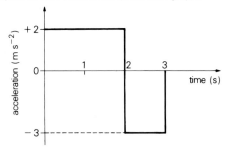

a) Determine the speed after 3 seconds.

b) How far has the object travelled in this time?

17 The displacement-time graph for the motion of three objects is shown. In each case calculate the acceleration.

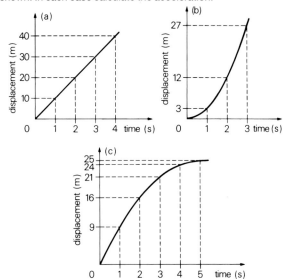

18 The acceleration of a car varies as shown.

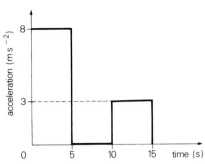

If the initial velocity is zero, draw a speed-time graph. How far did the car travel during the period 10 s to 15 s?

19 A helicopter is rising vertically at 8 m s⁻¹. An object is released from it and falls. The object hits the ground 3 s later.
  a) What is the velocity of the object as it hits the ground?
  b) Determine the height of the object when it was released.

20 For each of the following situations, sketch possible velocity-time graphs. A ball is
  a) thrown vertically upwards and caught when it returns to the starting point.
  b) dropped to the floor and caught after the first bounce.
  c) rolled along a horizontal surface and then accelerated down a sloping ramp.
  d) rolled along a horizontal surface, up an incline, and then back down to stop finally on the horizontal surface.

21 An object is accelerated uniformly from rest. The displacement-time graph is shown.
  Giving actual values, draw
  a) the corresponding velocity-time graph.
  b) the corresponding acceleration-time graph.

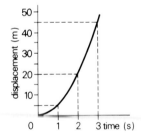

22 A ball rolls over the edge of a horizontal surface as shown.

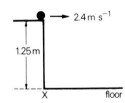

  a) How long will it take to hit the floor?
  b) Calculate the vertical component of the velocity as it hits the floor.
  c) If the horizontal velocity of the ball is 2.4 m s⁻¹, determine the angle at which the ball hits the floor.
  d) How far from point X did the ball land?

23 A rolling ball leaves the end of a sloping ramp at 5 m s⁻¹, as shown in the diagram.
  a) How long will it take to reach the ground?
  b) How far will it have travelled horizontally before hitting the ground?

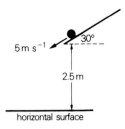

24 A sledge is moving at 6 m s⁻¹ along a horizontal surface. An object is projected vertically upwards from it at 12 m s⁻¹.

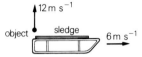

  a) Calculate the maximum height reached by the object.
  b) Calculate the horizontal distance travelled by the object before it falls back to the same height as the top of the sledge.
  c) Sketch the path taken by the object as seen by a stationary observer.
  d) What impression of the motion would someone on the sledge have?

25 A metal ball is launched at an angle of 30° and hits a horizontal surface at the same height as the top of the launcher. The point of impact is 34.6 m away and the ball takes 2 seconds to travel this distance.

  Find
  a) the horizontal component of the velocity of the ball
  b) the maximum height reached.

26 A projectile is fired with velocity *v* from A at an angle α to a horizontal site. It returns to the ground at R.

  The horizontal and vertical components of its velocity for the flight are shown in Graphs I and II respectively.

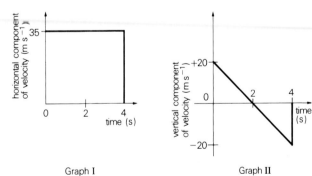

Graph I   Graph II

  a) How far from A is the projectile when it hits the ground at R?
  b) There is a disused building 15 m high, midway between A and R. What is the distance between the top of this building and the projectile as it passes directly over the building?
  c) Calculate the initial speed and direction of the projectile.

SEB

27 In an experiment to investigate how different factors affect the stopping of an unladen van, a series of speed-time graphs is obtained. In these graphs the speed is recorded from the instant the driver is asked to apply the brakes. One such graph is shown.

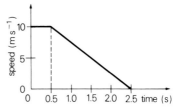

The following are deduced from the series of graphs.

Initial speed of van	Thinking distance	Braking distance	Overall stopping distance
(m s^{-1})	(m)	(m)	(m)
10	5	10	15
20	10	40	50
30	15	90	105

a) i) What is meant by the term 'thinking distance'?
ii) Explain why thinking distance varies directly as the van's speed.
b) Using the information from the table, reproduce the speed-time graph for the case in which the initial speed of the van is 30 m s^{-1}.

SEB

28 In a game, three boys, Bill, John and Peter, started at the same place P and each ran to one of the three positions marked A, B and C. The distances are marked.

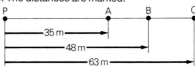

The graph of velocity against time from the start is shown for each boy.

a) Which position did Bill arrive at and what was his average speed for the journey?

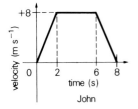

b) Copy and complete the following table for the first four seconds of John's journey and use the results to plot a graph of his displacement against time for this period.

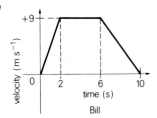

Time (s)	0	1	2	3	4
Displacement from start (m)					

c) i) Where was Peter and what was he doing 8 seconds after starting?
ii) What was he doing 10 seconds after starting?

SEB

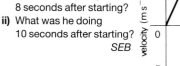

29 The diagram represents the apparatus set up to determine a value for g, the acceleration due to gravity. A steel ball B is held by an electromagnet E at a height h vertically above switch S$_2$. When switch S$_1$ is opened, the electric clock is started and E is disconnected from the electrical supply. The ball falls and strikes S$_2$ which opens and stops the clock.

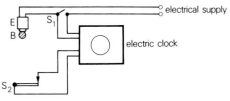

a) Show that the time t for a ball to fall freely from rest through a height h is given by $t = \sqrt{(2h/g)}$.
b) It is found that when $h = 0.600$ m, the recorded time of fall is 0.400 s. Using the above relationship what value do these results give for g?
c) The class decides to repeat the experiment for different values of h, and from the results the graph below is drawn of t against $\sqrt{h}$. Time t is in seconds and h is in metres.

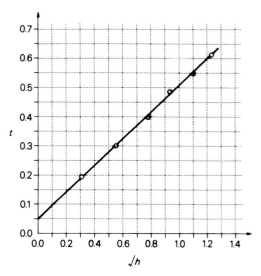

i) Suggest why the graph does not pass through the origin.
ii) From the graph of t against $\sqrt{h}$ find the true time for the ball to fall through a height of 1.44 m.
iii) What value does this now give for g?

SEB

30 A ball is projected at 15 m s^{-1} horizontally from the top of a vertical cliff and reaches the horizontal ground 45 m from the foot of the cliff.
a) Draw accurate graphs, with the appropriate numerical scales, of
i) the horizontal speed of the ball against time
ii) the vertical speed of the ball against time for the period from its projection until it hits the ground.
b) By using a vector diagram or otherwise, find the velocity of the ball 2 s after its projection giving both speed and direction. State any assumptions you have made.

SEB

31 A ball rolls off a roof at 15 m s⁻¹. What is the vertical component of velocity after 1 second?

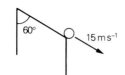

32 The speed-time graph for a train is shown.
Calculate the distance travelled in the first 25 seconds.

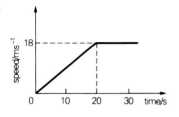

33 A projectile has the positions shown after equal intervals of time. Write down the horizontal and vertical distances at the end of the next time interval.

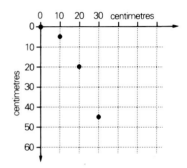

34 A girl on the back of a lorry travelling at 6 m s⁻¹ due West throws a ball due North at 2 m s⁻¹. Calculate the velocity of the ball relative to the ground.

35 a) The acceleration of a vehicle on a sloping air track may be measured using the apparatus shown.

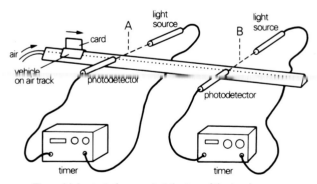

The vehicle starts from rest at the top of the track.
The time taken by the card on the vehicle to pass through a light beam is recorded by the timer.
The time taken by the vehicle to travel from A to B is measured to be 2.0 s.
Explain how you could find the acceleration of the vehicle. Your answer should include a list of the measurements you would take and a description of how you would calculate the acceleration.

b) A ball-bearing was rolled along a bench and fell to the floor. A strobe photograph was taken to record the motion of the ball-bearing. The strobe flash rate was 10 Hz and the resulting strobe photograph is represented below.

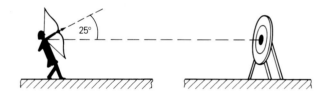

i) What is the time interval between each image in the photograph?
ii) What is the time of flight of the ball-bearing measured from the time it leaves the bench top to the time it strikes the floor?
iii) Calculate the horizontal velocity of the ball-bearing as it rolls along the bench.
iv) The ball-bearing strikes the ground with a vertical component of velocity of 4.0 m s⁻¹. Calculate the magnitude and direction of the velocity with which the ball-bearing strikes the floor.

SEB

36 An archer fires an arrow at a target 60 m distant. The arrow leaves her bow at 28 m s⁻¹ at an angle of 25° to the horizontal as shown.

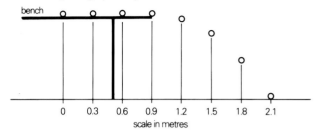

a) What is the horizontal component of the velocity of the arrow?
b) How long will it take the arrow to reach the target?

SEB

37 A parachutist drops from a balloon floating above an airfield.

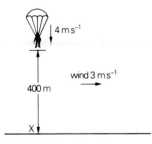

When he is 400 m above a point X on the airfield, he is falling at a constant vertical speed of 4 m s⁻¹. A steady wind blows him horizontally at 3 m s⁻¹. How far from X will he land?

SEB

2 Dynamics

2.1 Introduction

When a force acts on an object, it can produce a change in velocity either by changing its speed or by changing its direction. A force can also produce a change of shape. A change of velocity will only take place if the forces acting on the object fail to balance out. When the forces do balance, the object does not change its velocity. If the object is at rest, it remains at rest. If the object is moving, it continues to do so with the same speed and direction.

Figure 2.1 shows a multiflash photograph of a straw marker attached to a vehicle moving along a horizontal linear air track. In this case friction is negligible so that the net horizontal force is virtually zero. The distances between the images of the marker are equal, indicating a constant horizontal velocity.

Figure 2.1

An object can be moving at a steady speed but can change direction because of a resultant force. This is illustrated in Figure 2.2 which shows a multiflash photograph of a frictionless puck being whirled at constant speed in a circle. The attached string exerts a force which continually changes the direction of travel of the puck so that it travels in a circle rather than in a straight line.

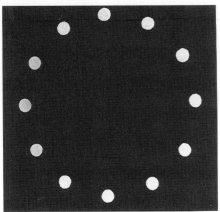

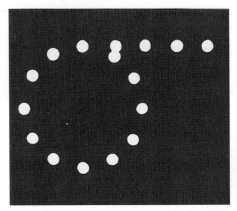

Figure 2.2   Figure 2.3

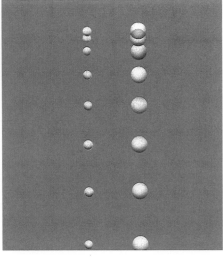

Figure 2.4

If the string breaks (Figure 2.3) the puck shoots off at a tangent to the circular path. The equal spacing between the images indicates constant speed. Newton summarised these observations in his First Law which can be formally stated:

'An object will remain at rest or will continue to move in a straight line at constant speed unless it is acted upon by a net or unbalanced force.'

Every object near the surface of the earth accelerates downwards. An example of this is shown in Figure 2.4.

The spacing between the images increases showing that the ball is accelerating. This acceleration is caused by the unbalanced force acting on the ball.

It can be shown experimentally that the acceleration a of an object is
    a) directly proportional to the applied force F if the mass is constant,

$$a \propto F$$

  and b) inversely proportional to the mass m if the applied force is constant,

$$a \propto 1/m$$

Combining these results, we get $a \propto \dfrac{F}{m}$

$$F \propto ma$$

This can be written $F = kma$

One newton is defined as the unbalanced force which gives an acceleration of $1\,\mathrm{m\,s^{-2}}$ to a mass of 1 kg.
   Hence, if $m = 1\,\mathrm{kg}$ and $a = 1\,\mathrm{m\,s^{-2}}$, then $F = 1\,\mathrm{N}$.
Using this in the equation $F = kma$, we find that $k = 1$ and we can write:

$$F = ma$$

This is a form of **Newton's Second Law**.

Example 1

A trolley with a marker attached is pulled by a stretched elastic cord the extension of which is kept constant. A multiflash photograph is taken at a flash rate of 10 Hz.
   If the mass of the trolley is 0.8 kg, find the unbalanced force acting on the trolley. The distances travelled by the marker in the time interval of 0.1 s are shown in the diagram.

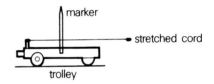

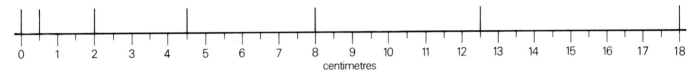

The acceleration can be found by constructing a table:

Distance moved in successive 0.1 s intervals	0.005 m	0.015 m	0.025 m	0.035 m	0.045 m	0.055 m
Time interval	0.1 s	0.1 s	0.1 s	0.1 s	0.1 s	0.1 s
Average speed in each 0.1 s interval (m s^{-1})	0.05	0.15	0.25	0.35	0.45	0.55
Increase in speed between successive 0.1 s intervals (m s^{-1})		0.10	0.10	0.10	0.10	0.10
Increase in speed between successive 1 s intervals (m s^{-1})		1.00	1.00	1.00	1.00	1.00
Acceleration (m s^{-2})		1.00	1.00	1.00	1.00	1.00

Table 1

From the table we can see that the acceleration is uniform and equal to $1\,\mathrm{m\,s^{-2}}$. The unbalanced force F acting on the trolley is given by

$$F = ma$$
$$= 0.8 \times 1 = 0.8$$

The unbalanced force acting on the trolley is 0.8 N.

Example 2

An unbalanced force of 25 N acts on a mass of 5 kg.
What is the acceleration produced?

Using $F = ma$

$$25 = 5 \times a \implies a = \frac{25}{5} = 5$$

The acceleration produced is 5 m s⁻².

Example 3

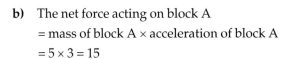

A net force of 24 N acts on two blocks A and B.

a) What is the acceleration of each block?
b) What is the net force acting on block A?

a) The blocks will move together so that

total mass $= 5 + 3 = 8\,\text{kg}$

the acceleration a is given by $a = \dfrac{F}{m} = \dfrac{24}{8} = 3$

The acceleration of each block is 3 m s⁻².

b) The net force acting on block A

$=$ mass of block A $\times$ acceleration of block A

$= 5 \times 3 = 15$

The net force acting on block A is 15 N.

Example 4

A person of mass 75 kg enters a lift. He presses the starting button and the lift descends with an acceleration of 1 m s⁻². The lift then descends at a steady speed before coming to rest with a deceleration of 1 m s⁻².
a) What is the force exerted on the person by the floor when the lift is stationary?
b) What is the force exerted by the floor on the person when the lift is accelerating?
c) Calculate the force exerted by the floor when the lift is decelerating.

a) The weight W of the person is given by

$W = mg = 75 \times -10 = -750$

This weight of 750 N acts downward
If R is the reaction force exerted by the floor

$R + W = ma$

But when the lift is stationary,

$$a = 0$$
$$\implies R - 750 = 0$$
$$R = 750$$

The force exerted by the floor is 750 N acting upwards.

$W=$ force exerted on the floor by the person
$R =$ force exerted on the person by the floor

b) When the lift accelerates downwards $a = -1\,\text{m s}^{-2}$

and $R + W = ma$

$$\implies R - 750 = 75 \times (-1)$$
$$R - 750 = -75$$
$$\implies R = -75 + 750 = 675$$

The force is 675 N acting upwards.

c) The lift is moving downwards but is decelerating. This indicates that there must be an unbalanced force acting upwards. The acceleration is thus directed upwards opposing the downward motion.

In this case $a = +1\,\mathrm{m\,s^{-2}}$

$$R + W = ma$$
$$\Rightarrow\quad R - 750 = 75 \times 1$$
$$R - 750 = 75$$
$$\Rightarrow\quad R = 75 + 750$$
$$R = 825$$

The force is 825 N and acts upwards.

Example 5

A mass of 0.05 kg is suspended inside a lift. The lift starts from rest, accelerates upwards at $0.4\,\mathrm{m\,s^{-2}}$, moves upwards at a steady speed of $0.6\,\mathrm{m\,s^{-1}}$ and then decelerates at $0.4\,\mathrm{m\,s^{-2}}$. Find the readings of the spring balance at each stage of the motion.

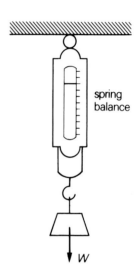

spring balance

The upward force R is provided by the spring in the balance and the equation relating the forces will be

$$R + W = ma$$

In each stage the magnitude of the weight will be the same and is given by

$$W = mg$$
$$= 0.05 \times -10 = -0.5$$

The weight is 0.5 N acting downwards.

Stage 1: the lift at rest

$$R + W = ma \qquad a = 0$$
$$m = 0.05\,\mathrm{kg}$$
$$W = -0.5\,\mathrm{N}$$
$$R - 0.5 = 0.05 \times 0$$
$$R = 0.5$$

The reading on the balance is 0.5 N

Stage 2: lift accelerating upwards

$$R + W = ma \qquad a = +0.4\,\mathrm{m\,s^{-2}}$$
$$m = 0.05\,\mathrm{kg}$$
$$W = -0.5\,\mathrm{N}$$
$$R - 0.5 = 0.05 \times 0.4$$
$$R - 0.5 = 0.02$$
$$R = 0.02 + 0.5$$
$$R = 0.52$$

The balance reads 0.52 N

Stage 3: lift moving at uniform velocity

$$R + W = ma \qquad a = 0$$
$$m = 0.05\,\mathrm{kg}$$
$$W = -0.5\,\mathrm{N}$$
$$R - 0.5 = 0.05 \times 0$$
$$R - 0.5 = 0$$
$$R = 0.5$$

The balance reading is 0.5 N

Stage 4: lift decelerating

$$R + W = ma \qquad a = -0.4\,\mathrm{m\,s^{-2}}$$
$$m = 0.05\,\mathrm{kg}$$
$$W = -0.5\,\mathrm{N}$$
$$R - 0.5 = 0.05 \times (-0.4)$$
$$R - 0.5 = -0.02$$
$$R = -0.02 + 0.5$$
$$R = 0.48$$

The reading on the balance is 0.48 N.

2.2 Force as a vector

The quantities displacement, velocity and force are vector quantities and are therefore added as vectors. The combined effect of two or more vectors is called the resultant of the vectors and is their vector sum. If two forces act on an object as shown in Figure 2.5 the resultant can be found using a scale diagram in which the length of the line represents the magnitude of the force and the angle at which the line is drawn represents the direction. The vectors are joined head to tail as indicated, Figure 2.6.

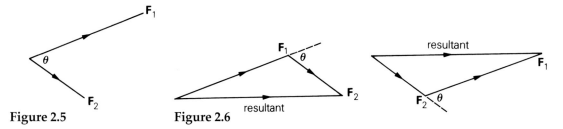

Figure 2.5   **Figure 2.6**

The same value for the magnitude and direction of the resultant is obtained irrespective of which vector is drawn first.

Example 6

Two forces of 15 N and 6 N act on an object at an angle of 80° between the directions of the forces. Find the resultant force. For the scale diagram choose 1 cm to represent a force of 2 N.

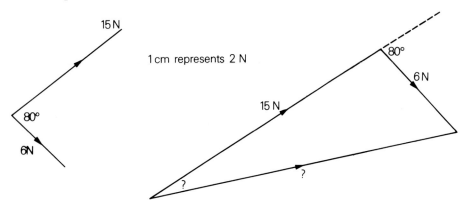

The length of the resultant vector is 8.6 cm so the resultant force is 8.6 × 2 which is 17.2 N. The angle between the resultant force and the 15 N is measured to be 20°.

2.3 Object acted upon by three forces

A brass ring is held at rest by pulling on it with three strings attached to three spring balances.

The readings of each balance are noted:

$F_1 = 12\,\text{N}$

$F_2 = 5\,\text{N}$

$F_3 = 13\,\text{N}$

Force F_1 acts at 67° to the horizontal
Force F_2 acts at 23° to the horizontal
Force F_3 acts vertically
Draw a scale diagram using
1 cm to represent 2 newtons.

The vector diagram forms a triangle.

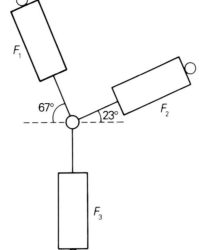

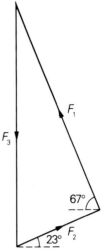

Figure 2.7   **Figure 2.8**

We can conclude that:

when an object is in equilibrium under the action of three forces, the three forces can be represented in magnitude by the three sides of a triangle.

Resolution of vectors

Two forces can be combined to give a single force called the resultant which as we have seen can replace these two forces. The reverse process is also possible, a single force being replaced by two forces called components. This splitting up into two separate forces is known as **resolution**.

This is shown in Figure 2.9 and as indicated in the vector triangle in Figure 2.10, $\mathbf{F}_x$ and $\mathbf{F}_y$ combined, form the single force $\mathbf{F}$.

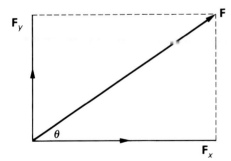

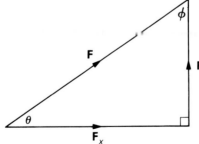

Figure 2.9   **Figure 2.10**

From the triangle in Figure 2.10, $\dfrac{\mathbf{F}_y}{\mathbf{F}} = \cos\phi$ and $\dfrac{\mathbf{F}_x}{\mathbf{F}} = \cos\theta$

$$\Rightarrow \quad \mathbf{F}_y = \mathbf{F}\cos\phi \qquad \Rightarrow \quad \mathbf{F}_x = \mathbf{F}\cos\theta$$

2 Dynamics

Example 7

A skier, weight 800 N, is pulled up a slope at constant speed.
The slope is inclined at 25° to the horizontal and the tow rope makes an angle of 50° to the slope. If the force exerted by the tow rope is 250 N, calculate the work done on the skier in order to move him 30 m up the slope.

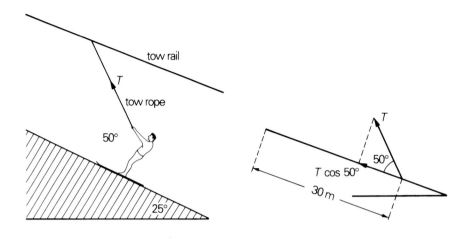

The tow rope makes an angle of 50° to the slope.
The component of the tension T acting parallel to the slope $= T \cos 50°$
$$= 250 \times 0.64$$
$$= 160.7$$

work done = force × distance
$$= 160.7 \times 30 = 4821 \text{ J}$$

The work done is 4821 J.

2.4 Free body diagram

When an object, sometimes referred to as a body, is in equilibrium under the action of two or more forces (i.e. there is no resultant force) the forces can be analysed using a vector diagram.
In order to construct the vector diagram it is useful to draw a free-body diagram. This is done by considering one point in the system at a time and isolating the forces acting on it.
The following illustrate the method.

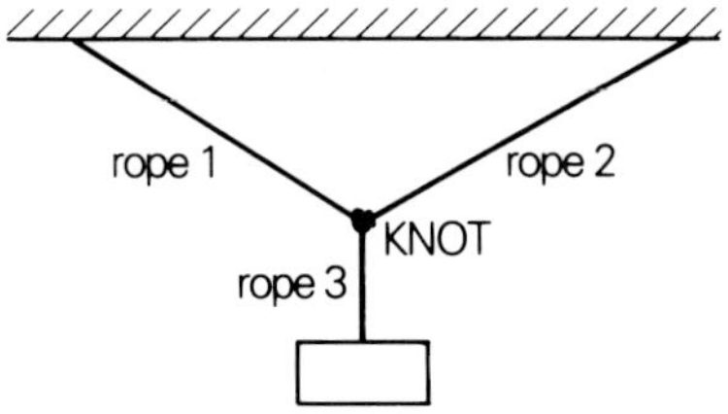

1. Block suspended by three ropes, Figure 2.11.
   Here we can draw free body diagrams for two chosen points in the system.

Figure 2.11

a) Free body diagram for the knot, Figure 2.12.

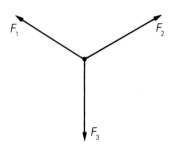

Figure 2.12

F_1 = force exerted by rope 1 on the knot
F_2 = force exerted by rope 2 on the knot
F_3 = force exerted by rope 3 on the knot

b) Free body diagram for the block, Figure 2.13.

Figure 2.13

F_3 = force exerted by rope 3 on the block
W = force of gravity acting on the block

2. Block resting on a frictionless slope, Figure 2.14.

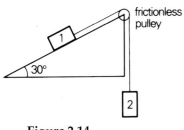

Figure 2.14

a) Free body diagram for mass 2, Figure 2.15.

Figure 2.15

F = force exerted by rope on mass 2
W_2 = force of gravity acting on mass 2

b) Free body diagram for mass 1, Figure 2.16.

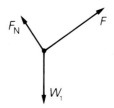

Figure 2.16

F = force exerted by rope on mass 1
W_1 = force of gravity acting on mass 1
F_N = force of slope, acting at right angles to surface, on mass 1

Example 8

A pendulum bob of weight 2 N is pulled to the right by a horizontal force F until the string makes an angle of 30° to the vertical.

a) What force would be needed for the string to sit at 30°?

b) What is the tension in the string under these conditions?

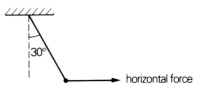

The free body diagram for the bob is shown on the right.

F = horizontal force
T = tension (force) in string
W = weight of bob

Construct a vector diagram for the three forces acting on the bob. Since it is in equilibrium under the action of three forces the diagram must form a triangle.

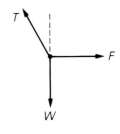

Scale: 1 cm represents 0.5 N

Draw a vertical line 4 cm long to represent the weight of the bob.

Add a line at right angles to the vertical line to represent the horizontal force.

Finally draw a line at 30° to the vertical to represent the tension in the string.

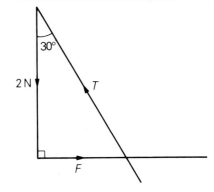

The sides of the triangle are measured

F is 2.3 cm long $F = 2.3 \times 0.5 = 1.2$ N
T is 4.6 cm long $T = 4.6 \times 0.5 = 2.3$ N

The answer can be checked using trigonometry, as shown on the next page.

In triangle ABC,
AB represents the weight which is 2 N
BC represents the horizontal force F

$$\text{but } \frac{BC}{AB} = \tan 30° = 0.58$$

$$BC = AB \times 0.58 = 2 \times 0.58 = 1.2$$

The horizontal force is 1.2 newtons.

$$\text{and } \frac{AB}{AC} = \cos 30°$$

$$AC = \frac{AB}{\cos 30°} = \frac{2}{0.87} = 2.3$$

The tension in the string T is 2.3 newtons.

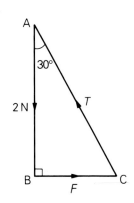

Example 9

A large bag of sand is suspended from
the ceiling by three ropes as indicated.
The weight of the bag is 70 N.
Find the forces acting on ropes 1 and 2.

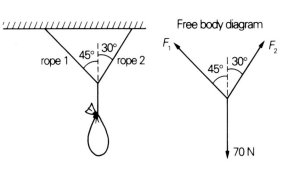

Free body diagram

Vector diagram
Scale: 1 cm represents 10 N

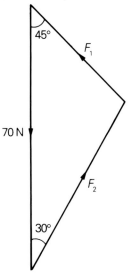

From the vector diagram:
length of vector representing F_2 = 5.1 cm

force F_2 = 51

length of vector representing F_1 = 3.6 cm

force F_1 = 36

The magnitudes of the forces in the ropes are 51 newtons and 36 newtons.

2.5 Momentum and collisions

This section is concerned with objects which collide.
In a collision between a vehicle and a wall, the total amount of damage can
perhaps indicate which physical quantities are important.
Consider the following

Figure 2.17 Mini moving slowly   **Figure 2.18** Mini moving fast

Figure 2.19 Bus moving slowly   **Figure 2.20** Bus moving fast

The mass of an object and the speed at which it is travelling affect the amount of damage; it can be concluded that:

'the greater the mass and the greater the speed at which it is travelling the more damage it would cause'.

Having identified mass and velocity as important factors in collisions, experiments can be carried out using colliding trolleys and measurements can be made of mass and velocity. These experiments can investigate the pattern of motion after the collision.

It is useful to use letters to indicate the mass of the moving objects and the velocities before and after the collision.

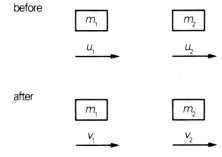

Collision experiments

Experiment 1

The arrangement used is shown in Figure 2.21.

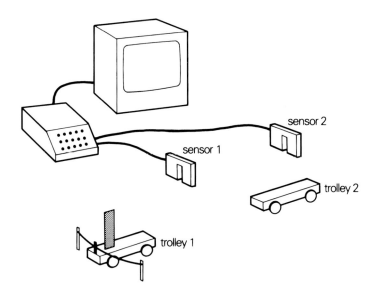

Figure 2.21

Trolley 1 is catapulted towards trolley 2 which is stationary. When they collide they stick together which means that they both move with the same common velocity.

The velocities of the trolleys are obtained photo-electrically and analysed by the computer.

When the marker interrupts the light beam in sensor 1, a pulse is sent to the computer.

The computer calculates the velocity u_1 of trolley 1 before the collision. On collision, the trolleys stick together and the marker interrupts the light beam in sensor 2.

The computer calculates the velocity v_1 of the trolleys after the collision; v_2 is the same as v_1.

Masses can be added to each trolley to change its mass.

A set of results is given in Tables 2 and 3.

| mass of trolley 1 | velocity of trolley 1 | | mass of trolley 2 | velocity of trolley 2 | | |
m_1 kg	u_1 $\mathrm{m\,s^{-1}}$	$m_1 u_1$ $\mathrm{kg\,m\,s^{-1}}$	m_2 kg	u_2 $\mathrm{m\,s^{-1}}$	$m_2 u_2$ $\mathrm{kg\,m\,s^{-1}}$	$m_1 u_1 + m_2 u_2$ $\mathrm{kg\,m\,s^{-1}}$
0.8	1.2	1.0	0.8	0	0	1.0
1.7	0.9	1.5	0.8	0	0	1.5
0.8	0.7	0.6	1.3	0	0	0.6
1.3	1.1	1.4	1.5	0	0	1.4

Table 2 Before the collision

| mass of trolley 1 | velocity of trolley 1 | | mass of trolley 2 | velocity of trolley 2 | | |
m_1 kg	v_1 $\mathrm{m\,s^{-1}}$	$m_1 v_1$ $\mathrm{kg\,m\,s^{-1}}$	m_2 kg	v_2 $\mathrm{m\,s^{-1}}$	$m_2 v_2$ $\mathrm{kg\,m\,s^{-1}}$	$m_1 v_1 + m_2 v_2$ $\mathrm{kg\,m\,s^{-1}}$
0.8	0.6	0.5	0.8	0.6	0.5	1.0
1.7	0.6	1.0	0.8	0.6	0.5	1.5
0.8	0.3	0.2	1.3	0.3	0.4	0.6
1.3	0.5	0.7	1.5	0.5	0.8	1.5

Table 3 After the collision

From the results it can be seen that the following relationship is confirmed.

$$m_1 u_1 + m_2 u_2 = m_1 v_1 + m_2 v_2$$

Example 10

Two identical vehicles collide on a linear air track, as shown below. The left-hand vehicle approaches at a constant velocity. The right-hand vehicle is stationary, but after the collision both vehicles travel to the right with the same constant velocity.

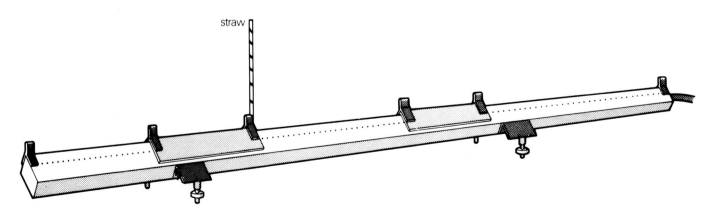

The diagram below is a representation of the stroboscopic photograph of the straw; the spacing is one-sixth full size and the flash rate is 10 Hz.

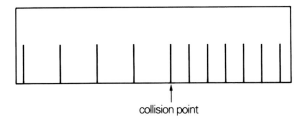

collision point

The mass of each vehicle is 0.2 kg.
Show that the product (mass × velocity) is the same before and after the collision.

flash rate = 10 per second
time interval = 0.1 second

From the photograph,
space between images before collision = 1 cm
actual distance = 6 × 1 = 6 cm

velocity of vehicle before collision = $\dfrac{\text{distance}}{\text{time}} = \dfrac{6}{0.1} = 60$

$= 0.60\,\text{m s}^{-1}$

Space between images after collision = 0.5 cm
actual distance = 6 × 0.5 = 3 cm

velocity of vehicles after collision = $\dfrac{\text{distance}}{\text{time}} = \dfrac{3}{0.1} = 30$

$= 0.30\,\text{m s}^{-1}$

total mass after collision = 0.2 + 0.2 = 0.4 kg
(mass × velocity) after   = 0.4 × 0.3 = 0.12 kg m s^{-1}
(mass × velocity) before = 0.2 × 0.6 = 0.12 kg m s^{-1}
The quantity (mass × velocity) is the same before and after the collision.

Experiment 2
In this experiment the vehicles do not stick together after the collision but move separately. Vehicles floating on a linear air track can be used to investigate such a collision, Figure 2.22.

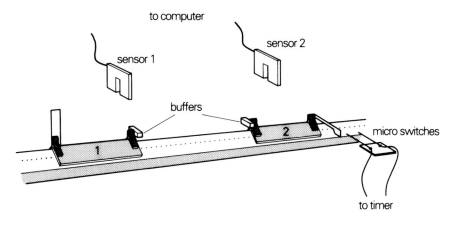

Figure 2.22

Vehicle 1 is catapulted towards vehicle 2 which is initially stationary. Both vehicles are fitted with rubber buffers so that they move off separately after impact.

Figure 2.23

Two or more vehicles can be clamped together in order to obtain different masses, Figure 2.23.

The marker on vehicle 1 interrupts the light beam of sensor 1 and a pulse is sent to the computer which calculates the velocity u_1 of vehicle 1 before the collision. After the collision the marker cuts the light beam of sensor 2 and the computer calculates the velocity v_1 of vehicle 1 after the collision.

In order to separate velocities of the vehicles after the collision the velocity of vehicle 2 is obtained in a different way. A light metal arm is attached to vehicle 2. This metal arm pushes against two thin rods which are connected to two microswitches which are connected to an electronic timer, Figure 2.24.

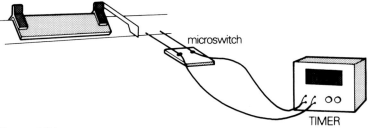

Figure 2.24

The first switch starts the timer and the second switch stops the timer. The distance between the rods is 0.1 metre so that the speed v_2 of vehicle 2 after the collision is given by

$$v_2 = \frac{0.1}{\text{time registered on the timer}}$$

Since vehicle 2 is stationary at the start, its velocity v_1 before the collision is zero.

A set of results is given in Tables 4 and 5.

m_1 kg	u_1 m s^{-1}	$m_1 u_1$ kg m s^{-1}	m_2 kg	u_2 m s^{-1}	$m_2 u_2$ kg m s^{-1}	$m_1 u_1 + m_2 u_2$ kg m s^{-1}
0.2	1.8	0.4	0.2	0	0	0.4
0.2	2.0	0.4	0.4	0	0	0.4
0.2	1.8	0.4	0.5	0	0	0.4
0.4	1.5	0.6	0.6	0	0	0.6
0.4	2.1	0.8	0.5	0	0	0.8

Table 4 Before the collision

m_1 kg	v_1 m s^{-1}	$m_1 v_1$ kg m s^{-1}	m_2 kg	v_2 m s^{-1}	$m_2 v_2$ kg m s^{-1}	$m_1 v_1 + m_2 v_2$ kg m s^{-1}
0.2	0.5	0.1	0.2	1.3	0.3	0.4
0.2	0.3	0.1	0.4	0.8	0.3	0.4
0.2	0.4	0.1	0.5	0.6	0.3	0.4
0.4	0.5	0.2	0.6	0.7	0.4	0.6
0.4	0.8	0.3	0.5	1.0	0.5	0.8

Table 5 After the collision

Investigation of the results from both experiments on collisions shows that the product (mass × velocity) has a special significance; (mass × velocity) is called **momentum**. For all objects involved in a collision, an equation can be used to describe the relationship between the values of the product (mass × velocity).

$$m_1 u_1 + m_2 u_2 = m_1 v_1 + m_2 v_2$$

This relationship is known as **the conservation of linear momentum** and can be written as

(total momentum before the collision) = (total momentum after the collision)

Example 11

A car moving at $30\,\mathrm{m\,s^{-1}}$ collides head-on with a small van which is stationary. The vehicles lock together. If the car has a mass of 900 kg and the van has a mass of 1200 kg, determine the common velocity of the vehicles after the collision.

By the principle of conservation of linear momentum:

$$m_1 u_1 + m_2 u_2 = m_1 v_1 + m_2 v_2$$

(momentum of car before collision) = (momentum of car plus van after collision)

$$900 \times 30 = (900 + 1200) \times v$$

$$v = \frac{900 \times 30}{2100} = 13$$

The velocity is $13\,\mathrm{m\,s^{-1}}$ after the collision.

Example 12

A trolley, mass 1 kg, moving at $1.2\,\mathrm{m\,s^{-1}}$ collides with a stationary trolley, mass 1 kg.
After the collision the first trolley slows down to $0.5\,\mathrm{m\,s^{-1}}$ and the other trolley moves off with velocity v_2.
Calculate the value of this velocity.

By conservation of linear momentum

$$m_1 u_1 + m_2 u_2 = m_1 v_1 + m_2 v_2$$
$$1 \times 1.2 + 1 \times 0 = 1 \times 0.5 + 1 \times v_2$$
$$v_2 = \frac{1.2 - 0.5}{1} = 0.7$$

The trolley moves off with a velocity of $0.7\,\mathrm{m\,s^{-1}}$.

2.6 Kinetic energy and collisions

In all collisions momentum is conserved.
Some of the kinetic energy is converted into heat which is generated during the impact.
This can be illustrated by calculating kinetic energies for the experimental results previously obtained in Section 2.5 (pages 33 to 37).

Results from experiment 1

total kinetic energy before $\frac{1}{2}m_1u^2$ (joules)	total kinetic energy after $\frac{1}{2}(m_1+m_2)v^2$ (joules)
0.6	0.3
0.7	0.5
0.2	0.1
0.8	0.4

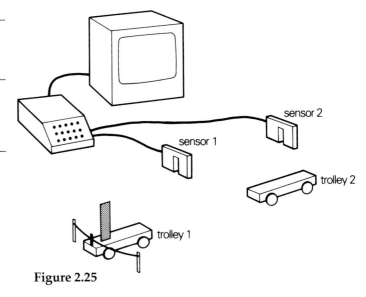

Figure 2.25

Results from experiment 2

total kinetic energy before $\frac{1}{2}m_1u_1^2+0$ (joules)	total kinetic energy after $\frac{1}{2}m_1v_1^2+\frac{1}{2}m_2v_2^2$ (joules)
0.32	$0.03 + 0.17 = 0.20$
0.40	$0.01 + 0.13 = 0.14$
0.32	$0.02 + 0.09 = 0.11$
0.45	$0.05 + 0.15 = 0.20$
0.88	$0.13 + 0.25 = 0.38$

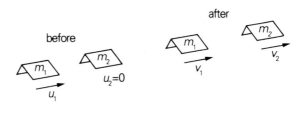

Figure 2.26

Collisions such as these in which there is a loss of kinetic energy are called **inelastic** collisions.

Example 13

A van, mass 1200 kg, is travelling at $30\,\text{m s}^{-1}$ when it collides with a stationary car, mass 800 kg.
If both vehicles lock together after the collision calculate the common velocity of the vehicles immediately after the accident and determine the loss of kinetic energy.

Let the velocity after the collision be v.
By conservation of momentum

$$m_1u_1 + m_2u_2 = m_1v_1 + m_2v_2$$
$$1200 \times 30 = (1200 + 800) \times v$$
$$v = \frac{1200 \times 30}{2000} = 18$$

the velocity after the collision is $18\,\text{m s}^{-1}$

kinetic energy before $= \frac{1}{2} \times 1200 \times 30^2 = 540\,\text{kJ}$

kinetic energy after $\;\; = \frac{1}{2} \times 2000 \times 18^2 = 324\,\text{kJ}$

There is a loss of kinetic energy of 216 kJ.

Elastic collisions

In an **elastic** collision, there is *no* loss of kinetic energy. Practical collisions are never perfectly elastic, but such a collision is approximated when two hard objects such as curling stones collide.
As in all collisions, momentum is conserved:

$$m_1u_1 + m_2u_2 = m_1v_1 + m_2v_2$$

and because $u_2 = 0$ and $v_1 = 0$, $\quad m_1u_1 = m_2v_2$
Since the collision is elastic, kinetic energy
is also conserved: $\qquad \frac{1}{2}m_1u_1^2 = \frac{1}{2}m_2v_2^2$

Figure 2.27

In the actual collision, the first curling stone does not stop immediately because the collision is not fully elastic, and the second curling stone moves off with a velocity slightly smaller than u_1.

Example 14

A single white snooker ball is hit towards a row of red balls lying along the cushion. Assuming an elastic collision, show that
a) one red shoots off the end of the row with the same velocity as that of the white before the collision,
b) it is impossible for the white ball and the red balls to move off together with a common velocity.

a) By conservation of momentum: $m_1u_1 + m_2u_2 = m_1v_1 + m_2v_2$

If the red ball has the same velocity v as the white, and the mass of each ball is m:

$$mv = mv$$

kinetic energy of white ball $= \frac{1}{2}mv^2$

kinetic energy of red ball $\;\;\; = \frac{1}{2}mv^2$

Kinetic energy is conserved.

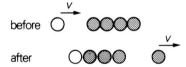

b) By conservation of momentum: $m_1u_1 + m_2u_2 = m_1v_1 + m_2v_2$

If the common velocity is v: $\qquad m_1u_1 + 0 = m_1v + m_2v$

and the mass of each ball is m: $\qquad mu_1 = mv + 4mv$

$$v = \tfrac{1}{5}u_1$$

kinetic energy before $= \frac{1}{2}mu_1^2$

kinetic energy after $\;\;\; = \frac{1}{2} \times (5m) \times (\tfrac{1}{5}u_1)^2$

$$= \tfrac{1}{5}(\tfrac{1}{2}mu_1^2)$$

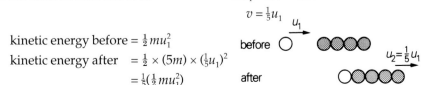

There is a loss of kinetic energy so that for an elastic collision, this is impossible.

2.7 Explosions

Explosions can be investigated by using two trolleys, one with a spring-loaded plunger, standing close to each other on a horizontal surface. When released, the plunger forces the trolleys apart, Figure 2.28.

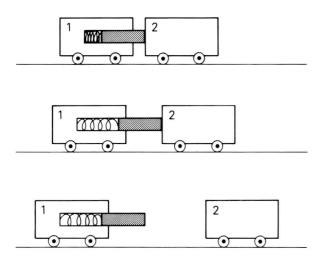

Figure 2.28

The mass of trolley 1, which is fitted with the plunger, remains unaltered but the mass of trolley 2 is varied by adding known masses to it.
The magnitude of the momentum of each trolley is calculated and entered in Table 6.

mass of trolley 1 is m_1; v_1 is velocity of trolley 1 after the explosion
mass of trolley 2 is m_2; v_2 is velocity of trolley 2 after the explosion

m_1 kg	v_1 m s^{-1}	$m_1 \times v_1$ kg m s^{-1}	m_2 kg	v_2 m s^{-1}	$m_2 \times v_2$ kg m s^{-1}
1	− 0.90	− 0.90	1	0.88	0.88
1	− 1.05	− 1.05	2	0.53	1.06
1	− 1.15	− 1.15	3	0.39	1.17
1	− 1.30	− 1.30	4	0.33	1.32

Table 6

Within the limits of the experiment, the momentum values for trolley 1 and trolley 2 have the same magnitude.
Before the explosion, both trolleys are stationary so that the momentum of each is zero.
If we take the direction of motion of each trolley into account so that one direction is taken to be positive and the other as negative, momentum will be conserved.
Taking motion to the right as positive and motion to the left as negative:

$$m_1 v_1 + m_2 v_2 = 0$$

It can be concluded from this that momentum is a vector quantity.

Example 15

A girl and her brother are on an ice rink.
They push each other apart.
Calculate the speed of the girl if the boy moves off at $0.6\,\text{m s}^{-1}$.

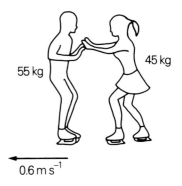

By conservation of momentum:

$$m_1 v_1 + m_2 v_2 = 0$$
$$-45 \times v_1 + 55 \times 0.6 = 0$$
$$v_1 = \frac{55 \times 0.6}{45}$$
$$= 0.7$$

The girl moves off with a speed of $0.7\,\text{m s}^{-1}$.

2.8 Impulse

Suppose that an object, mass m, is acted upon by a net force F for a time t which causes the velocity to change from u to v.

By Newton's Second Law $F = ma$

but the acceleration $a = \dfrac{v - u}{t}$

and substituting for a in the first equation we get

$$F = \frac{m(v - u)}{t}$$
$$= \frac{mv - mu}{t}$$

but mv = final momentum
and mu = initial momentum
so that $(mv - mu)$ is the change in momentum. It follows that

$$\text{net force} = \frac{\text{change in momentum}}{\text{time during which force acts}}$$

and this can be written

force × time during which it acts = change of momentum

$$Ft = mv - mu$$

The product Ft is called the impulse of the force and the unit of impulse is the newton-second which is the same as the unit of momentum, kg m s^{-1}.

Forces which act over short time intervals are, in general, not constant. A typical variation of force with time is shown in Figure 2.29. In such a case the impulse is given by the area under the graph, which is indicated by the shading. Thus the change in momentum produced equals the area under the force-time graph.

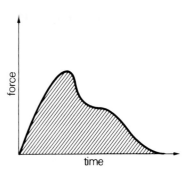

Figure 2.29

Often the exact variation of the force is not known and the average force $\overline{F}$ is used so that the equation becomes

$$\overline{F}t = mv - mu$$

where $\overline{F}$ = average force acting during the time interval.

Example 16

A billiard cue hits a stationary ball, mass 0.2 kg, which is at rest. The ball moves off with a velocity of 3 m s^{-1} and the time of contact between the ball and the cue is 0.015 s. Calculate the average force exerted by the cue on the ball.

$$\overline{F} = \frac{mv - mu}{t} \qquad \text{where } v = 3 \text{ m s}^{-1}$$
$$u = 0$$
$$m = 0.2 \text{ kg}$$
$$t = 0.015 \text{ s}$$

$$\overline{F} = \frac{0.2 \times 3 - 0.2 \times 0}{0.015}$$

$$= \frac{0.6}{0.015}$$

$$= 40$$

The force exerted by the cue is 40 N.

2.9 Newton's Third Law

Newton's Third Law states

'To every action force, there is an equal and opposite reaction force.'

This could be demonstrated using the equipment shown in Figure 2.30.

A spring-loaded trolley is placed close to but not touching another trolley on a horizontal surface. The metal plunger of trolley A and the metal edge of trolley B are connected to the start terminals of an electronic timer using long thin wire. When the plunger is triggered, it makes contact with the edge of trolley B and the electronic timer records the contact time. Each trolley shoots off and the card attached to it cuts a light beam causing the electric clock to operate. This allows the velocity of each trolley to be calculated.

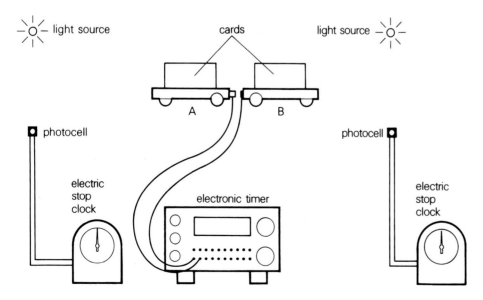

Figure 2.30

The following results were obtained.

trolley A			*trolley B*	
length of card	0.1 m		length of card	0.1 m
time on clock	0.32 s		time on clock	0.25 s
mass m_A	1.20 kg		mass m_B	0.90 kg
time of contact	0.05 s		time of contact	0.05 s

$$\text{speed of A} = \frac{\text{length of card}}{\text{time on clock}}$$

$$= \frac{0.1}{0.32}$$

$$= 0.31 \text{ m s}^{-1}$$

$$\text{speed of B} = \frac{\text{length of card}}{\text{time on clock}}$$

$$= \frac{0.1}{0.25}$$

$$= 0.40 \text{ m s}^{-1}$$

We can use these results and the law of conservation of momentum to calculate the average force exerted on each trolley

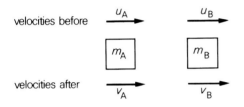

velocities before

velocities after

Figure 2.31

From the results:

$$u_A = 0 \qquad\qquad u_B = 0$$

$$v_A = -0.31 \text{ m s}^{-1} \qquad\qquad v_B = 0.40 \text{ m s}^{-1}$$

To calculate the average force we use:
$$\bar{F} = \frac{mv - mu}{t}$$

$$\bar{F}_A = \frac{m_A v_A - m_A u_A}{t}$$

$$= \frac{1.20 \times (-0.31) - 0}{0.05}$$

$$= -\frac{0.37}{0.05}$$

$$= -7.4$$

$\bar{F}_A$ is -7.4 N

$$\bar{F}_B = \frac{m_B v_B - m_B u_B}{t}$$

$$= \frac{0.90 \times 0.40 - 0}{0.05}$$

$$= \frac{0.36}{0.05}$$

$$= 7.2$$

$\bar{F}_B$ is 7.2 N

We can see that, within the limits of experimental error

$$\bar{F}_A = -\bar{F}_B \qquad\qquad \text{thus confirming Newton's Third Law.}$$

The average force acting on each trolley will be 7.3 N.

2 Dynamics

Example 17

Two trolleys A (mass 1 kg) and B (mass 3 kg) are attached with an elastic cord and pulled apart by a distance of 1 m on a horizontal surface.

They are released simultaneously and collide at point P. Find the displacements s_A and s_B.

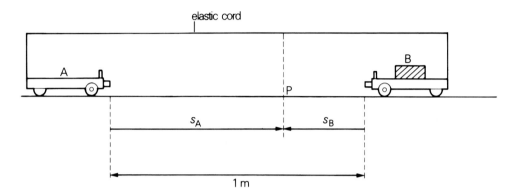

Because of Newton's Third Law, the average force $\overline{F}_A$ exerted on trolley A by the elastic cord has the same magnitude as the average force $\overline{F}_B$ exerted on trolley B by the elastic cord, but it will act in the opposite direction.

$$\overline{F}_A = -\overline{F}_B$$

The work done on trolley A by the cord $= \overline{F}_A s_A$

This will provide the trolley with kinetic energy given by $\frac{1}{2} m_A v_A^2$ where v_A = velocity of A just before impact

$$\overline{F}_A s_A = \frac{1}{2} m_A v_A^2$$

In the same way $\overline{F}_B s_B = \frac{1}{2} m_B v_B^2$

but $m_A = 1$ kg and $m_B = 3$ kg $\quad \Rightarrow \quad \overline{F}_A s_A = \frac{1}{2} v_A^2 \quad \dots [1]$

$$\Rightarrow \quad \overline{F}_B s_B = \frac{3}{2} v_B^2 \quad \dots [2]$$

The initial momentum is zero and since there is no external force acting on the whole system, the momentum just before impact is also zero.

$$m_A v_A + m_B v_B = 0$$

$$m_A v_A = -m_B v_B \quad \Rightarrow \quad v_A = -3 v_B$$

If we divide the energy equations [1] and [2] and substitue $-3v_B$ for v_A we have

$$\frac{\overline{F}_B s_B}{\overline{F}_A s_A} = \frac{\frac{3}{2} v_B^2}{\frac{1}{2} v_A^2}$$

$$\frac{\overline{F}_B s_B}{\overline{F}_A s_A} = \frac{3 v_B^2}{v_A^2} \quad \Rightarrow \quad \frac{-\overline{F}_A s_B}{\overline{F}_A s_A} = \frac{3 v_B^2}{(-3 v_B)^2}$$

$$\frac{-s_B}{s_A} = \frac{3 v_B^2}{9 v_B^2} \quad \Rightarrow \quad \frac{-s_B}{s_A} = \frac{1}{3}$$

$$s_A = -3 s_B$$

The total distance between the trolleys at the start is 1 m.

The magnitude of s_A must be 0.75 m and of s_B must be 0.25 m.

If we wish to indicate the vector direction of the displacements, we can write

$$s_A = +0.75 \text{ m and } s_B = -0.25 \text{ m}$$

Summary

Newton's Second Law is expressed by the equation $F = ma$

The newton is defined as that force which gives a mass of 1 kg an acceleration of $1\,\mathrm{m\,s^{-2}}$.

Force is a vector quantity.

The resultant of two forces which do not act along the same straight line is found by vector addition.

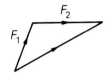

When an object is in equilibrium under the action of three forces, the vector diagram is a triangle.

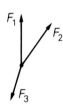 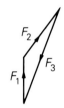

Momentum is a vector quantity.

Momentum is the product of mass times velocity.

The Principle of Conservation of Linear Momentum states that:

'for any collision between two objects moving along the same straight line, momentum is conserved provided there are no external forces acting on the objects'

For any collision or explosion

total momentum before = total momentum after

In an inelastic collision momentum is conserved but there is a loss of kinetic energy.

In a perfectly elastic collision both momentum and kinetic energy are conserved.

Newton's Third Law states that, when two objects interact, they exert forces on each other which are equal in magnitude but opposite in direction.

impulse = force × time

When a force is variable, the impulse is given by the area under the force-time graph.

impulse = change of momentum

$$Ft = mv - mu$$

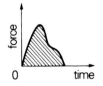

Problems

1   Describe an experiment which could be conducted to estimate the unbalanced force acting on a trolley which is accelerated uniformly along a horizontal surface by a stretched elastic cord.
How could you check the answer you obtain for the force?

2   A train, mass 250 tonnes, experiences a total frictional resistance of 10 kN as it accelerates at $2\,\mathrm{m\,s^{-2}}$ along a horizontal track.
   a)   Calculate the total driving force required to produce this acceleration.
   b)   Assuming that the frictional resistance remains the same, calculate the driving force required to maintain the same acceleration up an incline which makes an angle of 8° to the horizontal.

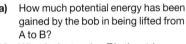

3   The string of a pendulum is held at an angle of 45° as shown. The mass of the bob is 0.1 kg and the length of the pendulum is 1 m.
   a)   How much potential energy has been gained by the bob in being lifted from A to B?
   b)   What is the tension T in the string when it is let go?

4   An object, mass 5 kg, falls freely towards the surface of a planet with an acceleration of $5\,\mathrm{m\,s^{-2}}$.
   a)   What is the force of gravity, acting on the object, due to the planet?
   b)   At what height will the object have gained 150 joules of potential energy if it were raised from the surface of the planet?

5   An elastic cord is stretched between two supports as shown.

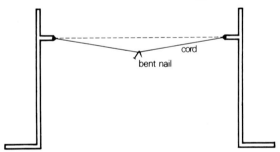

A bent nail is suspended on the cord; the cord is released and the nail is catapulted vertically upwards.
Explain how you would estimate the potential energy stored in the cord.

6   a)   Which physical quantity is defined as the change in momentum per unit time?
   b)   In which unit is the quantity measured?

7   a)   A golf club exerts an average force of 2.8 kN on a ball of mass 0.05 kg. If the contact time is $4 \times 10^{-4}\,\mathrm{s}$, determine the velocity of the ball as it leaves the club.
   b)   A vehicle, mass 0.1 kg, moves along a horizontal linear air track at a constant speed of $0.2\,\mathrm{m\,s^{-1}}$. If it is in contact with an elastic cord for 0.3 s and rebounds with a speed of $0.16\,\mathrm{m\,s^{-1}}$, calculate the average force acting on the vehicle.

8 Which physical quantities are represented by the shaded areas shown in the graphs?

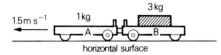

(a)   (b)

9 Two trolleys are exploded apart on a horizontal surface. If trolley A moves off at 1.5 m s⁻¹, calculate the velocity of B. Calculate the kinetic energies of the trolleys just as they move off.

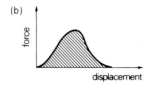

10 A ball mass 0.1 kg is dropped from a height of 3.2 m.
   a) How long will it take to hit the ground?
   b) Construct a graph showing how the kinetic energy varies with time until the ball hits the ground.

11 A spring is attached to the lid of a cocoa tin and a weight of 1 N is hung at the end. A pointer is fixed to the spring and sticks out from a slit which is cut in the side of the tin. Explain what you would expect to happen to the pointer in the following situations.
   a) the tin is allowed to fall down vertically
   b) the tin is thrown vertically upwards
   c) the tin is placed on a trolley which is then pushed along a horizontal surface.

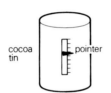

12 The force acting on an object, mass 1.5 kg, varies with time as shown.
   a) Determine the impulse of the force over this 3 second period.
   b) What is the change in momentum of the object after 3 s?
   c) Calculate the kinetic energy of the object at the end of 3 s if the initial velocity of the object was zero.

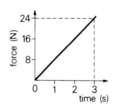

13 A rocket-powered sledge has a mass of 210 kg unloaded. During a test run an astronaut, mass 85 kg with equipment, sits on the sledge and is accelerated along a frictionless horizontal track. The speed is measured and automatically recorded, the results of which are given in the graph.

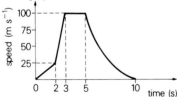

   a) What distance was covered in the first 5 seconds?
   b) Calculate the thrust provided during the first 2 seconds.
   c) Was the decelerating force acting on the sledge constant?

14 The unbalanced thrust on an object, mass 100 kg, varies as shown.
   a) If the initial speed of the object is zero, draw a speed-time graph for the object for the 20 second period.
   b) Calculate the distance travelled by the object during this time.

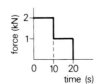

15 A boxer exerts an average force of 200 N on a punchbag for a time of 0.15 s. The mass of the bag is 40 kg.
   a) What is the velocity of the bag after it leaves the glove?
   b) How high would the bag rise vertically above the starting position?
   c) Describe a method by which the average force exerted by a boxing glove could be estimated.

16 When a catapult is used to fire a stone, it exerts an average force of 12 N. The stone has a mass of 0.043 kg and acquires a speed of 7 m s⁻¹. Estimate the time of contact between the catapult and the stone. How could the average force exerted by the elastic of the catapult be estimated?

17 An electric train has a mass of 2.5×10^5 kg. It makes a journey between two stations on a horizontal track. The speed changes with time as indicated on the graph. The effective resistance opposing the motion of the train is 20 kN.

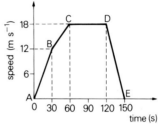

   a) Calculate the acceleration during each section of the motion.
   b) Determine the total force applied during section BC.
   c) What is the driving power of the train during period CD?

18 Two blocks slide towards each other, collide and stop.

   a) Is momentum conserved?
   b) Calculate the loss of kinetic energy.
   c) Where has the kinetic energy gone?

19 An object, mass 0.8 kg, slides from rest down an incline. It slides 2 m down the incline, falling a vertical height of 1.5 m and attaining a speed of 2 m s⁻¹

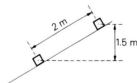

   a) Calculate the loss of potential energy.
   b) What is the kinetic energy of the object?
   c) Determine the force of friction acting on the object.

20 The motion of a 5 kg radio-controlled car is represented on the graph.
   a) What was the initial speed of the car?
   b) Draw a graph showing the unbalanced force acting on the car during the 12 seconds shown.
   c) Calculate the distance travelled by the car.

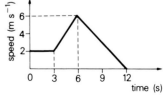

21 A vehicle on a linear air track has a mass of 80 g. It is catapulted by an elastic cord which is pulled back a short distance. When released the vehicle moves off at 0.4 m s^{-1} after being in contact with the cord for 0.045 s.

a) Calculate the momentum of the trolley.

b) What is the average force exerted by the cord?

c) Estimate the original potential energy stored in the stretched cord.

22 A student of mass 70 kg investigates the motion of a lift. He stands on a weighing machine in the lift on its downward journey in a high building. For 2 seconds immediately after the lift starts, the weighing machine reads 560 N; then for a further 6 seconds it reads 700 N, and for the final 2 seconds it reads 840 N.

a) Describe the motion of the lift during its journey.

b) Calculate the magnitude and direction of the resultant force acting on the student during each stage of the journey.

c) Draw a graph of acceleration against time for the journey. The axes of the graph should clearly indicate the values of the acceleration at different times.

SEB

23 In an experiment to check the calibration of a spring balance a trolley of mass 4.0 kg is pulled down a friction-compensated track. Positions of the marker straw attached to the trolley are obtained from a stroboscopic photograph.

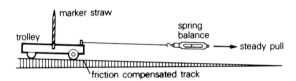

A section of the resulting stroboscopic photograph is shown. The flash rate of the stroboscope was 10 flashes per second and the spring balance registered a steady reading of 0.90 N.

a) Determine the resultant force applied to the trolley.

b) Suggest **two** reasons which might account for the difference between the calculated resultant force and the spring balance reading. Explain how each reason accounts for the observed difference.

SEB

24 A vehicle is travelling along a horizontal linear air track. A card on the vehicle passes through a light beam before the vehicle is stopped by a stretched elastic band. While the vehicle is being stopped, the centre of the elastic moves from O to P.

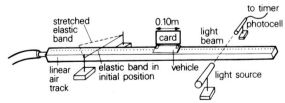

Results obtained from one run of the vehicle are:

Mass of vehicle and card = 1.1 kg

Length of card = 0.10 m

Time through light beam = 0.25 s

Stopping distance OP = 0.050 m

a) Calculate

i) the average force exerted by the elastic band on the vehicle while it is being stopped:

ii) the time taken by the elastic band to stop the vehicle.

b) Describe how you would measure the maximum stretch OP of the elastic band experimentally.

SEB

25 In driving a pile into the ground, a hammer of mass 500 kg falls freely from rest through a height of 5.0 m on to a pile of mass 1500 kg. The pile and hammer then move together as the pile is driven 0.12 m into the ground.

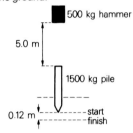

a) Determine the speed of the hammer just before it hits the pile.

b) **i)** Using the Principle of Conservation of Momentum, calculate the common speed of pile and hammer immediately after the collision.

ii) State one assumption which you must make to justify your application of momentum conservation in part **b) i)**.

c) From the moment just after collision until the system comes to rest, what is the change in

i) the total kinetic energy of pile and hammer

ii) the total potential energy of pile and hammer?

d) By considering these energy changes, or otherwise, calculate a value for the average resistive force which the ground offers to the motion of the pile during its movement into the ground.

SEB

26 A train consists of an engine and a line of three wagons. Each wagon has a mass of 20 000 kg. The resistive forces due to friction acting on the wagons can be assumed constant at all speeds and equal to 1000 N on each wagon.

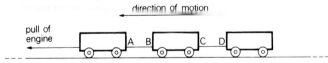

a) When the train is moving along a straight, horizontal stretch of track, the engine exerts a constant pull of 45 000 N on the front wagon.

Calculate **i)** the acceleration of the train;

ii) the tension in the coupling chain, AB.

b) With the same engine pull continuing to act, the train moves on to a straight, downhill section, the slope of which just compensates for the resistive forces acting on the wagons. During this part of the run state whether the tension in the coupling chain CD is less than, equal to, or greater than the tension in coupling chain AB. **Explain** your choice.

c) Finally the train moves on to another straight, horizontal track and the engine pull is reduced until the train is running at a constant speed. Again **explain** how the tension in coupling chain CD will compare with the tension in coupling chain AB.

SEB

27 In a laboratory experiment a vehicle on a track is set in motion by a catapult incorporating a number of identical elastic cords. The diagram shows the arrangement of the catapult system.

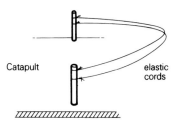

Catapult   elastic cords

a) What practical steps would you take to ensure that friction is made negligible and how would you check that this has been done?

b) The speed achieved by the vehicle when catapulted by different numbers of elastic cords is recorded in the table on the right.

Number of cords N	Speed in m s⁻¹ v
1	0.41
2	0.57
3	0.69
4	0.80

    i) From theoretical considerations, what relationship would you expect between N and v?

    ii) Show whether the results verify this relationship.

c) State any **two** practical factors likely to lead to discrepancies in the results.

SEB

28 In an experiment, a block of mass 1.00 kg is released from rest from a point A 2.00 m up a slope as shown in the diagram. The block slides down to the point B at the bottom of the slope where its speed is measured. This is repeated several times, the block being released from the same point A each time but with the slope adjusted so that the initial height h is different on each occasion.

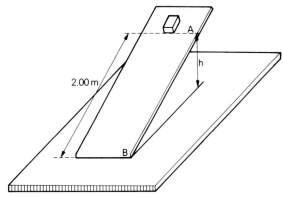

The speeds of the block for four different initial heights are shown in the table.

Height h (m)	0.60	1.00	1.40	1.80
Speed at B (m s⁻¹)	2.50	3.85	4.90	5.80
Potential energy at A (J)				
Kinetic energy at B (J)				

a) **i)** Copy the table and complete it to show the potential energy of the block at A and the kinetic energy of the block at B.

    ii) Account for the difference between the potential energy at A and the corresponding kinetic energy at B.

b) Calculate the average frictional force acting on the block during the experiment when h = 1.00 m.

c) **i)** Plot a graph of the kinetic energy at B against the initial height h

    ii) Use this graph to find a value for the initial height h which makes the slope friction-compensated for this block.

SEB

29 Two vehicles travel in the same direction along the same straight line. After 5 seconds the vehicles collide and stick together. The velocity time graphs for the motion of each vehicle are shown below.

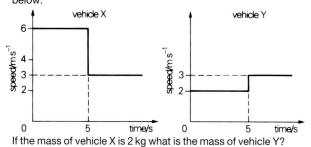

If the mass of vehicle X is 2 kg what is the mass of vehicle Y?

30 A clockwork car, mass 200 g, is set on a plank which floats on a cushion of air.
The mass of the plank is 500 g.
If the car moves to the right with a speed of 0.4 m s⁻¹ calculate the speed of the plank.

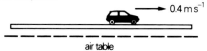

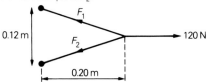

air table

31 A catapult is extended a distance of 0.20 m by a force of 120 N. Find the value of forces F_1 and F_2.

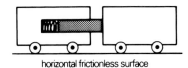

32 Two trolleys of mass 2 kg and 4 kg are moving along a level track together at 2 m s⁻¹.

horizontal frictionless surface

A spring-loaded plunger is operated and this causes the 2 kg trolley to stop and the 4 kg trolley to move off with increased speed. Calculate the speed of the 4 kg trolley.

33 An acrobat stands on a tightrope. The rope makes an angle of 7° on each side.

If his weight is 800 N, calculate the tension in each half of the rope.

34 A crane supports a 2 tonne package as indicated in the diagram. Find, using a scale diagram, values for the force in the cable F_1 and the force in the crane arm F_2.

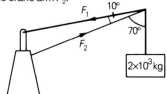

35 Two vehicles on a linear air track collide.
Vehicle A approaches vehicle B with a speed of 2 m s⁻¹ while vehicle B is at rest.
After the collision vehicle A is moving with speed 0.8 m s⁻¹

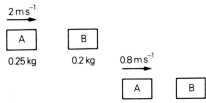

Calculate   **a)** the velocity of vehicle B
             b) loss of kinetic energy during the collision.

36 A rocket is on a launch vehicle resting on a linear air track. When the rocket is lit it shoots off and the vehicle recoils.

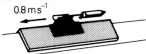

If the recoil velocity of the vehicle is 0.8 m s⁻¹ and the mass of the vehicle is 0.3 kg calculate the impulse exerted on the vehicle by the rocket. If the rocket takes 0.25 seconds to leave the vehicle find the average force exerted on the vehicle.

37 An object is held in the position shown by two strings.
If the force of friction at the pulley is negligible find the values of forces T_1 and T_2.

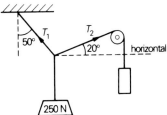

38 A weight of 5 kN hangs over a pulley. Two ends of the rope are anchored to the wall and the ceiling making angles as indicated. Assuming the pulley to be frictionless find the magnitudes of forces F_1 and F_2.

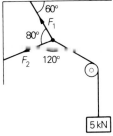

39 A light spring has a mass of 0.2 kg suspended from its lower end. A second mass of 0.1 kg is suspended from the first by a thread.

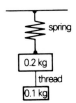

The arrangement is allowed to become stationary and then the thread is burned through. At this instant what is the upward acceleration of the 0.2 kg mass?

SEB

40 A girl on a sledge slides down a slope. The total mass of the girl and the sledge is 100 kg. The record of their journey from A to D is indicated on a combined stopwatch-speedometer attached to the sledge. The readings of this instrument at positions A, B, C and D are shown.

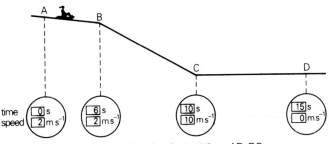

a) Which stage of the journey takes the shortest time: AB, BC or CD?
b) Describe the motion of the sledge during each of these stages.
c) Calculate the average retarding force acting on the sledge during stage CD.
d) If the girl lies flat along the sledge after passing A, suggest possible new readings on the stopwatch-speedometer as the sledge passes B.

SEB

41 a) In an experiment at an accident research unit, a moving car P was made to collide with a second stationary car Q. On impact, the two cars stuck together and afterwards skidded to rest.

The graph shows the velocity of car P throughout the experiment.

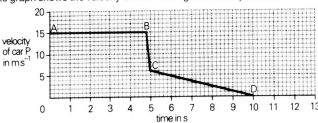

   i) Which section of the graph corresponds to the collision between the cars?
   ii) Which section of the graph corresponds to the cars skidding to rest?
   iii) State the velocity of car Q at the time corresponding to point B on the graph.
b) A dummy of mass 70 kg was firmly fixed in car P using a seat belt. Information from the graph indicates a deceleration during the collision of 45 m s⁻².
   i) Calculate the force exerted by the seat belt on the dummy.
   ii) Describe carefully what would have happened to the dummy if it had not been wearing a seat belt. Explain your answer in terms of Newton's laws of motion.
c) **i)** Calculate the deceleration of the cars as they skidded to rest.
   ii) The experiment was repeated with identical cars when the road was wet. When a graph was drawn of the velocity of the moving car, it was found to be identical to the above graph up to point C. What difference would you expect to find in the section CD of the graph? Explain your answer.

SEB

42 Two vehicles are fired from opposite ends of a horizontal frictionless air-track using catapults X and Y constructed from single identical elastic bands. Vehicle A has a mass of 0.3 kg and vehicle B has a mass of 0.1 kg.

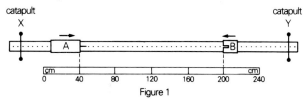

Figure 1

Two seconds after passing the positions shown in Figure 1, the vehicles collide and stop opposite the 80 cm mark as shown in Figure 2.

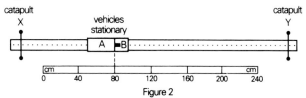

Figure 2

a) Copy and complete the following table for the motion of the vehicles before the collision.

Quantity	unit	vehicle A	vehicle B
mass	kg	0.3	0.1
speed	m s^{-1}		
momentum	kg m s^{-1}		
kinetic energy	J		

b) What is the total momentum i) before the collision and ii) after the collision?
c) Which catapult was stretched more to fire its vehicle? Explain your answer.

SEB

43 A 2 kg mass is hanging by a string from the roof. A horizontal force H is applied to hold the string in the position shown in the diagram.

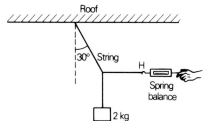

By drawing a scale diagram or otherwise, find the reading on the spring balance.

SEB

44 According to Newton's Third Law, forces always exist as equal and opposite partners.
Name the partner of each of the forces X and Y shown in the diagram.

SEB

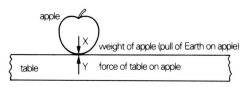

45 The diagram below shows apparatus used to investigate collisions.

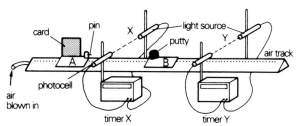

a) In one experiment vehicle B is initially at rest and vehicle A is moving at a steady speed. After passing X, vehicle A collides with vehicle B and remains joined to it.

The results are shown below.

mass of vehicle A	= 0.10 kg
mass of vehicle B	= 0.06 kg
length of card on vehicle A	= 0.10 m
time to pass photocell X	= 0.50 s
time to pass photocell Y	= 0.80 s

  i) Calculate the speed of vehicle A before the collision.
  ii) Calculate the speed of vehicles A and B after the collision.
  iii) Use these results to show that momentum is conserved in this collision.
b) This apparatus could be adapted to measure the speed of an air rifle pellet.
  Describe
  i) how the apparatus would be arranged,
  ii) the measurements which would be made, and
  iii) how the speed of the pellet would be calculated from these measurements.

SEB

46 A rocket of mass 2.2×10^6 kg is launched vertically. The rocket engines exert a constant force of 3.0×10^7 N.
a) Calculate the resultant force on the rocket at take-off.
b) Find the initial acceleration of the rocket as it takes off.
c) The table below shows the speed of the rocket at intervals of time after the launch.

Time (s)	0	10	20	30	40
Speed (m s^{-1})	0	40	90	150	220

State what the figures in the table indicate about the acceleration of the rocket during the first 40 seconds of flight.

SEB

47 A liquid-fuelled rocket is taking off vertically upwards.

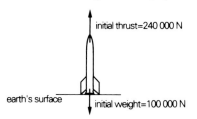

a) What is the initial acceleration of the rocket?
b) Assuming that the burning fuel provides a constant thrust, explain what would happen to the acceleration as the rocket rises.

SEB

48 a) The passenger cars on a roller-coaster at a fun-fair are pulled up to point A and released.

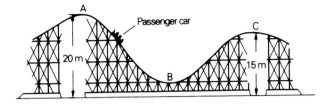

A safety officer requires to measure experimentally the speed of the cars as they pass the lowest point B on the track.
Describe how the safety officer could carry out the experiment.
Your description should include:
 i) a sketch of the apparatus used;
 ii) the procedure carried out and the measurements taken;
 iii) an indication of how the final result would be obtained.

b) During one run, a car and passengers of mass 800 kg are released from rest at point A, a height of 20 m above the ground. The car travels a distance of 120 m along the track until it reaches point C, a height of 15 m above the ground. A constant frictional force of 250 N acts between the car and the track as the car moves from A to C.
 i) State the energy changes which occur as the car moves from A to C.
 ii) Calculate the work done against friction in moving the car from A to C.
 iii) Find the kinetic energy of the car on reaching point C.

SEB

49 On an air track a lighter vehicle hits a heavier one and bounces back from it. The mass of the lighter vehicle is 0.1 kg and its speed before the collision is 8 m s⁻¹. After impact it rebounds at 2 m s⁻¹.

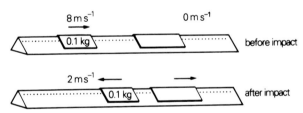

a) Calculate the size of the change of momentum of the heavier vehicle.
b) What additional information would be needed to calculate the average force exerted on the heavier vehicle due to the collision?

SEB

50 A water skier is being towed as shown by a boat travelling at constant speed.

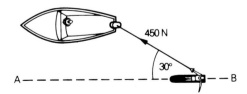

If the tension in the rope is 450 N, calculate the force acting along line AB opposing the forward motion of the skier.

SEB

51 A stationary snooker ball of mass 0.2 kg is hit by a cue so that the ball moves off with an initial velocity of 2 m s⁻¹. The time of contact between the cue and the ball is measured electronically to be 50 ms.

Calculate the average force exerted on the ball by the cue.

SEB

52 a) State the difference between vector quantities and scalar quantities. Give an example of each.

b) An oil-rig is being towed by two tugs A and B to its operating position in the North Sea. The angle between the two horizontal tow lines is 90°, and the rig is moving at a constant speed.

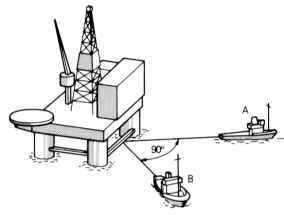

 i) If each tug exerts a pull of 2×10^6 N, calculate the size and direction of the resultant force exerted by the tugs.
 ii) What is the size and direction of the total force of friction acting on the oil-rig when it is moving at this constant speed?

SEB

53 a) Two girls are arguing about which of them is able to hit a hockey ball harder. Describe an experiment which they could carry out to measure the average force between a hockey stick and ball during the time of contact.
Your description should include:
 i) a labelled diagram of the apparatus
 ii) the experimental procedures
 iii) the measurements taken
 iv) an indication of how the average force would be found.

b) During a game of hockey, a stationary ball of mass 0.15 kg is struck by a player. The graph below shows how the force on the ball varies with time.

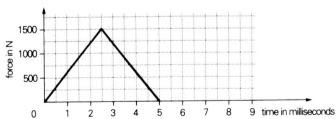

 i) Calculate the speed with which the ball leaves the hockey stick.
 ii) During an indoor practice game the same player hits a practice ball of the same mass but which is made from a softer material. The ball moves off with the same speed as before. Sketch a graph showing how the force on the practice ball might vary with time. Indicate how this graph compares with that shown above.

SEB

54 A cliff railway is used at a seaside resort to transport passengers up and down a slope of length 80 m, from the promenade to the top of a cliff. The vertical distance from the level of the promenade to the top of the cliff is 40 m.

The railway system consists of two cars, each of mass 9000 kg, connected by cable to each other via a large pulley which is driven by an electric motor in the upper station. The cars run on parallel tracks and as one car descends the slope the other car ascends.

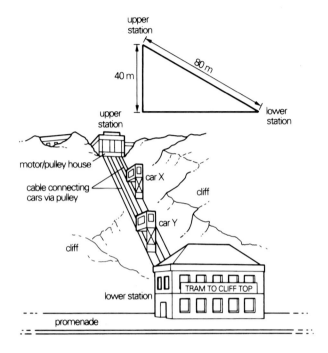

The frictional forces acting on the system can be assumed constant and equal to 6000 N on each car.

a) In one journey 20 passengers descended to the promenade in car X while 8 passengers ascended to the cliff top in car Y. The average mass of each passenger was 70 kg. The electric motor had to operate throughout the journey.

i) Why was the loss in the potential energy of the loaded car X not sufficient to raise car Y to the upper station?

ii) What was the change in the potential energy of the system as a result of this journey?

iii) How much work was done against the frictional forces in moving the cars?

iv) Calculate the average output power from the electric motor if the journey time was 30 seconds.

b) Explain how the tension in the cable attached to an ascending car might vary as it moves from the lower to the upper station, the middle part of the journey being covered at constant speed.

SEB

55 A physicist is asked to consider how a space probe might behave when launched from a certain planet. As a first step he assumes that the mass of the probe is constant at 1500 kg and that the engine exerts a constant force.

In a particular part of this study he imagines that the probe is rising vertically from the surface of the planet when its engine suddenly cuts out. The graph below shows how the velocity of the probe varies with time from the instant of lift off.

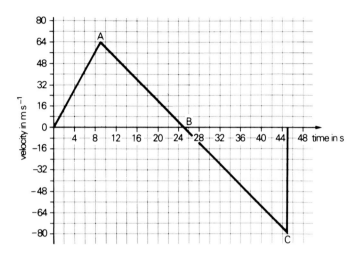

a) Suggest what happens to the probe 9, 25 and 45 seconds after lift off i.e. at points A, B and C on the velocity-time graph.

b) Find the greatest height above the surface of the planet reached by the probe.

c) Calculate the acceleration due to gravity on the planet.

d) Assuming that the planet has no atmosphere:

i) draw a sketch showing the forces acting on the probe during lift off;

ii) calculate the force exerted by the probe engine during this time.

e) In reality, although the force exerted by the engine remains constant, the mass of the probe varies as fuel is used. Draw a sketch graph to show how the velocity might change with time in this case. On your graph mark the points corresponding to points A, B and C mentioned in **a)**

SEB

3 Properties of matter

3.1 Introduction

In the investigation of the properties of gases it is normal to measure the three quantities, pressure, temperature and volume. The changes in these quantities can be explained in terms of the motion of particles. This chapter will consider the results for experiments on gases, and describe matter in terms of particles.

Pressure

Like the word 'work', pressure has many meanings in everyday use. For example, we talk of the pressure of exams, or pressure being exerted by the Government. In physics however, pressure is defined in terms of two other quantities, force and area. The following example illustrates the effects of different pressures.

When you stand in soft snow you sink into it. This is because your weight is acting over a small area, the area of your feet. However, if you wear snow shoes you find that you can walk over the snow without sinking in, Figure 3.1.

Your weight has not changed but has simply been spread over a much larger area by the snow shoes.

Without snow shoes a force is exerted on a small area and so the force on unit area is large. In this case we say that the **pressure** is large and so you sink into the snow. When wearing snow shoes, the same force is exerted over a much larger area and so the force on unit area is much smaller. We say that the pressure is smaller and so this time you do not sink. To be more exact, we define pressure as follows,

$$\text{pressure} = \frac{\text{force acting at right angles to an area}}{\text{area}}$$

i.e. $p = \dfrac{F}{A}$

where p = pressure, F = force, A = area

Figure 3.1 Soldier using snow shoes

Units

As the SI unit of force is the newton (N) and the SI unit of area is the square metre (m^2) it follows that the unit of pressure is the newton per square metre, written as $N\ m^{-2}$. This unit has been named the pascal (Pa) after Blaise Pascal, a Frenchman who did many experiments involving gas and liquid pressures.

$1\ \text{Pa} = 1\ N\ m^{-2}$

However the pascal is a very small unit and so we will often use the kilopascal (kPa) where $1000\ \text{Pa} = 1\ \text{kPa}$.

Example 1

Calculate the pressure produced by a force of 50 N acting down on a metal sheet of area $0.01\ m^2$.

$p = \dfrac{F}{A}$

$p = \dfrac{50}{0.01}$

$p = 5000$

The pressure produced is 5000 Pa.

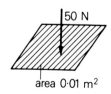

50 N

area 0·01 m²

Example 2

A person, weight 750 N, stands on snowshoes each of which has an area of 0.2 m². Calculate the pressure on the snow.

$$\text{pressure} \quad = \quad \frac{\text{force}}{\text{area}} \quad = \quad \frac{750}{2 \times 0.2} \quad = \quad 1875 \text{ pascals}$$

The pressure on the snow is 1875 Pa.

3.2 The Bourdon pressure gauge

In the experiments discussed in this chapter we shall use a Bourdon pressure gauge to measure gas pressures. Figure 3.2 shows front and rear views of the pressure gauge.

Figure 3.2 Bourdon pressure gauge

Figure 3.3

This pressure gauge works on the same principle as the familiar party-tooter often found in Christmas crackers, Figure 3.3. The harder you blow into the party-tooter, the more the paper tube uncurls. The Bourdon gauge consists of a hollow curved metal tube. An increase in pressure in the tube causes it to uncurl and a system of cogwheels makes a pointer move round a scale. A decrease in pressure results in the pointer moving in the opposite direction. In some Bourdon gauges, although the gauge is not connected to anything, the pointer is not at zero. This is because the air around us exerts a pressure which we call **atmospheric pressure**. The value of atmospheric pressure changes from day to day but is approximately 1×10^5 Pa or 100 kPa. The gauge in Figure 3.2 is indicating the atmospheric pressure.

The Bourdon gauge has many uses in industry, for example on gas cylinders, pumps and boilers. Figure 3.4 shows a type of Bourdon gauge which can be seen on many car dashboards. It is used to measure the oil pressure in the engine.

Figure 3.4 Oil pressure gauge

Checking the calibration

Using the apparatus shown in Figure 3.5 the pressure of a gas can be changed by applying a force on a piston in a syringe.

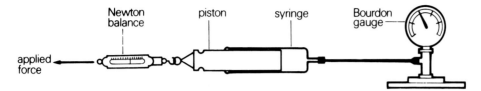

Figure 3.5 Calibration of Bourdon gauge

If we measure the force and the area of the piston we can calculate the change in pressure from the equation $p = \dfrac{F}{A}$. If the calibration of the gauge is correct, the change in pressure recorded by the gauge should equal our calculated pressure change.

Typical results from this experiment are shown below:

Original pressure reading on gauge	$p_1 = 102\ 000\ \text{Pa}$
Final pressure reading on gauge	$p_2 = 72\ 000\ \text{Pa}$
Change in pressure recorded by gauge	$(p_1 - p_2) = 30\ 000\ \text{Pa}$
Force applied to piston	$F = 30\ \text{N}$
Radius of piston	$r = 0.018\ \text{m}$
Area of circular piston	$(A = \pi r^2) = 0.001\ \text{m}^2$
Calculated pressure change	$F/A = 30\ 000\ \text{Pa}$

These results show that the pressure change calculated from F/A agrees with that recorded by the gauge. We have therefore checked that the calibration of the Bourdon gauge is correct.

3.3 Kinetic Theory

The basic assumption of the Kinetic Theory is that all matter consists of particles which are in constant motion at any temperature above absolute zero. Air particles cannot be seen as they are extremely small. However, evidence for their motion was discovered in 1827 by Robert Brown.

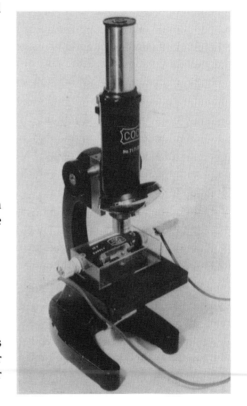

Brownian motion

Robert Brown, a Scottish botanist, carried out an experiment which showed that when tiny pollen grains suspended in water are viewed under a microscope they are seen to be in constant motion. At first it was thought that this motion was a form of life but further experiments with non-living particles showed that the motion was always present.

In the laboratory we can look at the Brownian motion of smoke particles using the apparatus shown in Figure 3.6.

Light from the lamp is focused by the glass rod on the glass cell. A dropper filled with smoke from smouldering string is used to fill the glass cell and a glass cover will then seal the cell. When the microscope is correctly adjusted, the smoke which consists of tiny specks of ash can be seen reflecting the light from the lamp. The smoke particles are seen to move jerkily through short distances in

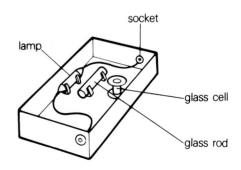

Figure 3.6 Brownian motion apparatus

many different directions. The first accurate explanation of this Brownian motion was given by Albert Einstein in 1905. According to the Kinetic Theory, the air particles surrounding a speck of ash are moving randomly and colliding with it. Although a speck of ash is much larger than the air particles, it is small enough to be affected by collisions with them. These randomly occurring collisions produce unbalanced forces which cause the speck of ash to move. The air particles are moving in all directions so that the collisions come from all directions. The motion of a speck of ash is therefore random, i.e. it moves, but not in any particular direction, Figure 3.7.

According to the Kinetic Theory, at a higher temperature the air particles have more kinetic energy and so are moving faster. This means that at higher temperatures the collisions are more violent and so the specks of ash are jostled around faster.

Figure 3.7 Random motion of specks of ash

3.4 Behaviour of gases

Robert Boyle investigated the relationship between the pressure p and the volume V for a fixed mass of gas at constant temperature. The apparatus shown in Figure 3.8 can be used for this investigation. The results when plotted give Figure 3.9. If $1/V$ is plotted against p, the straight line graph in Figure 3.10 is obtained.

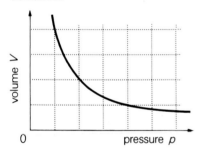

Figure 3.9   Figure 3.10

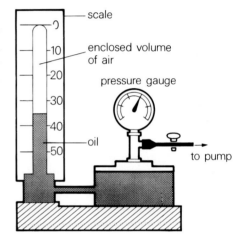

Figure 3.8 Boyle's Law apparatus

This illustrates that

$$p \propto \frac{1}{V} \text{ (mass and temperature constant)}$$

$pV = $ constant (mass and temperature constant)

This is known as **Boyle's Law** which can be written

$$p_1V_1 = p_2V_2 \quad \text{where } V_1 \text{ is the volume at pressure } p_1$$
$$\text{and } V_2 \text{ is the volume at pressure } p_2$$

Example 3

A cylinder contains $0.2\,\text{m}^3$ of oxygen at a pressure of $3 \times 10^5\,\text{Pa}$. What volume will this oxygen occupy at a pressure of $1 \times 10^5\,\text{Pa}$ if the temperature is unchanged?

$$p_1V_1 = p_2V_2 \qquad V_1 = 0.2\,\text{m}^3; \qquad V_2 = \text{final volume}$$
$$p_1 = 3 \times 10^5\,\text{Pa}; \qquad p_2 = 1 \times 10^5\,\text{Pa}$$

$$\Rightarrow 3 \times 10^5 \times 0.2 = 1 \times 10^5 \times V_2$$
$$\Rightarrow \qquad V_2 = \frac{3 \times 10^5 \times 0.2}{1 \times 10^5}$$
$$\Rightarrow \qquad V_2 = 0.6$$

The new volume will be $0.6\,\text{m}^3$.

The pressure exerted by a gas is caused by the bombardment of the sides of the container by the gas molecules. If the temperature is increased, the kinetic energy of the molecules will also increase and the pressure will be greater because of more frequent collisions by particles colliding with greater energy.

The relationship between pressure and temperature can be investigated by heating a fixed mass of gas at constant volume over a range of temperatures, Figure 3.11, and measuring the corresponding pressures.

A graph of the results from such an experiment is shown in Figure 3.12. If the experiment is repeated with a larger flask, a different set of results is obtained. When the results of both experiments are plotted and the lines extended backwards, they both intersect the temperature axis at –273°C, Figure 3.13.

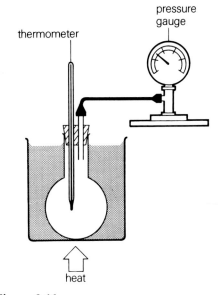

Figure 3.11

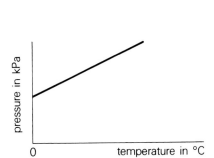

Figure 3.12

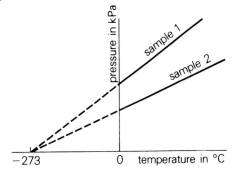

Figure 3.13

In general this is true for any graph of pressure against temperature for a fixed mass of gas.

The temperature –273°C is known as absolute zero and is the starting point for the absolute temperature scale.

The unit of measurement of the absolute scale is the kelvin (K) and when pressure is plotted against temperature the pressure line passes through the origin, Figure 3.14.

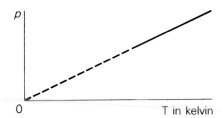

Figure 3.14

This means that

$$p \propto T \quad \text{(mass and volume constant)}$$

where T is the absolute temperature measured in kelvin

$$\Rightarrow \quad \frac{p}{T} = \text{constant}$$

This is known as the **Pressure Law**

$$\frac{p}{T} = \text{constant}$$

$$\Rightarrow \quad \frac{p_1}{T_1} = \frac{p_2}{T_2}$$

where p_1 is the pressure at absolute temperature T_1 and p_2 is the pressure at absolute temperature T_2

To convert a celsius reading into kelvin, 273 is added to the celsius reading.

kelvin = celsius + 273

Note that a temperature change of one kelvin is the same as a temperature change of one degree celsius.

Example 4

A sample of gas has a volume of $50 \, cm^3$ and a pressure of $120 \, kPa$ at room temperature of 20°C.

If the volume is constant what is the pressure at a temperature of 70°C?

$$\frac{p_1}{T_1} = \frac{p_2}{T_2}$$

$$\begin{aligned} p_1 &= 120 \, kPa & p_2 &= ? \\ T_1 &= 20 + 273 = 293 \, K \\ T_2 &= 70 + 273 = 343 \, K \end{aligned}$$

$$p_2 = \frac{120 \times 343}{293} = 140$$

The final pressure is 140 kPa.

3.5 Explanations based on Kinetic Theory

Although the Kinetic Theory has its limitations, it is useful because it provides an explanation of many properties of gases.

Boyle's Law: $p \propto 1/V$ (at constant T)

Consider a volume V of gas at pressure p. If the volume is reduced without change in temperature, the particles will collide more frequently with the container walls. This will produce a larger force. Also the area of the container walls has been reduced and both the increased force and reduced area will lead to an increase in the gas pressure,

i.e. as V decreases, p increases.

Pressure Law: $p \propto T$ (at constant V)

Consider a fixed volume of gas at temperature T and pressure p. If the temperature of the gas increases, this means that the kinetic energy and therefore the speed of the particles must increase. As the volume is constant this will lead to an increased gas pressure because the particles will be colliding more violently and more frequently with the container walls,

i.e. as T increases, p increases.

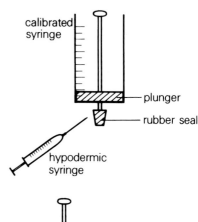

3.6 Density

When a solid melts, there is very little change in volume. However, when a liquid is changed to a gas, there is a large increase in volume.

Two experiments can provide us with an estimate of the change in volume when a liquid changes to a gas and when a solid changes to a gas.

Liquid to gas

The plunger of a calibrated syringe is pushed to the bottom to exclude all air and the nozzle is sealed with a rubber cap, Figure 3.15. A small measured volume of water is then injected through the rubber seal by means of a hypodermic syringe. The large calibrated syringe is then immersed in a beaker of salt solution which is boiling at a temperature just above 100°C. The sample of water turns into steam which pushes back the plunger. The volume of steam produced is read off the scale of the syringe. It is found that the water produces a volume of steam that is about 1600 times greater than the volume of water.

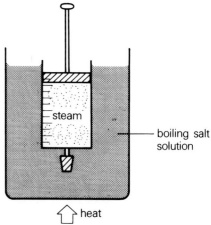

Figure 3.15

Solid to gas

A small test tube containing about $1\,cm^3$ of solid carbon dioxide is connected by tubing to an inverted gas jar, Figure 3.16. The gas jar is calibrated for measuring volume and is initially filled with water. As the solid carbon dioxide vaporizes, it is collected in the gas jar. It is found that the volume of gas produced is about 800 times greater than the volume of solid.

Results from experiments such as these indicate that the volume occupied by particles of a gas is of the order of one thousand times greater than when in the liquid or solid state.

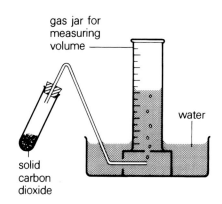

Density

Although the volume of the particles has increased on heating, the mass of the particles, whether in the gaseous or the liquid state, has remained unchanged. If we take equal volumes of the liquid and of the gas, their mass would be very different.

The mass per unit volume of a substance is called its **density** ρ.

Figure 3.16

$$\text{density } \rho = \frac{\text{mass}}{\text{volume}}$$

$$\Rightarrow \quad \rho = \frac{m}{V}$$

The SI units for density are $kg\,m^{-3}$.

Example 5

A block of metal has the measurements shown.

The mass of metal is found to be $540\,g$.

Calculate the density of the metal.

$$\begin{aligned}
\text{volume} \quad &= 5 \times 5 \times 8 = 200\,cm^3 \\
&= 2 \times 10^{-4}\,m^3 \\
\text{mass} \quad &= 540\,g = 0.540\,kg \\
\text{density} \quad &= \frac{\text{mass}}{\text{volume}} = \frac{0.54}{2 \times 10^{-4}} = 2700
\end{aligned}$$

The density of the metal is $2700\,kg\,m^{-3}$.

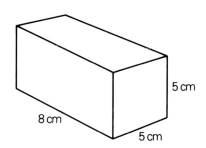

Example 6

An experiment is carried out to find the density of a liquid.

An empty beaker is placed on a balance. The mass of the empty beaker is noted. $25\,cm^3$ of liquid is measured accurately using a pipette. This is poured into the beaker and the new mass is noted.

Calculate the density of the liquid from the results.

$$\begin{aligned}
\text{mass of empty beaker} \quad &= 95.6\,g \\
\text{mass of beaker + liquid} &= 115.7\,g \\
\text{volume of liquid} \quad &= 25\,cm^3.
\end{aligned}$$

$$\begin{aligned}
\text{mass of liquid} \quad &= 115.7 - 95.6 = 20.1\,g \\
&= 0.02\,kg
\end{aligned}$$

$$\text{volume of liquid} = 25\,cm^3 = 2.5 \times 10^{-5}\,m^3$$

$$\text{density} = \frac{\text{mass}}{\text{volume}} = \frac{0.02}{2.5 \times 10^{-5}} = 800$$

The density of the liquid is $800\,kg\,m^{-3}$.

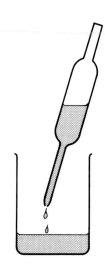

Density of air

The density of air is very low but it can be determined if a sensitive balance is available.

A strong glass flask is fitted with a stopper, glass tube and rubber tube with clip attached. This is fitted to a vacuum pump and the air is withdrawn. The clip is closed and the empty flask is weighed. The clip is opened and air at atmospheric pressure enters the flask.

The flask full of air is weighed. Typical results are given below.

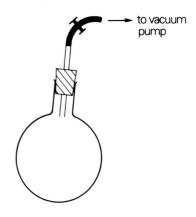
to vacuum pump

$$\text{mass of empty flask} \qquad = 186.1\,\text{g}$$
$$\text{mass of flask full of air} \qquad = 186.8\,\text{g}$$
$$\text{volume of flask} \qquad = 500\,\text{cm}^3$$

$$\text{mass of air} \quad = 186.8 - 186.1 = 0.7\,\text{g} = 0.7 \times 10^{-3}\,\text{kg}$$
$$\text{volume of air} \ = 500\,\text{cm}^3 = 5 \times 10^{-4}\,\text{m}^3.$$
$$\text{density} \qquad = \frac{\text{mass}}{\text{volume}} = \frac{0.7 \times 10^{-3}}{5 \times 10^{-4}}$$
$$\qquad\qquad = \ 1.4$$

The density of air at room temperature and atmospheric pressure is 1.4 kg m^{-3}.

This method gives a reasonable estimate of the density of air but is not entirely satisfactory because the flask may contain water vapour which will give a false result.

In general, solids and liquids do expand a little when heated: the same mass will then occupy a slightly larger volume, and the density will be smaller. An accurate value of the density should also state the temperature at which it was measured.

A change in temperature or in pressure can produce a large change in the volume of gas. The value of a gas density must state the temperature and the pressure at which it was measured. The conditions chosen are usually a temperature of 0°C and a pressure of 1.01×10^5 Pa: this is known as **Standard Temperature and Pressure** (s.t.p.).

Table 1 shows the densities of some solids, liquids and gases.

solids and liquids	density at 20°C / kg m^{-3} × 10^3
cork	0.25
olive oil	0.92
water	1.00
naphthalene	1.15
perspex	1.19
glycerol	1.26
aluminium	2.70
glass	3.00
iron	7.86
silver	10.50
lead	11.40
mercury	13.60
gold	19.30

Example 7

A sample of oxygen with a density of 1.43 kg m^{-3} at s.t.p. occupies a volume of 5.00×10^{-3} m^3 at s.t.p. What is the mass of the sample?

$$\rho = \frac{m}{V} \qquad\qquad \rho = 1.43\,\text{kg m}^{-3}$$
$$\qquad\qquad\qquad V = 5.00 \times 10^{-3}\,\text{m}^3$$
$$\Rightarrow \ 1.43 = \frac{m}{5.00 \times 10^{-3}}$$
$$\Rightarrow \quad m = 1.43 \times 5.00 \times 10^{-3}$$
$$\Rightarrow \quad m = 7.15 \times 10^{-3}$$

The mass of the sample is 7.15 × 10^{-3} kg

gases	density at s.t.p. / kg m^{-3}
hydrogen	0.09
helium	0.18
nitrogen	1.25
air	1.29
oxygen	1.43
carbon dioxide	1.98

Table 1 Densities

3.7 Spacing of particles

Figure 3.17 shows a model of the structure of a liquid in which it is assumed that the particles are spherical. This shows that when the particles are closely packed together, the spacing d is equal to the particle diameter d_o. If the liquid is compressed, this is resisted by a repulsion force between the particles. If the particles are pulled apart, this is resisted by an attraction force between the particles.

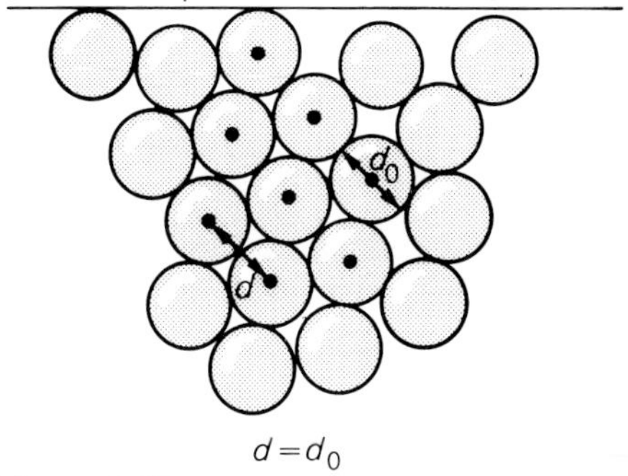

As we saw earlier, the change in volume which takes place when a sample of liquid changes into a gas is by a factor of the order of 1000 times. To estimate the change in spacing which will take place, it is assumed that each particle is enclosed in a cubical box, Figure 3.18. The sides of the box have a length equal to the particle diameter d_o. The volume is therefore d_o^3

When the liquid becomes a gas, the size of the particles does not change but they become more widely spaced and the volume occupied by one particle will be 1000 times greater than the original volume.
The new volume is $1000\,d_o^3$ which can be represented by a cube of side x, Figure 3.18. In this case the new volume will be x^3.

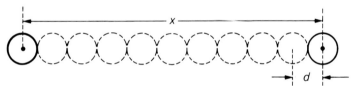

$$x^3 = 1000\,d_o^3$$
$$\Rightarrow x = \sqrt[3]{1000\,d_o^3}$$
$$\Rightarrow x = 10\,d_o$$
$$\Rightarrow x = 10\,d \quad \text{since } d = d_o$$

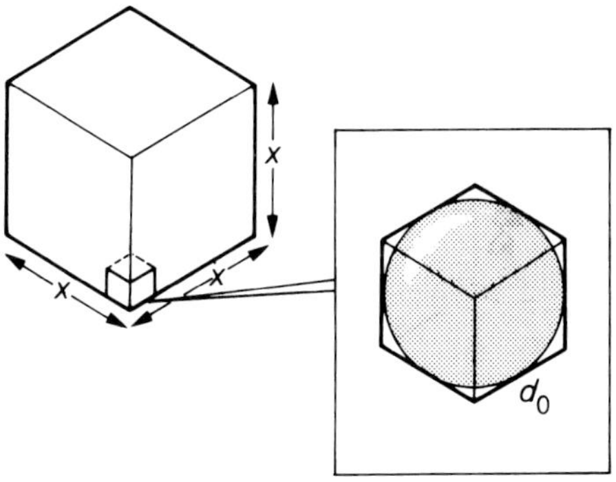

Thus in a gas the particle spacing is about 10 times greater than that of the liquid, Figure 3.19.

Figure 3.19

surface of liquid

Figure 3.17

$$d = d_0$$

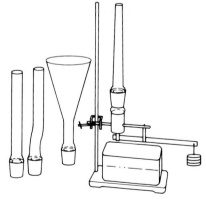

Figure 3.18

3.8 Pressure in a liquid

The French scientist Blaise Pascal (1623–1662) investigated the pressure in a liquid.
 Figure 3.20 shows a set of vessels known as Pascal's vases. These are used to show that the depth of water determines the pressure exerted on the pressure disc and not the amount of water in each case.
 A disc is held firmly in place by a lever at the end of which weights can be added, Figure 3.21.
 The parallel-sided vessel is used first. Water is poured into the vessel until at a particular height h, the water starts to drip out. This shows the downward force on the disc from the liquid is just sufficient to overcome the upward force on the disc from the lever system.

Figure 3.20

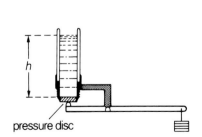

pressure disc

Figure 3.21

The experiment is repeated with different shapes of vase. In each case the height of water which causes the water to drip out is the same regardless of the shape of the vessel.

This shows that the pressure is determined by the depth of the liquid, and not by the shape of the vessel.

The pressure at any depth acts equally in all directions

This can be illustrated by stretching a thin rubber membrane over a thistle funnel. This is then connected to a sensitive Bourdon gauge which registers any change in pressure.

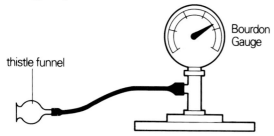

Figure 3.22

The funnel is then placed at a given depth in water and set at various angles. In each case the pressure reading is the same, indicating that at a given depth the pressure of the liquid acts equally in all directions.

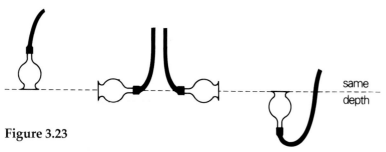

Figure 3.23

The pressure in a given liquid increases with depth

The relationship between depth and pressure can be investigated by floating a flat-bottomed tube loaded with lead shot in water, Figure 3.24.

A scale fitted inside the tube allows the depth to be measured.

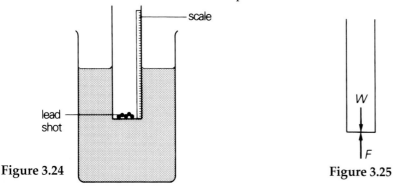

Figure 3.24   **Figure 3.25**

When the tube floats, the pressure of the liquid on the base of the tube supports it. If the weight of the tube plus lead shot is W and the area of the base is A, the tube floats so that the upward force acting on it balances the weight.

$W = F$ where the upward force is F (Figure 3.25).

The upward force acts over an area A so that the pressure acting upwards on the base of the tube is given by

$$p = \frac{F}{A}$$

but $F = W$

$$\Rightarrow \quad p = \frac{W}{A}$$

This pressure is provided by the liquid.

If the tube is made heavier by adding lead shot, it will sink to a greater depth where the liquid pressure is greater.

The experiment is carried out by adding lead shot until the tube floats with a specified depth below the surface.

The tube is weighed.

It is loaded with more lead shot until it sinks to the next depth.

It is weighed again.

This process is repeated and a set of results is given in Table 2.

depth h (m)	total weight of tube W (N)
0.07	0.21
0.08	0.23
0.09	0.26
0.10	0.29
0.11	0.32
0.12	0.35

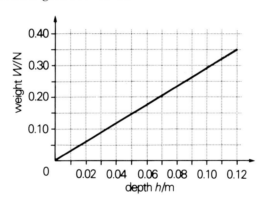

Table 2   **Figure 3.26**

When the results are plotted a straight line graph passing through the origin is obtained, Figure 3.26.

The graph shows that the weight of the tube W is directly proportional to the depth h.

As previously shown, the pressure of the liquid p is directly proportional to the weight W.

$$p \propto h$$

It can be concluded that the pressure is directly proportional to the depth.

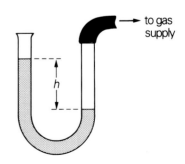

A manometer containing water can be connected to a gas tap. The greater pressure on the right hand side forces the water up on the left hand side. The difference in level h indicates the difference in pressure between each side of the U-tube, Figure 3.27.

Figure 3.27

The pressure at a given depth depends on the density of the liquid

To illustrate the effect which the density of the liquid has on the pressure, a flat-bottomed tube is floated in the liquid.

Lead shot is added until the depth achieved is some constant value, for example 8 cm.

The weight of lead shot is noted and as previously demonstrated this weight W is directly proportional to the pressure of the liquid.

The tube is floated in water to a depth of 8 cm and the weight noted.

The tube is cleaned and dried and then floated in another liquid.

Lead shot is added until the tube sinks to a depth of 8 cm in the liquid.

The weight of lead shot plus tube is noted.

This is repeated for liquids of known density.

A set of results is given in Table 3.

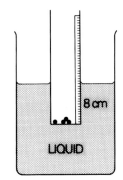

Figure 3.28

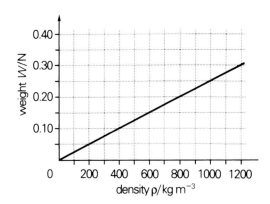

liquid	density ρ (kg m^{-3})	weight W (N)
glycerol	1260	0.32
vinegar	1050	0.26
water	1000	0.25
olive oil	920	0.23
turpentine	870	0.22
ethanol	800	0.20

Table 3   **Figure 3.29**

A graph of W plotted against ρ gives a straight line graph through the origin, Figure 3.29.

This shows that

$$W \propto \rho$$

and since the upward force acting on the base F is equal to W

$$F \propto \rho$$

but the pressure p of the liquid

$$p = \frac{F}{A}$$

so that $p \propto \rho$

It can be concluded that the pressure is directly proportional to the density of the liquid.

3.9 **Buoyancy**

When an object is hung at the end of a spring balance, Figure 3.30, the weight W exerts a downward force which is supported by the upward force T of the spring.

As the object is lowered into a liquid, the spring balance reading decreases, giving a minimum reading when the object is totally immersed, Figure 3.31.

The reduction of the balance reading is due to the buoyant force F_B or upthrust which is exerted on the object by the liquid. It is this buoyant force which produces buoyancy or 'floating power'. The forces acting on the immersed object are balanced, so that

$T = W - F_B$ where T = force exerted by the spring
W = weight of the object
F_B = buoyant force due to the liquid

If an object is less dense than a liquid, it will float and displace only a small volume of the liquid. The buoyancy force will be equal to the weight of the object, and to the weight of the liquid displaced, Figure 3.32.

$F_B = W$

Materials with a density close to, but less than, the density of a liquid will still float but with much more of their volume submerged. The buoyancy force again equals the weight of the object, Figure 3.32(b).

An object which has a density greater than that of the liquid will sink into the liquid. In this case, the buoyant force is less than the weight of the object – by how much depends on the densities of the object and of the liquid.

For most purposes, an object which has a density greater than that of a liquid will sink in that liquid. However in a liquid, pressure increases with depth, and so density increases with depth. In this case, if a liquid is deep enough, an object will sink into the liquid to a depth where the density of the object (which doesn't change) equals the density of the liquid at the greater depth.

For a floating object that is pushed below the surface with a force P, Figure 3.33, the forces acting on the object are balanced:

$P = F_B - W$

If the force P is now removed, the buoyant force F_B pushes the object up to the surface because this force is greater than the weight W of the object. The object rises and floats on the surface.

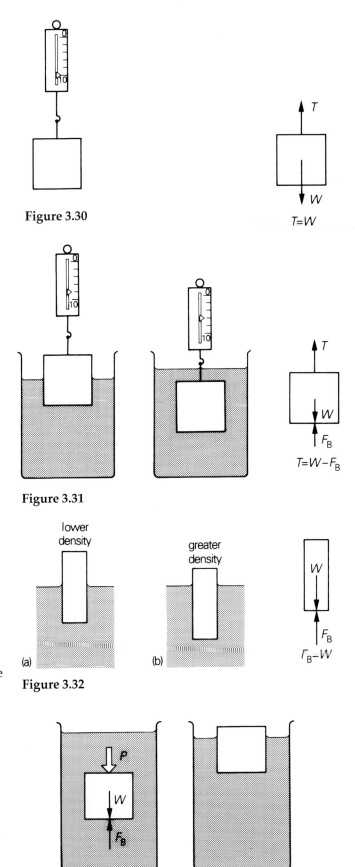

Figure 3.30

$T=W$

Figure 3.31

$T=W-F_B$

lower density

greater density

(a)   (b)

F_B-W

Figure 3.32

$P=F_B-W$

Figure 3.33

3.10 Hydrometer

The proportion of an object which is immersed depends on the density of the liquid in which it floats. The same object will float to a greater depth in a liquid of density 800 kg m⁻³ than it would in a liquid density 1000 kg m⁻³. This fact is used in the **hydrometer**. A glass tube with a loaded bulb at one end floats in a liquid and its scale indicates the density. The hydrometer will sink further in liquids of lower density and the scale can be calibrated.

In the photograph, Figure 3.34, a hydrometer floats in a liquid with a density less than that of water.

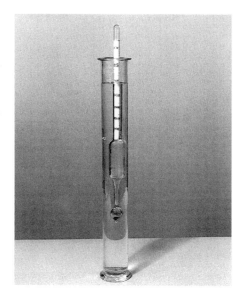

Figure 3.34

3.11 Hot air balloon

When an object floats in a fluid (liquid or gas) it experiences an upthrust.

A hot air balloon, floating in air makes use of this, Figure 3.35.
A burner raises the temperature of the air inside the balloon making it less dense than the surrounding air.

The denser air outside the balloon produces an upthrust which lifts the balloon upwards.

Figure 3.35

3.12 Submarines

Ships float because a large part of the inner volume is air making the average density less than the density of water.

In a submarine, ballast tanks are fitted. These can be filled with water or with air.

When on the surface the tanks are mainly full of air.

In order to dive, the tanks are filled with water. The weight of the submarine is now greater than the upthrust and the submarine sinks.

Figure 3.36

Figure 3.37

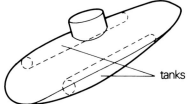
tanks

Summary

$$pressure = \frac{force\ acting\ normal\ to\ an\ area}{area\ over\ which\ force\ acts}$$

The SI unit of pressure is the pascal (Pa):
$1\ Pa = 1\ N\ m^{-2}$.

A Bourdon gauge is an instrument for measuring gas or liquid pressure.

The unit of temperature on the kelvin temperature scale is the kelvin (K). A kelvin is the same size as a degree celsius. Absolute zero (0 K) on the kelvin scale corresponds to −273°C on the celsius scale.

$$kelvin = degrees\ celsius + 273$$

The Gas Laws can be summarized as below,
where p = gas pressure,
V = volume,
T = kelvin temperature
and m = mass of gas.

Pressure Law   (constant V and m)

$$p \propto T$$

$$\Rightarrow \quad \frac{p_1}{T_1} = \frac{p_2}{T_2}$$

Boyle's Law   (constant T and m)

$$p \propto \frac{1}{V}$$

$$\Rightarrow \quad p_1 \times V_1 = p_2 \times V_2$$

The Brownian motion of specks of ash in air is due to collisions with the moving air particles.

According to the Kinetic Theory, all matter consists of particles which are in constant motion at any temperature above absolute zero. The average kinetic energy of the particles is directly proportional to (varies directly as) the Kelvin temperature. Gas pressure is produced by the particles colliding with the walls of their container.

$$density = \frac{mass}{volume}$$

The spacing of molecules in solids and liquids is approximately one tenth the spacing in a gas.

The pressure in a liquid acts equally in all directions throughout the liquid.

$$pressure \propto depth$$
$$p \propto h$$
$$pressure \propto density$$
$$p \propto \rho$$

Problems

1   A syringe has a piston with cross-sectional area $2\ cm^2$. The piston is pushed with a force of 12 N. Calculate the pressure.

2   A drawing pin has a sharp point with area $0.01\ mm^2$. What is the pressure exerted by the point when the head is pushed with a force of 8 N?

3   Explain how you would estimate the density of air at atmospheric pressure and room temperature.

4   In an experiment the temperature of a fixed mass of gas is kept constant. The pressure is altered and various readings of pressure and volume are taken. These are listed in the table

pressure (k Pa)	101	116	122	135	180	210	250
volume (cm³)	45	39	37	34	25	22	18

Plot a graph of pressure against volume.
What is the relationship between pressure and volume?

5   A fixed mass of gas is kept at constant temperature but the pressure is increased from 1.01×10^5 Pa to 3.00×10^5 Pa. If the original volume was $0.2\ m^3$, determine the final volume.

6   The pressure of a fixed mass of gas is 200 kPa at 40°C and the volume is $1.5\ m^3$. The temperature is increased to 100°C but the volume remains the same. What is the new pressure?

7   Explain why the use of large tyres helps to prevent a tractor from sinking into soft ground.

8   If you want to rescue someone who has fallen through the ice on a pond, would it be safer to walk or crawl across the ice towards him? Explain.

9   An elephant exerts a force of 5 000 N by pressing his foot on the ground. If the area of his foot is $0.02\ m^2$, calculate the pressure exerted by his foot.

10   A tank contains 1 000 kg of water. If the base of the tank has an area of $20\ m^2$, calculate the pressure exerted by the water on the base.

11   The pressure of air in a car tyre is 2.5×10^5 Pa at a temperature of 27°C. After a motorway journey the pressure has risen to 3.0×10^5 Pa. Assuming that the volume of the tyre has not changed,
a)   calculate the resulting temperature of the air in the tyre
b)   explain the change in pressure in terms of the motion of the air particles in the tyre.

12   Change the following celsius temperatures into kelvin temperatures,
a)   −273°C,   b)   −150°C,   c)   500°C.

13   Change the following kelvin temperatures into celsius temperatures,
a)   0 K,   b)   272 K,   c)   500 K.

14   A weather balloon contains $100\ m^3$ of helium when atmospheric pressure is 90 kPa. If atmospheric pressure changes to 100 kPa, calculate the new volume of helium at the same temperature.

15   A bicycle pump has its barrel full of air at a pressure of 1.0×10^5 Pa. The pressure in the tyre which is to be inflated is 1.5×10^5 Pa. If the original volume of air in the barrel is $600\ cm^3$ and there is no temperature change during the movement of the piston, what will be the new volume of air in the pump when the tyre valve is just beginning to open?

16 a)   A syringe with a close fitting plunger is attached to an uncalibrated Bourdon gauge. The plunger can be pushed down in the syringe by placing weights on top of the plunger.

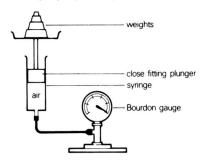

Describe how you would calibrate the Bourdon gauge using this arrangement.

b)   An experiment is carried out to investigate how the pressure of a gas varies with temperature. The experimental arrangement is shown below.

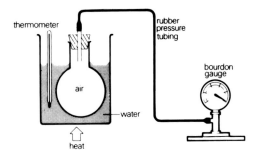

The water bath is heated until the water is boiling. As the water cools, readings of pressure are taken at a number of different temperatures.

i)   Why is it desirable to allow the water to cool slowly?

ii)   Give an explanation in terms of the behaviour of the particles of the gas for the change in pressure as the gas cools.

iii)   Redraw the following axes and sketch the graph of the results you would expect from this experiment.   *SEB*

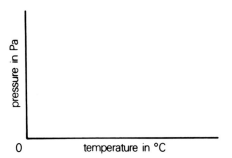

17   A block of solid carbon dioxide measures 1 cm × 1 cm × 1 cm and has a mass of 0.0016 kg.
What is the density of the solid CO_2?
If the density of gaseous carbon dioxide is 1.98 kg m^{-3} at s.t.p., estimate the volume of gaseous carbon dioxide at s.t.p. obtained from this block.
How does the average spacing of the molecules in the solid CO_2 compare with that of the gas?

18   A closed flask with a volume of 400 cm^3 contains gas which has a mass of 5×10^{-4} kg. The temperature of the gas is 15°C.
What is the density of the gas?
The flask is cooled to 0°C. What can you say about
  i)   the pressure of the gas   **ii)**   the density of the gas
  iii)   the average kinetic energy of the molecules of the gas compared to the values at 15°C?

19   In an agricultural project it is necessary to determine the average volume of a particular type of small seed. The apparatus below is devised to achieve this.

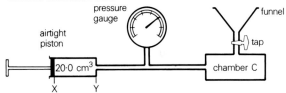

a)   With the tap open and the piston at X, the pressure gauge indicates that atmospheric pressure is 1.02×10^5 Pa. The tap is closed and the piston is slowly pushed to Y. The gauge now reads 1.62×10^5 Pa. The internal volume between X and Y is 20.0 cm^3.
Calculate the volume of air that is now in the apparatus, i.e. from Y into and including chamber C.

b)   The tap is again opened and the piston returned to X. A sample of seeds is now poured through the funnel into C and the tap is closed. After the piston has been slowly pushed to Y, the pressure gauge reads 1.95×10^5 Pa.
  i)   Calculate the new volume of air in the apparatus now.
  ii)   What is the volume of the sample of seeds in C?

c)   Explain briefly the effect (if any) on the accuracy of the measurement of the volume of the seed sample, if the volume inside the apparatus from Y into and including C was made very large compared with the volume between X and Y.

d)   Describe how you would find the average volume of a single seed. (Counting all the seeds in the sample is not practicable).
SEB

20   A quantity of gas is trapped in a cylinder by a close fitting piston. The cylinder also contains a heating coil.

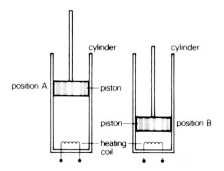

a)   The piston is pushed down from position A to position B and held there.
  i)   State what change occurs in the pressure of the trapped gas.
  ii)   Use a particle model of the gas to explain this change.

b)   The heating coil is switched on and the piston is held in position B.
  i)   State what happens to the molecules of the gas during the time the heating coil is on.
  ii)   State what change occurs in the pressure of the gas during this time.
  iii)   Use a particle model of the gas to explain this pressure change.
SEB

21 A boy used the following apparatus to test a hypothesis that 'the pressure of a gas is directly proportional to its temperature'.

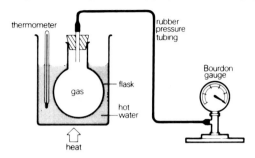

He obtained the following results:

Temperature °C	0	20	40	60	80	100
Pressure kN/m²	90	96	103	110	117	123

a) Comment on the volume of the enclosed air during the experiment.

b) Draw a graph of the results and use the graph to show how a relationship between pressure and temperature of a gas may be deduced.

c) Rewrite the original hypothesis in a fully and more correct form.

d) A classmate criticized the experiment because some of the air was not at the temperature recorded on the thermometer. Suggest one way to reduce this error.

SEB

22 When home-made wine is being made, it may be necessary to measure its density. Describe how this could be done by floating a loaded tube in a sample of the wine as shown below.

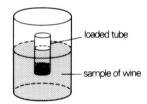

Include in your description

a) an outline of the relevant theory, and

b) how the necessary measurements are made. *SEB*

23 A skin diver, operating at a depth of 15 m and at a pressure of 2.5×10^5 Pa, carries his air supply in a steel cylinder on his back. When full, the cylinder contains 0.060 m³ of air at a pressure of 1.6×10^7 Pa.

Calculate

a) the volume of air available to him at this depth;

b) the time that the air would last if he requires air at a flow rate of 0.30 m³ per minute. *SEB*

24 a) A pupil uses the apparatus shown in the diagram to perform an experiment to find the relationship between the pressure and the volume of a fixed mass of gas at constant temperature.

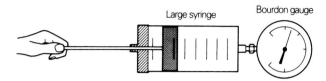

The following results are obtained:

Pressure (kPa)	90	60	45	36
Volume (m³)	0.0010	0.0015	0.0020	0.0025

i) Use all the results in the table to find the relationship between the pressure and the volume of the gas. Show your working and state the relationship.

ii) Why is it so important to keep the gas temperature constant?

b) A balloon filled with hydrogen gas is released from sea level. As the balloon rises it expands in volume. It is designed to burst when the volume becomes 4 times its original volume at sea level.

i) When the balloon leaves sea level, its volume is 3.0 m³ and the pressure is 100 kPa. What is the pressure inside the balloon when it is just about to burst, assuming its temperature remains constant?

The graph shows the variation of air pressure with height above sea level, assuming the temperature does not change.

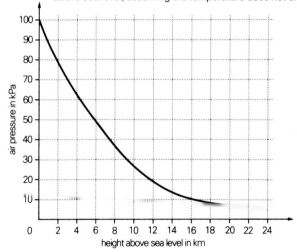

ii) When the balloon bursts, the pressure inside the balloon is approximately equal to the pressure outside. Assuming this, at what height does the balloon burst?

c) For a fixed mass of gas, use the kinetic theory of gases to explain the change in pressure when

i) the volume of the gas increases with no change in temperature;

ii) the temperature of the gas decreases with no change in volume. *SEB*

4 Resistors in circuits

4.1 Introduction

A polythene rod rubbed with a duster becomes negatively charged as a result of friction: the rod gains electrons from the duster. Similarly, a nylon rod can be positively charged by friction because it loses electrons to the duster.

There are only two types of electric charge: positive and negative. A pair of charges gives rise to an **electric force** between them. If two rods that have been oppositely charged are brought near to each other, there is a force of attraction between them. Two rods having the same type of charge repel each other.

The movement of air during a thunderstorm causes thunder clouds to be charged by friction. Very large quantities of positive and negative charge are built up: when these are discharged, a huge spark of lightning results. Figure 4.1.

A flow of electron current occurs when an electric fire is switched on: electrical energy is converted to heat energy and light energy.

There are two ways of detecting charge:
a) by measuring the **flow** of charge, e.g. electric current,
b) by measuring the **force** between charges, e.g. the charged polythene and nylon rods.

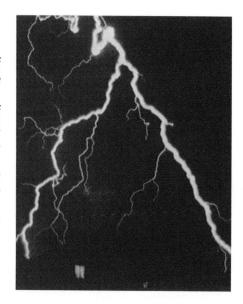

Figure 4.1 Lightning

4.2 Electric field

The gravitational force of attraction of the mass of the Earth for other masses can be described in terms of a gravitational field. The force between charged particles can similarly be described in terms of an **electric field**.

The fundamental unit of charge is the charge on an electron which is equal and opposite to the charge on a proton. However, in describing electric forces, we shall be concerned only with the effects of groups of these charged particles which are spread over the surface of an object: these are simply described as the **charge** on an object.

In Figure 4.2, the two small objects Q_1 and Q_2 are identical and both are negatively charged. They are placed some distance apart, but there is a force of repulsion between them because they both have a negative charge.

Figure 4.3 shows a small charged object Q_3 and a large object Q_4 which is also charged. The charge on Q_4 is spread over a larger surface so that the forces of repulsion are more complicated: the forces are in many directions and the electrons are at various distances from each other.

To simplify the problem, we must consider only very small charged objects called **point charges**.

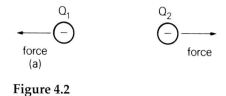

Figure 4.2

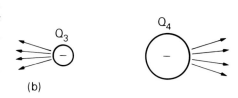

Figure 4.3

Direction of electric field force

In Figure 4.2, the force exerted by charge Q_1 on charge Q_2 is directed from Q_1 to Q_2 along the line joining them. There is an equal electric force in the opposite direction from Q_2 to Q_1.

The apparatus shown in Figure 4.4 is used to investigate the electric field. The glass dish contains oil on which is sprinkled a little grass seed. Two metal 'point' electrodes dip into the oil, and they are connected to a high voltage supply. When the supply is switched on, the electrodes become positively and negatively charged and the seeds form a pattern as shown. The lines in the pattern indicate the direction of the electric force, and the pattern shows the electric field between the two electrodes.

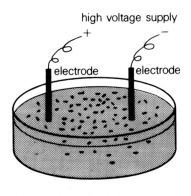
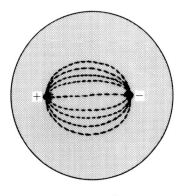

high voltage supply

electrode   electrode

dish containing oil and grass seed   pattern of seeds in oil

Figure 4.4

4.3   Field patterns and lines of force

The field strength g of the Earth's gravitation has an approximate value of 10 newtons per kilogram. This means that the gravitational force of attraction is proportional to the gravitational field strength *and* the mass which is near the earth.

In a similar way the electric field strength near a charged object has a value, which is measured in newtons per coulomb. It is also the case that the electrical force on a charge is proportional to the electrical field strength *and* the amount of charge at that point in the field.

The two types of field with their lines of force are shown in Figure 4.5. The arrows on the lines of force indicate the direction in which the mass or positive charge moves. If the object creating the electric field force is positively charged, then the arrows on the lines of force are reversed, Figure 4.6, so that they still indicate the direction of movement of a positive charge.

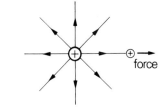

Figure 4.6

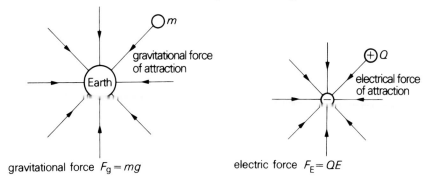

gravitational force $F_g = mg$ electric force $F_E = QE$

Figure 4.5 Gravitational and electric field patterns

An electric field pattern may be plotted from the shadows cast on a screen from a lamp, Figure 4.7. The direction of each line of force is found from the shadow cast by a thin metal foil that is charged and held on an insulating rod between the charged metal plates. Each line of force can be marked on the screen. Figure 4.8 shows the electric field patterns obtained in this way for various arrangements.

The variation in strength of the electric field is indicated by the spacing of the lines of force; the closer the spacing, the stronger is the field. Notice that the lines

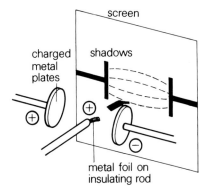

Figure 4.7

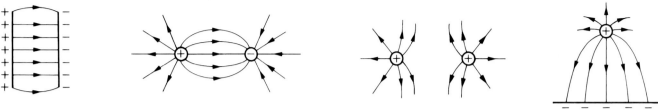

Figure 4.8 Electric field patterns

of force between a pair of parallel charged metal plates are evenly spaced showing that the electric field is uniform.

In calculations concerning a charge in an electric field, we shall always assume that the field is uniform.

4.4   Potential difference and work done

If the lines of force in an electric field are evenly spaced, the field is uniform. This means that a charged particle experiences the same force throughout the electric field.

A positive charge Q is placed in a uniform electric field caused by a potential difference of V volts being applied across the space, Figure 4.9.

In order to move a positive charge from the right-hand side to the left-hand side a certain amount of work W must be done, due to the opposing force effect of the field.

If W joules of work are needed to move Q coulombs of charge, then $\dfrac{W}{Q}$ joules are needed to move 1 coulomb of charge.

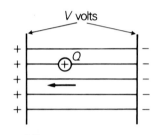

Figure 4.9

Now the greater the potential difference V, the greater is the field strength and hence the greater the work required to move the charge.

The work done per coulomb is a measure of the potential difference

i.e. V is proportional to $\dfrac{W}{Q}$

If 1 joule of work is done in moving 1 coulomb of charge, then the potential difference is defined as 1 volt.

Therefore $V = \dfrac{W}{Q}$

Example 1

The charge on an électron is $- 1.6 \times 10^{-19}$C. Calculate the increase in energy if an electron is accelerated from rest through a uniform field caused by a p.d. of 20 V.

$$Q = - 1.6 \times 10^{-19} \text{C}; \quad V = 20 \text{ V}$$

$$V = \frac{W}{Q}$$

∴ Work done by field $W = QV$

$$\Rightarrow \quad W = - 1.6 \times 10^{-19} \times 20 = - 3.2 \times 10^{-18}$$

The electron gains 3.2×10^{-18} joules.

4.5 Movement of charged particles in electric fields

The electron beam in the tube of a cathode ray oscilloscope moves parallel to an electric field in the electron gun and at right angles to an electric field between the Y-plates, Figure 4.10.

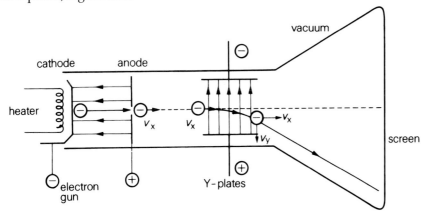

Figure 4.10

Electrons released from the heated cathode are accelerated by the uniform electric field between the cathode and anode. On reaching the anode they travel at a constant velocity v_x until they reach the region of electric field between the Y-plates. The passage of electrons through this region, where the field is at right angles to their motion, resembles the trajectory of a projectile when projected horizontally through the Earth's gravitational field, and in fact the electrons follow a similar parabolic path. The horizontal velocity v_x of the electrons remains constant as they travel from the electron gun through a vacuum towards the Y-plate region. In this region there is an acceleration towards the lower, positive plate and they gain a vertical component of velocity v_y as well as maintaining their horizontal velocity v_x. The electron beam strikes the screen, having been deflected by the electric field. The electric field between the Y-plates depends on the p.d. applied to them and so the deflection of the beam can be used to compare p.d.'s. In a solid the application of an electric field to a conducting material causes the 'free electrons' to drift. In a circuit, the applied potential difference sets up an electric field within the conductors, giving the conduction electrons their drift velocity.

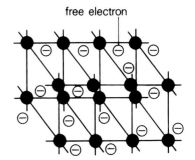

Figure 4.11 Metal atoms

4.6 Electrical conduction in solids

A material through which electric charge can flow is called a **conductor**. A material through which electric charge will *not* flow is called an **insulator**. Conduction may take place through gases, liquids or solids, but here we shall consider solids.

Most solid conductors are metals. It is useful to build up a model of the process of conduction. Figure 4.11 depicts a piece of metal with one 'free electron' per atom. The black circles represent the nuclei and fixed electrons of the metal atoms. Atoms have nuclei surrounded by electrons, most of which are bound tightly to the nucleus. However in metal atoms, some of the outer electrons are free to move. These are shown in the diagram and are called 'free electrons'. The American scientist Edwin Hall showed experimentally that in most metals one or two 'free electrons' per atom are available for conduction of electricity.

Figure 4.12 Edwin Hall

4 Resistors in circuits

These electrons have relatively high speeds (about $10^6\,\mathrm{m\,s^{-1}}$) in random directions. When a conductor is placed in a circuit containing a battery, this general movement becomes directed towards the positive terminal, Figure 4.13. There is a drift of all the free electrons at a speed of about $10^{-4}\,\mathrm{m\,s^{-1}}$ as soon as the circuit switch S is closed. The electron current is from negative to positive terminal (conventional current is in the reverse direction).

Potential difference and resistance

The energy required to drive the electron current round the circuit is provided by a chemical reaction in the battery or by the mains power supply. The **potential difference** across any component X in a circuit can be measured by placing a voltmeter in parallel with it, Figure 4.14. The component X is said to have a **resistance** if a potential difference (p.d.) is needed in order to drive a current through it.

The graph in Figure 4.15 shows the relationship usually obtained between the current I through a resistor (component X) and the potential difference V across it. This shows that the current varies directly as the potential difference.

$$I \propto V \text{ or } V \propto I$$
$$\Rightarrow \quad V = \text{constant} \times I$$
$$\Rightarrow \quad \frac{V}{I} = \text{constant} = R$$

where the constant R is called the resistance. The ratio V/I is the resistance of the component.

The resistance can be thought of as a measure of the potential difference needed to drive a current of 1 ampere through the component. If 1 volt is required to drive a current of 1 ampere through a component, it is said to have a resistance of 1 ohm.

$$R = \frac{V}{I}$$

If $V = 1$ volt, $\quad I = 1$ ampere, $\quad$ then $R = 1$ ohm

1 ohm = 1 volt per ampere

$$1\,\Omega = 1\,\mathrm{V\,A^{-1}}$$

Example 2

What potential difference is required to drive a current of 1 A through a resistor
a) of value $2\,\Omega$ **b)** of value $120\,\Omega$?

A $1\,\Omega$ resistor requires 1 V to drive a current of 1 A
A $2\,\Omega$ resistor requires ? V to drive a current of 1 A
– twice the resistance: twice as difficult, so twice the voltage needed, i.e. 2 V.

So, the $120\,\Omega$ resistor requires 120 V to drive a current of 1 A.

The electrical energy in a circuit, supplied by the source, is converted to other forms of energy in the components which make up the circuit. The amount of electrical energy converted into other forms of energy when the coulomb of charge passes from one point in the circuit to another is called the **potential difference** between the two points.

If 1 coulomb of charge passes between two points A and B in a circuit and releases 1 joule of energy, then we say that there is a potential difference of 1 volt between A and B, Figure 4.16.

If the p.d. is 2 volts, then 2 joules of energy is released per coulomb of charge which passes between A and B.

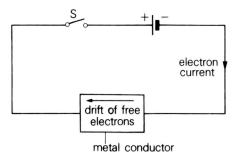
Figure 4.13 Conduction in a metal

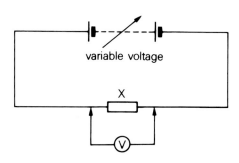
Figure 4.14 Measuring potential difference

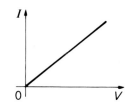
Figure 4.15 Current-voltage graph for a resistor

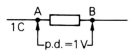
Figure 4.16 Source connected to a resistor

If the p.d. is V volts then V joules of energy is released per coulomb of charge which passes between A and B.

If Q coulombs of charge pass between A and B when the p.d. is V volts then the energy released, W, is given by $W = QV$.

The rate of flow of charge is the electric current I, where $I = Q/t$. We can express the energy released by the equation

$$W = QV = ItV \text{ joules}$$

Example 3

Calculate the energy converted in a 4 ohm resistor when connected to a 12 volt source for 2 minutes.

$$R = \frac{V}{I} \;\Rightarrow\; 4 = \frac{12}{I} \;\Rightarrow\; I = 3 \text{ amperes}$$

$$W = ItV \qquad t = 2 \times 60 \text{ seconds}$$

$$\Rightarrow \quad W = 3 \times 2 \times 60 \times 12 = 4320$$

4320 joules of energy are converted in the 4 ohm resistor.

4.7   Electromotive force

A source of electrical energy, such as a battery, provides an electromotive force (e.m.f.) to drive an electron current through the circuit. The e.m.f. of the source governs the electrical energy supplied to each unit charge that passes through the source, i.e. the number of joules of energy per coulomb of charge. Alternatively, the e.m.f. of the source is the work done on unit charge when it passes through the source.

The units of e.m.f. are the same as those of p.d.

$$1 \, J \, C^{-1} \equiv 1 \, V$$

The e.m.f. of a source is the potential difference across the terminals when no current is flowing, i.e. on open circuit. If a current is flowing, the terminal potential difference (t.p.d.) is lower than the e.m.f. as explained on the next page.

When, however, a current is flowing through a series of resistors in a circuit, Figure 4.17, then the sum of the energies which are produced in each resistor is equal to the total energy provided by the source. This is because energy is conserved.

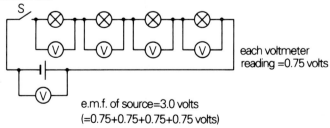

each voltmeter
reading =0.75 volts

e.m.f. of source=3.0 volts
(=0.75+0.75+0.75+0.75 volts)

Figure 4.17

This means that the e.m.f. of the source equals the sum of the p.d.'s around the circuit.

Internal resistance

Consider the circuit in Figure 4.18. We might expect the potential difference V across the resistor R to be the same as the e.m.f. of the source. In reality a set of results for various values of R is obtained like those in the table below.

resistor value $R\ \Omega$	100	10	5	2	1
voltmeter reading V volts	2.0	1.7	1.4	1.0	0.7

Table 1

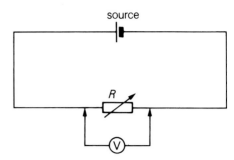

Figure 4.18 Measuring internal resistance

We find that the value of the external resistance R affects the terminal potential difference. This is because the cell used as a source has an **internal resistance** which resists the current.

Measurement of internal resistance

The circuit in Figure 4.19 is used for determining the value of the internal resistance r of a cell of e.m.f. 1.8 V by measuring the current and the t.p.d. for various values of external resistance R.

Table 2 below shows a typical set of results.

current I amperes	0.0	0.1	0.2	0.3	0.4	0.5	0.6	0.7	0.8
t.p.d. V volts	1.8	1.6	1.4	1.2	1.0	0.8	0.6	0.4	0.2

Table 2

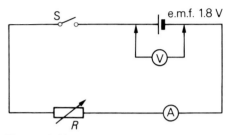

Figure 4.19

These results are plotted on a graph of t.p.d. against current, Figure 4.20. Notice that when switch S is open and no current flows, the t.p.d. has a maximum value which is equal to the e.m.f. of the cell: the cell is on 'open circuit'.

The graph is a straight line of the form

$$y = mx + c$$

where m is the gradient of the line and c is the intercept on the vertical axis.

$\Rightarrow\quad V = mI + c$

$\Rightarrow\quad V = -2.0I + 1.8$

because the gradient of the line is -2.0 and the intercept on the vertical axis is $+1.8$ V (the e.m.f. E).

$\Rightarrow\quad V = E - Ir$ where $r = -m$, the gradient.

The terminal potential difference V is less than the e.m.f. by some quantity Ir where r is the internal resistance of the cell. The value of Ir is sometimes called the 'lost volts'.

Because $m = -2.0$, the internal resistance r of the cell is $2.0\ \Omega$.

Energy is lost in driving the current through the chemicals which make up the cell, and this causes the cell to have an internal resistance r.

Note also the value 0.9 A of the intercept on the horizontal axis. This shows that the maximum current which the cell is capable of delivering (i.e. when the cell is on short-circuit) is 0.9 A.

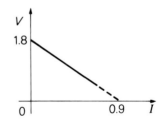

Figure 4.20

Example 4

A circuit contains a battery of e.m.f. 4.0 V and internal resistance $1.5\ \Omega$. If the external resistor has a value of $6.5\ \Omega$, find the value of

a) the current in the circuit   **b)** the t.p.d.   **c)** the short-circuit current.

In the circuit on the right, the battery is shown as an e.m.f. of 4.0 V and an internal resistance r of $1.5\ \Omega$ in series.

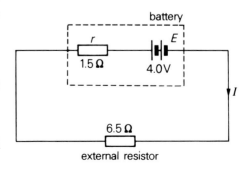

a) Total circuit resistance = 6.5 + 1.5 = 8.0 Ω
e.m.f. of battery = 4.0 V

$$I = \frac{V}{R}$$

$\Rightarrow \quad I = \frac{4.0}{8.0} = 0.5$

The current in the circuit is 0.5 A.

b) The t.p.d. is equal to the p.d. across the external resistor.

$$V = IR$$

$\Rightarrow \quad V = 0.5 \times 6.5 = 3.25$

The t.p.d. is 3.25 V

c) The short-circuit current is the current when the voltage V is zero.

$$V = E - Ir$$

$\Rightarrow \qquad 0 = 4.0 - I \times 1.5$

$\Rightarrow \quad 1.5 \times I = 4.0$

$\Rightarrow \qquad I = \frac{4.0}{1.5} = 2.7$

The short-circuit current is 2.7 A.

Example 5

Calculate the internal resistance of each of the following sources of e.m.f. when inserted in the circuit shown on the right.

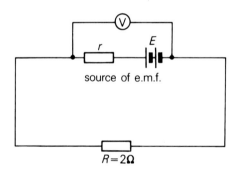
source of e.m.f.

$R = 2\,\Omega$

a) a U2 dry cell,   e.m.f. = 1.5 V,   t.p.d. = 1.2 V
b) a car battery,   e.m.f. = 12.0 V,   t.p.d. = 11.7 V
c) a calculator battery,   e.m.f. = 9.0 V,   t.p.d. = 3.6 V

$$V = E - Ir \quad \text{where} \quad r \text{ is internal resistance of source.}$$

but $\qquad I = \dfrac{E}{R + r} \qquad\qquad R$ is external resistance

$\Rightarrow \qquad V = E - \left(\dfrac{E}{R + r}\right)r$

$\Rightarrow \quad V(R + r) = E(R + r) - Er$

$\Rightarrow \quad VR + Vr = ER$

$\Rightarrow \qquad r = \dfrac{R(E - V)}{V}$

a) For the U2 dry cell $E = 1.5\,V$, $V = 1.2\,V$, $R = 2\,\Omega$

$\therefore \qquad r = \dfrac{2(1.5 - 1.2)}{1.2} = 0.5$

Internal resistance of U2 cell = 0.5 Ω.

b) For the car battery $E = 12.0\,V$, $V = 11.7\,V$, $R = 2\,\Omega$

$\therefore \qquad r = \dfrac{2(12.0 - 11.7)}{11.7} = 0.05$

Internal resistance of car battery = 0.05 Ω.

c) For the calculator battery $E = 9.0\,V$, $V = 3.6\,V$, $R = 2\,\Omega$

$\therefore \qquad r = \dfrac{2(9.0 - 3.6)}{3.6} = 3.0$

Internal resistance of calculator battery = 3.0 Ω.

4.8 Potential dividers

We now consider ways of varying the available potential difference. For this purpose we assume that the power supply has zero internal resistance and a fixed e.m.f.

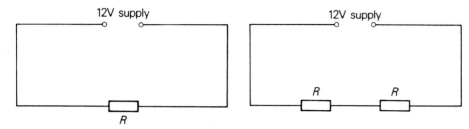

Figure 4.21 **Figure 4.22**

In Figure 4.21 the external resistor R is supplied with energy: 12 joules of energy for every coulomb of charge which passes through it ($12\,\text{J}\,\text{C}^{-1} \equiv 12\,\text{V}$).

If two identical external resistors are connected across the supply, Figure 4.22, the current through each resistor is the same: the rate of transformation of electrical energy to heat is the same for each resistor. The energy passing round the circuit is still $12\,\text{J}\,\text{C}^{-1}$, so 6 joules of energy is released for every coulomb of charge passing through each resistor. This means that the potential difference across each resistor is 6 volts, Figure 4.23.

$$V_1 + V_2 = 12$$

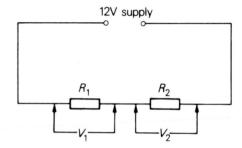

Figure 4.23

In general, for any number of resistors in series in a circuit, the total energy supplied by the source is the sum of the energies supplied to the resistors.

Figure 4.24 shows four unequal resistors in **series**. The total resistance in a series circuit is the sum of the resistances of the individual resistors.

$$R = R_1 + R_2 + R_3 + R_4$$

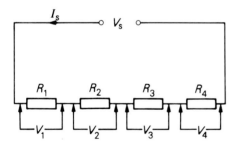

Figure 4.24

Because the resistors are in series, the current in each is the supply current I_s; multiply both sides of the above equation by I_s:

$$I_sR = I_sR_1 + I_sR_2 + I_sR_3 + I_sR_4$$

Then, because $V = I \times R$,

$$V = V_1 + V_2 + V_3 + V_4$$

The series of resistors in Figure 4.24 thus provides a range of potential differences.

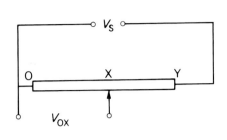

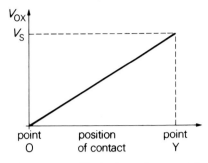

Figure 4.25 Potential divider

Figure 4.26 Variation of potential

The range of possible p.d.'s can be increased by using a continuous length of resistance wire. Figure 4.25 shows a source of e.m.f. of V_s volts and how various p.d.'s can be tapped off. The position of the contact point X on the resistance wire controls the p.d. V_{ox} between points O and X. Moving the contact from O to Y changes the p.d. V_{ox} as in the graph in Figure 4.26. The maximum value of V_{ox} is V_s when the contact is at point Y.

Halfway between O and Y, the p.d. is half V_s.

One-third of the way from O to Y the p.d. is one-third of V_s.

By tapping off various lengths of the resistance wire, smaller divisions of the total potential can be obtained. This arrangement is called a **potential divider**, the resistor OY being referred to as a **load resistor**.

This useful arrangement can provide a completely variable range of p.d.'s by varying the position of a contact point on a variable resistor (rheostat) as shown in Figure 4.27.

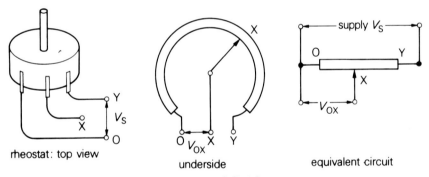

rheostat: top view

underside

equivalent circuit

Figure 4.27 Variable resistor as a potential divider

Example 6

A potential divider consists of a rheostat of resistance 25 ohms and is connected across a supply. If a constant current of 60 milliamperes passes through the rheostat, what range of p.d.s can it provide?

With the contact at point O, the p.d. is zero,

i.e. $V_{ox} = 0$ because X and O coincide.

With the contact at point Y, the p.d. V_{oy} is V_s,

i.e. $V_{oy} = V_s = I_s R$

The total resistance R of the divider is 25 ohms

The current I_s through this resistor is 60×10^{-3} amperes

$\Rightarrow \quad V_{oy} = 60 \times 10^{-3} \times 25 = 1.5$

$\Rightarrow \quad$ maximum voltage obtainable is 1.5 V

The potential divider can provide a range of voltages from 0 V to 1.5 V.

4.9   Resistors in parallel

In the circuit of Figure 4.28 the resistors R_1 and R_2 are connected in **parallel** to a supply of V_s volts giving a supply current of I_s amperes.

The system can be represented by an equivalent circuit shown in Figure 4.29 in which R_p is the equivalent resistance and I_s is the supply current.

A current I_s travels to a pair of parallel resistors and then separates at the junction into two currents I_1 and I_2, Figure 4.30.

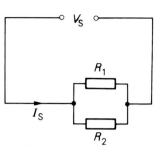

Figure 4.28

From Figure 4.30, $I_s = I_1 + I_2$

Also the two resistors are in parallel:

$\Rightarrow$ p.d. across R_1 = p.d. across R_2 = V_s

$\Rightarrow$ $I_1 \times R_1 = I_2 \times R_2 = V_s$

$\Rightarrow$ $I_1 = \dfrac{V_s}{R_1}$ and $I_2 = \dfrac{V_s}{R_2}$

From Figure 4.29, $I_s = \dfrac{V_s}{R_p}$

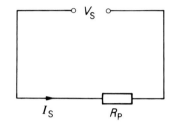

Figure 4.29

But $I_s = I_1 + I_2$

$\Rightarrow$ $\dfrac{V_s}{R_p} = \dfrac{V_s}{R_1} + \dfrac{V_s}{R_2}$

Divide both sides of this equation by V_s:

$$\frac{1}{R_p} = \frac{1}{R_1} + \frac{1}{R_2}$$

This important relationship gives the equivalent resistance of two resistors in parallel. In general, for more than two resistors in parallel, the equation becomes

$$\frac{1}{R_p} = \frac{1}{R_1} + \frac{1}{R_2} + \frac{1}{R_3} + \frac{1}{R_4} + \dots$$

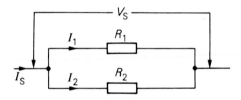

Figure 4.30

Example 7

Calculate the equivalent resistance of four resistors of 2 ohms, 3 ohms, 4 ohms and 5 ohms connected in parallel.

$$\frac{1}{R_p} = \frac{1}{2} + \frac{1}{3} + \frac{1}{4} + \frac{1}{5}$$

$$= \frac{30 + 20 + 15 + 12}{60} = \frac{77}{60}$$

$\Rightarrow$ $R_p = \dfrac{60}{77}$ (remember to invert the fraction)

$= 0.779$

The equivalent resistance of the four resistors is 0.78 ohms.

Example 8

Calculate the total resistance of the network in Figure 4.31.

The circuit has a 'parallel' pair of resistors in series with the 2 ohm resistor, and all these are in parallel with a 5 ohm resistor.

a)   The equivalent resistance R of the 'parallel' pair of resistors: 3 ohms and 4 ohms.

$$\frac{1}{R} = \frac{1}{3} + \frac{1}{4} = \frac{4 + 3}{12} = \frac{7}{12}$$

$\Rightarrow$ $R = \dfrac{12}{7}$

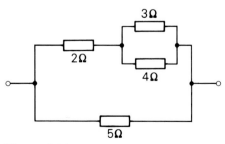

Figure 4.31

b)   The equivalent resistance R' of the top arm of the circuit:
2 ohms and $\frac{12}{7}$ohms. These are in series, so

$$R' = 2 + \frac{12}{7} = \frac{26}{7}$$

c)   The equivalent resistance R'' of the whole circuit:
$\frac{26}{7}$ ohms and 5 ohms in parallel.

$$\frac{1}{R''} = \frac{1}{\frac{26}{7}} + \frac{1}{5} = \frac{7}{26} + \frac{1}{5}$$

$$\Rightarrow \quad \frac{1}{R''} = \frac{35 + 26}{130} = \frac{61}{130}$$

$$\Rightarrow \quad R'' = \frac{130}{61} \approx 2.1$$

The total resistance of the network is approximately 2 ohms.

4.10   Wheatstone bridge circuit

The Wheatstone bridge circuit, a resistor network for determining resistance, was devised by the English physicist Sir Charles Wheatstone. It can provide accurate measurements of resistance and does not depend for its accuracy on the accuracy of a meter. It does however require a **sensitive** meter. The form of circuit most often encountered is shown in Figure 4.32. G represents a sensitive centre-zero galvanometer.

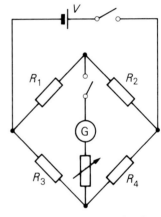

Figure 4.32 Wheatstone bridge circuit

It is often helpful to consider this circuit re-drawn as in Figure 4.33. (The galvanometer has been omitted.)

Consider AC as a potential divider made from two resistors R_1 and R_2. Applying Ohm's Law:

p.d. across R_1 $V_{AB} = I_1 R_1$

p.d. across R_2 $V_{BC} = I_1 R_2$

$$V = V_{AB} + V_{BC}$$

Consider DF as another potential divider in parallel with the first:

p.d. across R_3 $V_{DE} = I_2 R_3$

p.d. across R_4 $V_{EF} = I_2 R_4$

$$V = V_{DE} + V_{EF}$$

If the resistor values are chosen so that $V_{AB} = V_{DE}$ then it follows also that $V_{BC} = V_{EF}$ since the sum of the individual p.d.'s gives the supply p.d. which is V.

$$\Rightarrow \quad I_1 R_1 = I_2 R_3 \qquad \Rightarrow \quad \frac{R_1}{R_3} = \frac{I_2}{I_1}$$

and $I_1 R_2 = I_2 R_4 \qquad \Rightarrow \quad \dfrac{R_2}{R_4} = \dfrac{I_2}{I_1}$

so that $\dfrac{R_1}{R_3} = \dfrac{R_2}{R_4}$ or $\dfrac{R_1}{R_2} = \dfrac{R_3}{R_4}$

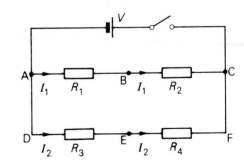

Figure 4.33

Now when $V_{AB} = V_{DE}$, then a galvanometer connected between points B and E registers zero current (null deflection) since points B and E are at the same potential: there is no potential difference between them and so $V_{BE} = 0$.

When the resistor values are selected so that the meter reads zero current, the bridge is said to be **balanced**.

In practice three of the resistors in this circuit are accurately known standard resistors while the fourth one is of unknown value to be determined using the bridge. By choosing a suitable ratio for resistors R_1 and R_2 and then gradually adjusting the value of R_3 until the bridge is balanced, it is possible to find R_4 from the ratio

$$\frac{R_1}{R_2} = \frac{R_3}{R_4}$$

The size of the current in the galvanometer depends on the extent to which the resistor values are not in the correct ratio. A protective variable resistor is inserted in series with the sensitive galvanometer in order to minimize the risk of damage when the 'out of balance' current is high, Figure 4.32.

Example 9

The Wheatstone bridge shown in Figure 4.34 is balanced. If $R_1 = 120\,\Omega$, $R_2 = 400\,\Omega$ and $R_3 = 80\,\Omega$, what is the value of the unknown resistor X?

Since the bridge is balanced $\dfrac{R_1}{R_2} = \dfrac{R_3}{X}$

$$\Rightarrow \qquad X = \frac{R_2 \times R_3}{R_1}$$

$$\Rightarrow \qquad X = \frac{400 \times 80}{120} = 267$$

The value of the unknown resistor X is 267 ohms.

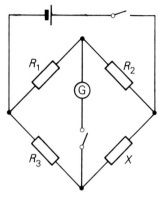

Figure 4.34

The unbalanced Wheatstone bridge

The circuit in Figure 4.35 represents a balanced bridge.

If the value of resistor R_1 is increased by a small amount ΔR, then the galvanometer indicates an out-of-balance current I. The set of results in Table 1 illustrates typical behaviour of this circuit.

Increase in resistance $\Delta R\,(\Omega)$	0	1.0	2.0	3.0	4.0	5.0	6.0	7.0	8.0	9.0	10
Out of balance current $I\,(\mu A)$	0	35	70	100	130	170	200	230	270	300	340

Table 1

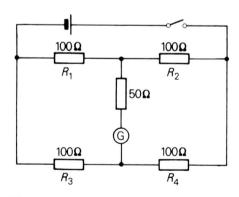

Figure 4.35

A graph of change in resistance ΔR against current I indicates that, for an initially balanced bridge, as the value of one resistor is changed by a small amount, the current is proportional to the change in resistance, Figure 4.36.

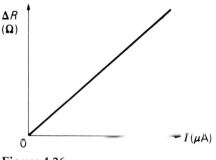

Figure 4.36

If resistor R_1 is replaced by a heat sensitive resistor called a thermistor then the out-of-balance current indicates temperature change, Figure 4.37. Alternatively, resistors R_1 and R_2 could be replaced by an identical pair of electrical strain gauges (resistors whose resistance alters with changes in stress) and the out-of-balance current would give information about mechanical strain, Figure 4.38. There are many applications of the Wheatstone bridge circuit.

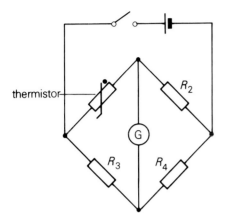

Figure 4.37 Measuring temperature

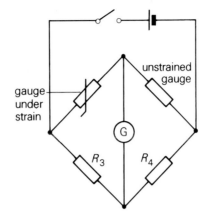

Figure 4.38 Measuring strain

Metre bridge

An alternative form of Wheatstone bridge circuit which uses only one standard resistor is called the metre bridge, Figure 4.39. With this arrangement two of the resistors are replaced by a one-metre length of uniform resistance wire with a movable contact P.

The position of the contact point P decides the ratio R_1 to R_2 since, provided the wire is of uniform thickness, the ratio can be expressed as the ratio of the two lengths of wire l_1 to l_2

i.e.
$$\frac{R_1}{R_2} = \frac{l_1}{l_2} = \frac{R_3}{R_4}$$

and since the wire is 1 metre long, $l_2 = 100 - l_1$

$$\Rightarrow \quad \frac{l_1}{100 - l_1} = \frac{R_3}{R_4}$$

This method provides an accurate determination of resistance: the error in the measurement of l_1 and l_2 can be less than 1% since these lengths can be measured to the nearest millimetre.

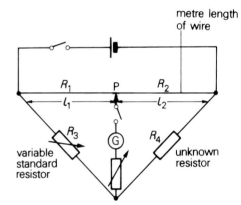

Figure 4.39 Metre bridge

Example 10

A metre bridge is balanced when the movable contact is 64 cm from the end of the wire, Figure 4.40. What is the value of the unknown resistor?

At balance $\quad \dfrac{l_1}{100 - l_1} = \dfrac{R_3}{R_4} \qquad l_1 = 64\,\text{cm} \quad R_3 = 100\,\Omega \quad R_4 = X$

$$\Rightarrow \quad \frac{64}{100 - 64} = \frac{100}{X}$$

$$\Rightarrow \quad \frac{64}{36} = \frac{100}{X}$$

$$\Rightarrow \quad X = \frac{36 \times 100}{64}$$

$$X = 56.25$$

The unknown resistor has a value of 56 ohms.

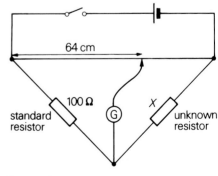

Figure 4.40

Summary

The direction of an electric field is given by the direction of the force on a positive charge placed in the field.

The magnitude of an electric field is given by the magnitude of the force on a unit positive charge placed in the field and is measured in newtons per coulomb, $N\,C^{-1}$.

The work done W in transferring Q coulombs of charge through a p.d. of V volts is given by $W = Q \times V$ joules.

The potential difference between two points is equal to the work done per unit charge in moving charge from one point to another.

$$V = \frac{W}{Q}$$

The rate of flow of charge is defined as the current.

$$\frac{Q}{t} = I \qquad \text{where } Q \text{ is the quantity of charge}$$
$$t \text{ is the time}$$
$$I \text{ is the current}$$

So $Q = I \times t$

For a current of 1 ampere, the quantity of charge that flows in 1 second past a given point is defined as the coulomb, C.

$$1\,C = 1\,A \times 1\,s, \quad 1 \text{ coulomb} = 1 \text{ ampere-second}$$

A component is said to have a resistance of 1 ohm when 1 volt is required to drive a current of 1 ampere through it.

$$R = V/I, \quad 1 \text{ ohm} = 1 \text{ volt per ampere}, \quad 1\,\Omega = 1\,V\,A^{-1}$$

If Q coulombs of charge pass between two points A and B where the p.d. is V volts, the energy released W is given by

$$W = Q\,V \text{ joules}$$

If a current I passes for t seconds through a p.d. of V volts, the energy released is

$$W = I\,t\,V \text{ joules}$$

The e.m.f. (electromotive force) of a source is the energy converted when a coulomb of charge passes through the source. If 1 joule of energy is supplied by every 1 coulomb of charge, then the e.m.f. is 1 volt.

An electrical source is equivalent to an e.m.f. with a resistor in series, where the resistor corresponds to the internal resistance.

The e.m.f. of a source is equal to the p.d. across the terminals of the source when no current is being delivered: on open circuit.

The terminal potential difference of a source is related to its e.m.f. and internal resistance by the equation:

$$V = E - I \times r \quad \text{where } V = \text{terminal potential difference}$$
$$E = \text{e.m.f. of source}$$
$$r = \text{internal resistance}$$
$$I = \text{current through the source}$$

Electrical power P is given by

$$P = I \times V$$
$$1 \text{ watt} = 1 \text{ ampere} \times 1 \text{ volt}$$

A potential divider may be used to provide fixed or variable p.d.'s from a given source, using fixed or variable resistors.

The total resistance in a series circuit is given by the sum of the individual resistors:

$$R_s = R_1 + R_2 + R_3 + \ldots$$

For resistors in parallel the total resistance can be calculated from:

$$1/R_p = 1/R_1 + 1/R_2 + 1/R_3 + \ldots$$

An ammeter is connected in series in a circuit. A good ammeter has a low resistance.

A voltmeter is connected in parallel in a circuit. A good voltmeter has a high resistance.

For the balanced Wheatstone bridge shown below:

$$\frac{R_1}{R_2} = \frac{R_3}{R_4}$$

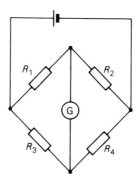

For an initially balanced bridge, as the value of one resistor is changed by a small amount, the galvanometer current is proportional to the change in resistance.

Problems

1. If a current of 40 mA passes through a lamp for 16 s, how much charge has passed any given point in the circuit?

2. A lightning flash lasted for 1 ms. If 5 C of charge was transferred during this time, what was the current?

3. The current in a circuit is 2.5×10^5 A. How long does it take for 500 C of charge to pass any given point in the circuit?

4. What is the p.d. across a 2 kΩ resistor if there is a current of 3 mA in it?

5. Draw a circuit diagram to show the experiment you would perform to determine the internal resistance of a battery. Explain what readings you would make and how you would calculate the internal resistance.

6. The terminal potential difference of a cell is 1.5 V on 'open circuit' and 1.4 V when connected in a circuit in which the current is 0.2 A. What is the internal resistance of the cell?

7. A 5 ohm resistor is connected to a 20 volt d.c. supply. Calculate the time for 3000 joules of energy to be converted in this resistor.

8. What size is the current in a circuit containing a battery of internal resistance 1.6 Ω and e.m.f. 4.2 V, connected to an external resistor of 2.6 Ω?

9. What is the terminal p.d. of a battery of internal resistance 1.8 Ω and e.m.f. 4.4 V when connected to an external resistor of 0.4 Ω?

10. What is the 'short-circuit' current for a battery of e.m.f. 4.5 V and internal resistance 0.9 Ω?

11. In order to determine the e.m.f. and internal resistance of a battery, a pupil used two 15 Ω resistors and an ammeter. When the two resistors were joined in parallel and connected to the battery the current was 2.0 A, and when connected in series the current was 0.75 A. Calculate the e.m.f. and internal resistance of the battery.

12. The circuit diagram shows two cells whose e.m.f.'s and internal resistances are known.

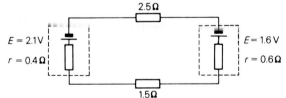

Calculate the current in the circuit.

13. Four identical cells each of e.m.f. 1.5 V and internal resistance 0.3 Ω are connected in series. What is the overall e.m.f. and internal resistance? What is the short-circuit current?

14. Six identical cells each of e.m.f. 1.5 V and internal resistance 0.3 Ω are connected in parallel. What is the overall e.m.f. and internal resistance? What is the short-circuit current?

15. Calculate the power of a 120 ohm heater which operates on a 20 volt supply.

16. An electrical source with internal resistance r is used to operate a heater of resistance R. What fraction of the total power is available at the heater?

17. a) A cell of e.m.f. E and internal resistance r is connected in series with an external resistor R.

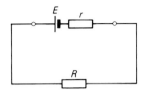

For this circuit, show that $R = \dfrac{E}{I} - r$, where I is the current in the circuit.

b) The e.m.f. and internal resistance of a d.c. supply are to be measured. The d.c. supply is connected in series with an ammeter and an external resistor R of variable resistance.

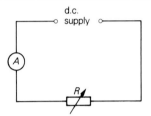

The current I is measured for various values of R. The results are shown in the table.

R (ohms)	5.00	10.0	15.0	20.0	25.0
I (amps)	0.667	0.400	0.286	0.222	0.182

i) It would appear from the relationship in part (a) that a graph of R against $\dfrac{1}{I}$ will be a straight line. (E and r being taken as constant.) Using the data in the table draw a graph to verify this statement. (Use graph paper.)

ii) From this graph calculate values for the e.m.f. and internal resistance of the d.c. supply. Explain your working.

SEB

18. The following series of resistors is connected to a 12 V supply.

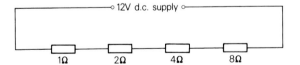

a) Calculate the p.d. across each resistor.
b) List all the possible p.d.'s obtainable from this resistor arrangement.

19. A potential divider has resistance 10 ohms. If a constant current of 300 mA flows through the divider what range of voltages can it provide?

20. Derive an expression for the combined resistance of two resistors in parallel.

4 Resistors in circuits

21 a) A d.c. supply has a constant e.m.f. of 12 V and an internal resistance of 3.0 Ω. A load resistor of resistance 1.0 Ω is connected across the supply terminals.
Calculate **i)** the power delivered to the load resistor;
 ii) the voltage across the supply terminals.
b) Calculation of the power delivered to various values of load resistor is repeated giving the following results:

R in ohms	0.6	1.0	2.5	3.5	5.0	9.0
P in watts	6.7		11.9	11.9	11.3	9.0

  i) Using suitable scales, draw a graph of P against R, including the point obtained in part **a)** i).
  ii) From your graph determine the value of load resistor to which maximum power is delivered from this supply.
  iii) Another 12 V d.c. supply has an internal resistance of 6.0 Ω. Suggest, with brief justification, the value of load resistor which should be connected to this supply for maximum power to be delivered to this load resistor.
c) On many signal generators there are two sets of output terminals – one set marked 6 Ω and the other marked 600 Ω. Suggest a reason for this provision.

SEB

22 Calculate the net resistance in the following circuit.

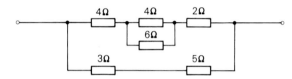

23 Derive an expression for the combination of two resistors in series.

24 An ammeter of resistance 10 ohms is used to measure the current in the circuit shown.
By how much does the measured current differ from the expected current?

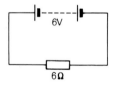

25 Calculate the total equivalent resistance between points X and Y in the circuit shown.

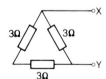

26 The circuit shown represents a Wheatstone bridge circuit.

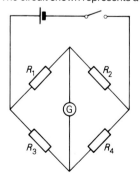

Explain the use of this circuit and derive an expression for the balance condition.

27 The Wheatstone bridge circuit shown below is balanced.

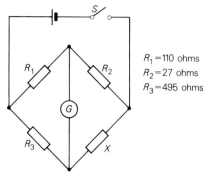

$R_1 = 110$ ohms
$R_2 = 27$ ohms
$R_3 = 495$ ohms

Calculate the value of the unknown resistor X.

28 Describe how the out-of-balance current in a Wheatstone bridge circuit can be used to measure temperature.

29 a) Describe an experiment to investigate how the rate at which heat is produced in a coil of wire varies with the current in the wire. Include in your answer:
  i) a labelled diagram of the apparatus used;
  ii) a description of the experimental measurements made;
  iii) details of any measures taken to minimise experimental error.
b) In such an experiment the following results were obtained.

Rate of heat production (J s⁻¹)	1.9	3.2	11	16	24
Current in wire (A)	0.7	0.9	1.6	2.0	2.4

  i) Use these results to determine graphically the relationship between the rate of production of heat and the current in the wire.
  ii) From the graph determine the resistance of the wire.

SEB

30 To find an unknown resistance R, a pupil sets up the following circuit where the voltmeter can be connected across either XY or XZ.

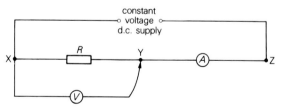

The results obtained are shown in the table.

Voltmeter connected across	Voltmeter reading V	Ammeter reading mA
XY	1.00	50
XZ	1.10	50

a) The current is the same for both positions of the voltmeter. From this information, what can you deduce about the voltmeter?
b) Find the resistance R and the resistance of the ammeter.
c) If the voltmeter is disconnected and another voltmeter of resistance 180 Ω is connected across XY, what would be the readings on the ammeter and this new voltmeter?

SEB

31 Instead of using a transformer, bulbs may be connected in series with a 'mains dropping' resistor R across the 240 V supply as shown.

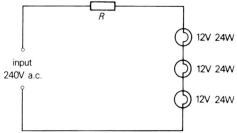

a) Calculate the value of R which allows the three bulbs to be run at their correct brightness.
b) What fraction of the input power is used by the bulbs?
c) Give the reason why the power used by the bulbs is less than the input power.

SEB

32 The diagram shows a metre bridge circuit used to find the resistance of X.

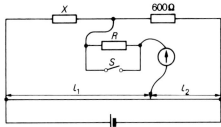

a) Explain the functions of resistor R and switch S.
b) Explain why a balance point in the middle section of the bridge wire gives a more accurate value of X.
c) If at balance point $l_1 = 60 \pm 1$ cm and $l_2 = 40 \pm 1$ cm, calculate the resistance of X and give the error limits of your answer.
d) Indicate two sources which contribute to the error in the measurements l_1 and l_2.

SEB

33 Two pupils set out to find the resistance of an unknown resistor X.
a) Pupil A sets up a metre bridge circuit using resistance box R, the resistance of which may be varied from 1 Ω to 10000 Ω.
Balance point is found when R = 3000 Ω and LM = 107 mm.

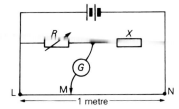

i) Calculate the resistance of X.
ii) Suggest any change pupil A could make to increase the accuracy of the result.

b) Pupil B sets up an ammeter-voltmeter circuit. The reading on the ammeter is 90 µA and the reading on the voltmeter is 1.5 V.
i) Calculate the resistance of X.
ii) Suggest any change pupil B could make to increase the accuracy of the result.

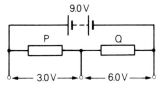

c) Discuss whether method (a) or method (b) is more accurate.

SEB

34 a) A 10 Ω resistor is connected across a battery of e.m.f. 6 V with internal resistance of 2 Ω.
i) What is the current in the circuit?
ii) What is the potential difference between the battery terminals?
b) To investigate the characteristics of a power supply unit a girl uses an ammeter and a resistance box in the following circuit.

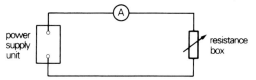

i) For this circuit derive the expression

$$R = \frac{E}{I} - r$$

where E is the e.m.f. of the power supply unit,
r is its internal resistance,
R is the total external resistance,
and I is the current in the circuit.
She collects values of I and R and draws the following graph.

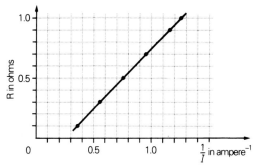

ii) Explain why she chooses to draw a graph of R against $\frac{1}{I}$.

iii) Extend the graph and deduce from it:
(A) the maximum current if the power supply unit were short circuited.
(B) the internal resistance of the power supply unit.
(C) the e.m.f. of the power supply unit.

SEB

35 The following circuit is used to provide output voltages of 3.0 V and 6.0 V from a 9.0 V battery of negligible internal resistance.

a) If the resistance of Q is 100 Ω, find the resistance of P.
b) When a 6 V, 0.060 A lamp is connected across the resistor Q, it does not operate at its normal brightness.
Give an explanation.

SEB

36 Three resistors are available. Their values are 4 Ω, 6 Ω, and 12 Ω. Describe how two, or all three, of the resistors might be combined to give each of the following resistances.
a) 10 Ω   **b)** 3 Ω   **c)** 8 Ω

SEB

4   Resistors in circuits

37 Certain resistors are constructed by depositing a thin film of conducting material on top of an insulating base. Connection to the film is made with gold pads at each end of the film as shown.

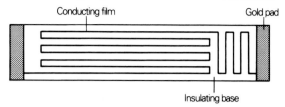

The resistance between the end gold connectors depends on the breadth of the conducting film. The results below show the resistance for various breadths of film of the same length and thickness.

Breadth (μm)	150	87	67	60	55
Resistance (Ω)	80	140	180	200	220

Find the relationship between the resistance and the breadth of the conducting film. You must show how the data were used to arrive at the relationship.

SEB

38 A platinum-film resistor is to be used to indicate changes in temperature.
To find the resistance at room temperature the resistor is placed in one of the arms of a Wheatstone bridge. A variable resistor and fixed resistors of 6.00 kΩ and 4.00 kΩ are placed in the other arms.

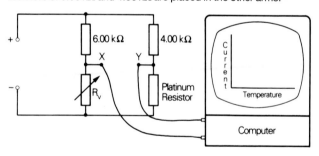

A computer is connected across XY and programmed to read the current between X and Y.
a) The computer shows that the current between X and Y is zero when the variable resistor is set at 162 Ω. Calculate the resistance of the platinum-film resistor at room temperature.
b) The computer is now programmed to plot a graph of the current in XY against the temperature of the platinum-film resistor. Suggest and explain the shape of graph you would expect as the temperature of the platinum-film resistor is increased.

SEB

39 In the following circuit, the p.d. across the 16 ohm resistor is 40 volts when switch S is **open**.

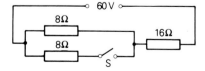

What is the p.d. across the 16 ohm resistor when the switch S is **closed**?

SEB

40 In the following circuit the current in the milliammeter is zero.

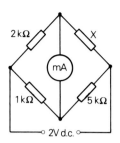

a) Calculate the resistance X.
b) Draw a circuit diagram to show how this value of resistance would be measured as accurately as possible using a suitable ammeter-voltmeter method.

SEB

41 On setting up the following bridge circuit, a pupil finds that no current flows in the galvanometer.

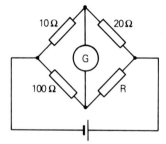

What is the resistance of the unknown resistor R?

SEB

42 Each cell in the circuit below has an e.m.f. of 2 V and an internal resistance of 1 Ω.

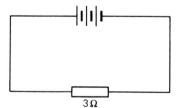

Calculate the current in this circuit.

SEB

5 Alternating current and voltage

5.1 Alternating current

The electricity supplied to homes is an alternating current at an alternating voltage of 240 V having a frequency of 50 Hz. An a.c. supply is used so that a transformer can step up or step down the voltage: less energy is wasted if the electrical power is transmitted at high voltage.

A supply of alternating current is generated using an a.c. generator. The generation of alternating current in a generator is illustrated in Figure 5.1.

When a coil is rotated in a magnetic field, an electromotive force E is induced which will drive a current I through the external circuit of resistance R. At any instant the current is given by $I = E/R$.

The slip rings and carbon brushes of this generator ensure that one output terminal is always connected to one side of the coil, whether that side is moving up or down through the magnetic field as it rotates. This means that the direction of the induced electromotive force changes every half revolution of the coil.

We can use an oscilloscope to give a trace which shows how the e.m.f. varies with time. The shape of the trace is the same as for a graph of e.m.f. against time; e.m.f. is on the vertical axis and time on the horizontal axis, Figure 5.2.

The induced e.m.f. varies between zero and a maximum value E_m known as the peak e.m.f. We can deduce how this variation takes place if we consider the coil as it rotates. Figure 5.3 shows the cross section of a coil as it rotates in a magnetic field.

The size of the induced e.m.f. is proportional to the rate at which the coil cuts through the field lines. If the resistance of the external circuit is constant, then the induced current I is proportional to the induced e.m.f. E.

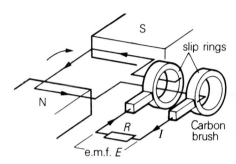

Figure 5.1 a.c. generator

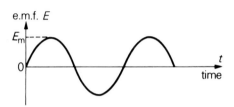

Figure 5.2 a.c. generator output

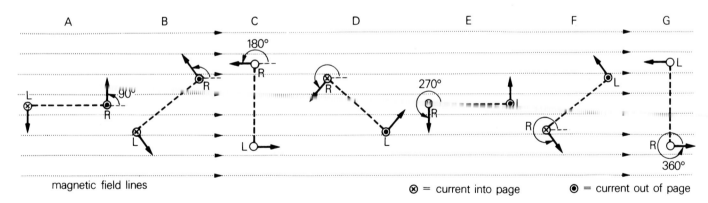

Figure 5.3 Coil rotating in a magnetic field

The direction of the induced current is shown at each stage. One side of the coil is labelled L and the other side R.

Consider the variation of current in the side of the coil marked R, Figure 5.3. When the side of the coil is moving at right angles to the magnetic field, the induced e.m.f. is a maximum. This occurs when the coil is in positions A and E. In these two cases the currents are in opposite directions. At positions B, D and F, the induced currents are less than maximum because the loop is moving at an angle to the field. At positions C and G, the sides of the coil are moving parallel to

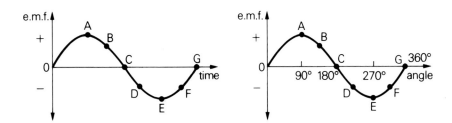

Figure 5.4 Generated e.m.f.

the magnetic field and are therefore not cutting the field lines, so the induced e.m.f. is zero, Figure 5.4.

The pattern of e.m.f. variation is repeated at regular intervals if the generator coil rotates at a constant rate. One complete pattern is called a cycle. The time to complete one cycle is the period T which is related to the frequency f:

$$T = \frac{1}{f}$$

Electricity supplied to homes has a frequency of 50 Hz, i.e. 50 cycles per second. So the period T of voltage variation is as follows.

$$T = \frac{1}{50} = 0.02\,\text{s}$$

This is the time taken for the generator coil to rotate through 360°, i.e. 2π radians.

Figure 5.5 shows the trace obtained on a cathode ray oscilloscope of the change in generator e.m.f. E with angle θ; it is a sine curve in which the e.m.f. varies between 0 V and the peak e.m.f. E_{m}.

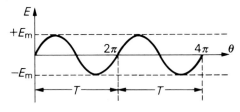

Figure 5.5

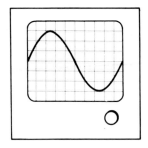

Figure 5.6   **Figure 5.7**

Frequency can be measured using a C.R.O. by comparing a waveform of unknown frequency with one of known frequency. The time-base is first adjusted until one complete wavelength is visible on the screen, Figure 5.6. Without altering the controls of the C.R.O. the frequency of the unknown is found by comparing the number of complete waves, Figure 5.7. There are two waves produced in the same time, and therefore the unknown frequency is twice the known one. In this case, if the known frequency is 50 Hz, the unknown frequency is 100 Hz.

The frequency of a wave can also be determined by referring to the time-base setting of the C.R.O.

The time-base is often calibrated in milliseconds per centimetre (ms cm^{-1}). This tells us how long it takes the trace to travel 1 cm to the right of the screen.

Example 1

The time-base of a C.R.O. is calibrated to 2 ms cm⁻¹. If four complete waves occupy 10 cm, what is the frequency of the wave?

The trace moves 1 cm in 2 ms
⇒ The trace moves 10 cm in 10 × 2 = 20 ms
⇒ The wave travels **one** complete wavelength in ¼ of 20 ms
⇒ The wave travels **one** complete wavelength in 5 ms = $\frac{1}{200}$ s
⇒ The frequency of the wave = 200 s⁻¹ = 200 Hz

The frequency of the wave is 200 Hz

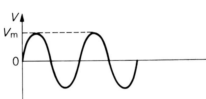

2 ms/cm

Comparison of a.c. and d.c.

The current and the p.d. of an a.c. supply vary continuously and so the effective value of these quantities is less than the maximum value.

The circuit in Figure 5.8 can be used to compare the heating effect of a d.c. supply with that of an a.c. supply. A light meter is placed to measure the output of lamp B first from a low voltage a.c. supply and then from a d.c. supply. Resistor R is adjusted until the lamp is equally bright from both sources. The peak voltage V_m of the a.c. supply and the equivalent steady voltage V_{dc} of the d.c. supply are measured on the calibrated screen of a C.R.O., Figure 5.9.

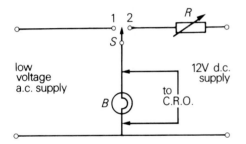

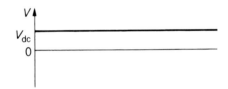

Figure 5.8 Comparison of a.c. and d.c. supplies

Figure 5.9

Typical results for three different lamps are shown in Table 1 below.

	V_m (volts)	V_{dc} (volts)	V_{dc}/V_m
lamp 1	12.0	8.5	0.7
lamp 2	3.0	2.1	0.7
lamp 3	2.0	1.4	0.7

Table 1

These show that the equivalent d.c. voltage V_{dc} for the same power output is about 70% of the maximum a.c. voltage V_m.

$$V_{dc} = 0.7 \, V_m$$

A more mathematical analysis indicates that an alternating voltage of peak value V_m delivers the same power as a d.c. voltage of $\frac{V_m}{\sqrt{2}}$. This is termed the root mean square voltage, V_{rms}.

$$V_{rms} = \frac{V_m}{\sqrt{2}}$$

Similarly the root mean square current I_{rms} is given by

$$I_{rms} = \frac{I_m}{\sqrt{2}}$$

Example 2

Calculate the peak voltage of a 240 V a.c. supply.

$$V_{rms} = \frac{V_m}{\sqrt{2}}$$

where V_{rms} = 240 V and V_m is the peak voltage

$\Rightarrow \qquad V_m = \sqrt{2} \times V_{rms} = \sqrt{2} \times 240 \approx 339$

The peak voltage of a 240 V a.c. supply is 339 V

Example 3

The peak value of an alternating current in a 10 Ω resistor is 3.0 A. Calculate the power developed in the resistor.

$$I_{rms} = 0.7\, I_m \qquad\qquad \text{power developed} = I_{rms}^2 \times R$$
$$\text{where} \quad I_m = 3.0\,\text{A} \qquad\qquad\qquad = 2.1^2 \times 10$$
$$\Rightarrow \ I_{rms} = 0.7 \times 3.0 = 2.1 \qquad\qquad\qquad = 44$$

The resistor develops a power of 44 W

5.2   Resistors in a.c. circuits

When some components are connected to a d.c. supply, their p.d.'s and currents do not reach their maximum values at the same instant: delays occur. The observation of these delays while we are using a varying a.c. supply is difficult unless we reduce the supply frequency to about 1 Hz. This can be achieved using a slow a.c. generator of the type shown in Figure 5.10, or by using the very low frequency output from a variable frequency signal generator.

Figure 5.10 Slow a.c. generator

Phase difference

Using the circuit in Figure 5.11 it is possible to observe the potential difference and current variation when a **resistor** is supplied with low frequency a.c.

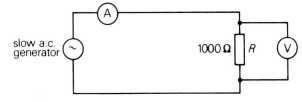

Figure 5.11 Phase in a resistor circuit

There is **no** difference in phase between the voltmeter readings and the ammeter readings as shown in Figure 5.12.

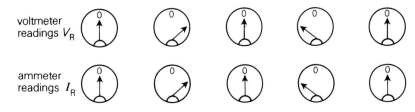

Figure 5.12

The current and voltage variations match, and we say that the current and voltage are **in phase**. This can be represented graphically as in Figure 5.13.

The current I_R and voltage V_R reach their maximum values at the same instant.

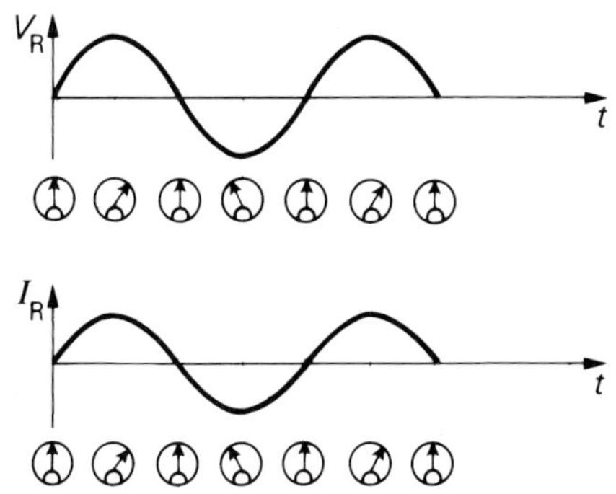

Measuring the opposition

The opposition of a component to alternating current in a circuit is called its **impedance**. Impedance is measured in ohms and is defined as the ratio of the r.m.s. potential difference to the r.m.s. current for the component in question. In fact, it is the potential difference across the component divided by the current in the component. When dealing with a.c. circuits, we use a.c. meters to give r.m.s. values.

The ratio V_R/I_R remains constant whatever their values: this means that the resistance remains constant. The ratio does not depend upon the frequency of the supply.

Figure 5.13

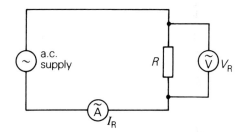

Figure 5.14

The impedance of a resistor is the same for both a.c. and d.c. and is its resistance R. For the resistor in Figure 5.14.

$$R = \frac{V_R}{I_R} \quad \text{where } V_R = \text{r.m.s. voltage across } R$$
$$I_R = \text{r.m.s. current in } R$$

Summary

V_{rms} is the root mean square voltage and represents the d.c. equivalent of an a.c. voltage variation

$$V_{rms} = \frac{V_m}{\sqrt{2}} = 0.7\, V_m$$

When a resistor is inserted in an a.c. circuit, the current and p.d. variation are in phase.

In an a.c. circuit

$$\text{resistance } R = \frac{V_R}{I_R} \quad \text{where } V_R \text{ is r.m.s. voltage across } R$$
$$\text{and } I_R \text{ is r.m.s. current in } R$$

The impedance of a resistor is independent of the frequency.

Problems

1 Describe an experiment to determine the relationship between peak voltage and root mean square voltage.
2 What is the peak voltage of a 12 V r.m.s. supply?
3 The peak value of an alternating current in a 3 Ω lamp filament is 4 A. Calculate the power of the lamp.
4 In the specification of a certain non-electrolytic capacitor, the maximum operating voltage is given as 63 volts d.c. What, therefore, is the greatest r.m.s. voltage allowed when this capacitor is used in an a.c. circuit?

SEB

6 Capacitance

6.1 Introduction

Capacitors are used for storing charge. They vary in shape, size and type according to their applications, Figure 6.1.

6.2 Capacitors

The circuit in Figure 6.2 can be used to illustrate some properties of a capacitor in a d.c. circuit.

When switch S is turned to position 1, the lamp L_1 glows brightly, dims and then goes out. The current is at a maximum immediately after the switch is closed and rapidly falls to zero, Figure 6.3(a). If the switch S is then turned to position 2, the lamp L_2 glows brightly, dims and then goes out even though the battery is no longer part of the circuit. The current is once again at a maximum immediately after the switch is closed and rapidly falls to zero although in this case the current is in the **opposite direction**, Figure 6.3(b).

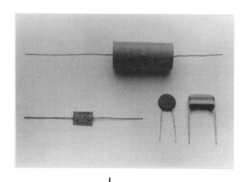

capacitor symbol

Figure 6.1 Capacitors

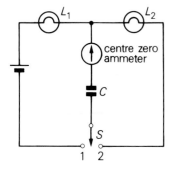

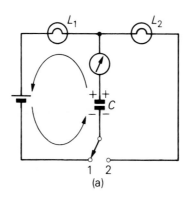

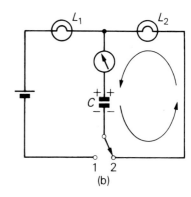

(a)

(b)

Figure 6.2

Figure 6.3

When a current passes for a certain time, a quantity of charge is transferred from one part of the circuit to another. Figure 6.3(a) shows the battery transferring electrons from the top plate to the lower plate of the capacitor. We say that the capacitor has been **charged**. In Figure 6.3(b) the capacitor releases the stored charge; electrons flow back to the top plate and we say that the capacitor is **discharging**.

A capacitor consists of two metal plates (or foils), separated by an insulating material. Figure 6.4 shows the construction of a typical capacitor.

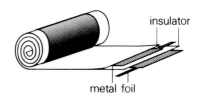

Figure 6.4 Capacitor construction

Charging the capacitor required a potential difference, so work was done in transferring charge between the plates. The relationship between the quantity of charge Q transferred to the plates and the potential difference V between them is investigated using the apparatus shown in Figure 6.5. The parallel plate capacitor shown consists of two metal foil plates whose separation and area of overlap can be varied. One form of this apparatus is called the 'Aepinus Capacitor', as shown; other forms have horizontally placed sheets of foil with insulating separators.

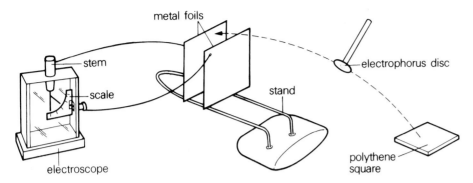

Figure 6.5

As charge is supplied to the capacitor plate, a potential difference is set up between the plates. Charge can be supplied using an electrophorus. When the electrophorus disc is placed on the negatively charged polythene square and earthed, the disc becomes positively charged by induction. An equal quantity of charge is transferred by the disc to the capacitor plate each time.

As more and more charge is transferred to the capacitor, more and more work is being done by the experimenter as he/she charges the capacitor. As the quantity of charge stored in the capacitor builds up, so too does the electric field between the parallel plates.

If one plate of the capacitor is connected to the case and the other to the stem of the electroscope, the deflection of the gold leaf gives a measure of the potential difference between the plates.

As more charge is transferred to the capacitor, the potential difference increases and is measured by the number of divisions of deflection of the gold leaf. This experiment provides results of the form shown in Table 1.

Quantity of charge transferred (number of charge transfers)	Q	1	2	3
potential difference (electroscope divisions)	V	2	4	6

Table 1

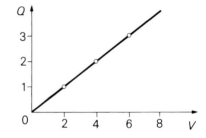

Figure 6.6

A graph of Q versus V has a constant slope and passes through the origin (Figure 6.6), so that Q and V are related by the equation, $Q = \text{constant} \times V$

This can be written

$$\frac{Q}{V} = \text{constant} \Rightarrow \frac{Q}{V} = C$$

The constant C defines the capacitance of the capacitor

$$\text{capacitance } (C) = \frac{\text{charge } (Q)}{\text{potential difference } (V)}$$

When Q is measured in coulombs and V is measured in volts, the capacitance is measured in farads.

If a charge of 1 coulomb (1 C) is transferred to the plate of a capacitor and this results in a potential difference between the plates of 1 volt (1 V), then the capacitance is 1 farad (1 F).

In practice one farad is a very large capacitance and most capacitors have much smaller values which may be expressed in microfarads (μF), nanofarads (nF) or picofarads (pF).

$$1\,\mu\text{F} = 1 \times 10^{-6}\,\text{F} \qquad 1\,\text{nF} = 1 \times 10^{-9}\,\text{F} \qquad 1\,\text{pF} = 1 \times 10^{-12}\,\text{F}$$

Example 1

What quantity of charge is needed to charge a 2.0 microfarad capacitor to a potential difference of 12 volts?

$$C = \frac{Q}{V} \quad \text{where } C = 2.0 \times 10^{-6}\,\text{F} \quad V = 12\,\text{V}$$

$$\Rightarrow \qquad 2.0 \times 10^{-6} = \frac{Q}{12}$$

$$\Rightarrow \qquad 12 \times 2.0 \times 10^{-6} = Q$$

$$\Rightarrow \qquad\qquad Q = 24 \times 10^{-6}$$

24 μC of charge is required to charge the capacitor.

Example 2

A charge of $3.0 \times 10^{-12}\,\text{C}$ transferred to the plate of a capacitor produces a potential difference of 2.0 mV. What is the capacitance of the capacitor?

$$C = \frac{Q}{V} \quad \text{where } Q = 3.0 \times 10^{-12}\,\text{C} \quad V = 2.0 \times 10^{-3}\,\text{V}$$

$$\Rightarrow \quad C = \frac{3.0 \times 10^{-12}}{2.0 \times 10^{-3}}$$

$$\Rightarrow \quad C = 1.5 \times 10^{-9}$$

The capacitor has a capacitance 1.5 nF.

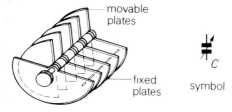

6.3 Factors affecting capacitance

Area of plates

The capacitance of a capacitor is directly proportional to the area of overlap of its plates.

The dependence of capacitance on the area of overlap has been used in the variable capacitor used for tuning a radio, Figure 6.7. Movement of the semicircular metal plates (vanes) relative to each other produces a variation of the capacitance.

Figure 6.7

Distance between capacitor plates

As the plate separation is increased, the potential difference V increases; since $C = Q/V$, this means that the capacitance decreases. In fact the capacitance increases as the plate separation d decreases.

This dependence of capacitance on plate separation is used in the 'trimmer' capacitor (used to make very fine adjustments to the tuning of a radio), Figure 6.8. The spacing of the metal plates is adjusted by turning the screw and hence the capacitance varies.

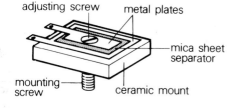

Figure 6.8 Trimmer capacitor

Material between capacitor plates

The dependence of capacitance on the type of material between the plates of the capacitor is expressed by the constant k.

The insulating material between the plates is called a dielectric and the constant k is the factor by which the capacitance is increased when that material is inserted between the plates. The k values given in Table 2 show that different materials influence the capacitance by different amounts.

material between plates	k factor
air	1.0
waxed paper	2.7
polyester	3.8
mica	7.0

Table 2

For general purposes, capacitors use waxed paper as the dielectric between the two metal foils as already shown in Figure 6.4. Other materials are chosen for special applications.

Another type of capacitor, the electrolytic capacitor has plates of aluminium foil, one of which has an oxide coating. There is a layer of chemical-soaked paper (electrolyte) between the foils. This type of capacitor is well sealed to prevent leakage, Figure 6.9. It is important to connect this type of capacitor with the correct polarity in a d.c. circuit as it can be damaged by incorrect connection. The electrolytic capacitor has its own symbol.

Capacitors have a 'working voltage' printed on them. This is the maximum recommended p.d. which should be applied to them without the risk of the insulation of the dielectric breaking down. This could result in a large current surge between the plates and rapid heating, leading to a dangerous explosion.

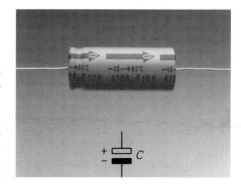

Figure 6.9 Electrolytic capacitor

6.4   Energy stored in a capacitor

In section 6.2, it was shown how the p.d. between the plates of a capacitor increased as the quantity of charge stored increased, Figure 6.10. The quantity of work done (or energy stored) can be found from the area under the Q versus V graph.

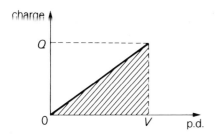

area of shaded triangle
$= \frac{1}{2} \times$ base $\times$ height
$= \frac{1}{2} \times V \times Q$

Figure 6.10 Energy stored in a cacpacitor

The energy stored in a capacitor $= \frac{1}{2} Q V$ joules.

Alternatively, since $C = \dfrac{Q}{V}$

$$\text{energy} = \tfrac{1}{2} C V^2 = \tfrac{1}{2} \frac{Q^2}{C}$$

Example 3

A $100\,\mu F$ capacitor is connected to a 12 V supply. Calculate the charge on the capacitor and the energy stored.

$$C = \frac{Q}{V} \qquad \text{where } C = 100\,\mu F \text{ and } V = 12\,V$$

$$\Rightarrow \quad Q = CV = 100 \times 10^{-6} \times 12$$

$$\Rightarrow \quad Q = 1.2 \times 10^{-3} \text{ coulombs}$$

$$\text{energy} = \tfrac{1}{2} Q V$$

$$= \tfrac{1}{2} \times 1.2 \times 10^{-3} \times 12 = 7.2 \times 10^{-3} \text{ joules}$$

The charge on the capacitor is 1.2×10^{-3} C and the energy stored is 7.2 mJ.

6.5 Capacitors in d.c. circuits

Charging a capacitor

The circuit in Figure 6.11 can help us to 'see' more clearly the current variation which takes place when a capacitor is charged from a d.c. supply.

The capacitor C is initially uncharged. When switch S is closed, electrons flow in an anti-clockwise direction: the lower plate becomes negatively charged and the upper plate positively charged. Thus there is a growth of potential difference across the capacitor. This potential difference opposes further flow of charge, thus reducing the charging current, Figure 6.12.

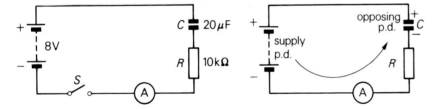

Figure 6.11

Figure 6.12 Charging a capacitor

Eventually enough charge has flowed to C so that the potential difference across C is equal to the supply potential difference (8 volts, in this case). At this stage, the potential difference across the capacitor is equal and opposite to that of the supply and so the net charge flow is zero. The variation of charging current with time is shown in Figure 6.13. The corresponding voltage variation is shown in Figure 6.14.

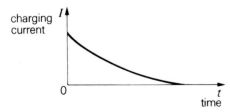

Figure 6.13 Change of current on charging a capacitor

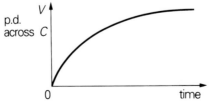

Figure 6.14 Change of voltage on charging a capacitor

Discharging a capacitor

The discharge of a capacitor can be observed in detail if it is first fully charged to a given potential difference with switch S at position 1 in the circuit in Figure 6.15.

The voltmeter indicates when the capacitor has been charged to the required potential difference. Switch S is then moved to position 2. Since the capacitor has a large potential difference across it, the charge flow from it is a maximum at the start. As charge flows from one capacitor plate to the other through R and the ammeter, Figure 6.16(a), the potential difference across them reduces and hence the discharge current reduces. The variation of discharge current with time is shown in Figure 6.16(b), and voltage variation is shown in Figure 6.16(c).

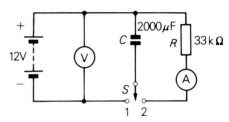

Figure 6.15

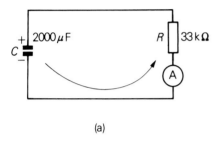
(a)

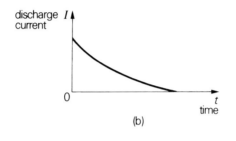
(b)

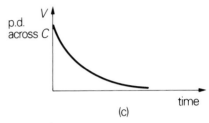
(c)

Figure 6.16

When a larger resistor R is substituted in the circuit, the current is reduced. Therefore the rate of flow of charge from the capacitor plates is reduced, with the result that it takes longer for the capacitor to discharge. Similarly, if a larger capacitor C is substituted then the total charge Q that it can store is increased; it therefore takes longer for the capacitor to discharge, Figure 6.17.

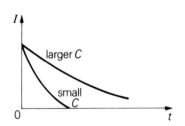

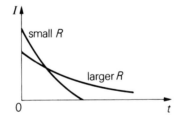

Figure 6.17 Capacitor discharge

These graphs of discharge show the variation of current in the opposite direction. If we show the charge and discharge currents for a capacitor using the same set of axes, we obtain the curves shown in Figure 6.18(a). The corresponding voltage variation is shown in Figure 6.18(b).

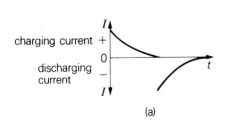
(a)

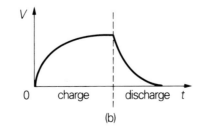
(b)

Figure 6.18 Charging and discharging a capacitor

6.6 Capacitors in a.c. circuits

Figure 6.19 shows a 200 µF capacitor connected in series with a slow a.c. generator and an ammeter.

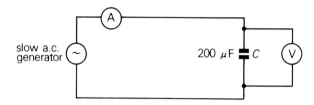

Figure 6.19 Phase in a capacitor circuit

There is a **difference** in phase between the voltmeter readings and the ammeter readings as shown in Figure 6.20.

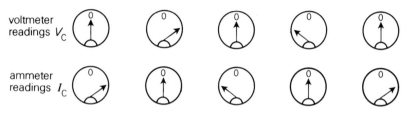

Figure 6.20

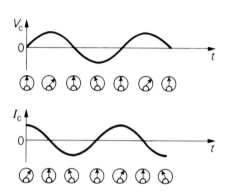

Figure 6.21

The current and voltage variations do not match and we say that the current and voltage are **out of phase**. This is shown graphically in Figure 6.21.

The current I_c reaches its maximum value before the voltage V_c reaches its maximum value. **The current leads the voltage**.

Factors affecting capacitor current

a) Frequency
The circuit in Figure 6.22 is used to investigate how the current I_c depends on the supply frequency. Table 3 shows the results obtained for a constant supply voltage, and these are plotted on the graph in Figure 6.23.

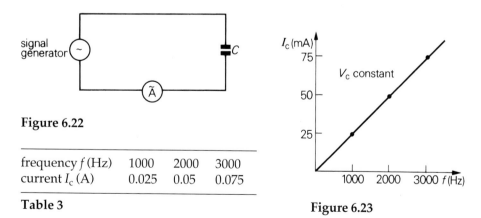

Figure 6.22

frequency f (Hz)	1000	2000	3000
current I_c (A)	0.025	0.05	0.075

Table 3

Figure 6.23

A straight line through the origin is obtained showing that the current I_c varies directly as the frequency.

$$I_c \propto f$$

b) Capacitance

The same circuit can be used to investigate how the current I_c depends on the capacitance C. Table 4 shows the results obtained for a constant supply voltage and signal generator frequency when various capacitors are inserted in the circuit. The results are plotted on the graph in Figure 6.24.

capacitance C (µF)	1000	2000	3000
current I_c (A)	0.03	0.06	0.09

Table 4

The graph shows that the current I_c varies directly as the capacitance.

$$I_c \propto C$$

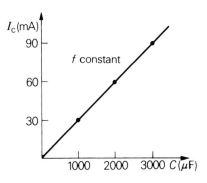

Figure 6.24

6.7 Some uses of capacitors

A d.c. supply has zero frequency, and so, since I_c is dependent on frequency, the current is zero.

Figure 6.25(a) shows the graph of an electrical signal that has both an a.c. component V_{ac} and a d.c. component V_{dc}. When this signal is supplied to the circuit shown in Figure 6.26 the voltage variation V_R across resistor R no longer includes the d.c. component, Figure 6.25(b). The capacitor has blocked the d.c. signal.

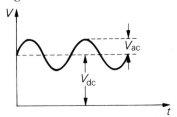
(a) signal containing a.c. and d.c.

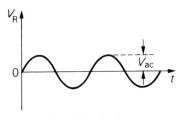
(b) d.c. signal blocked

Figure 6.25

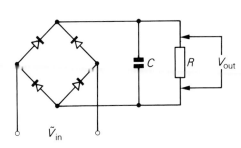

Figure 6.26

A capacitor can also be used to smooth rectified a.c. to give d.c. The circuit in Figure 6.27 can be used to demonstrate the smoothing action of a capacitor C. Without C, the variation in output voltage would be as shown in Figure 6.28(a). When capacitor C is included in the circuit, the output is smoothed to the form shown in Figure 6.28(b). The smoothing action is due to the charging and discharging of capacitor C. This output is called a ripple voltage.

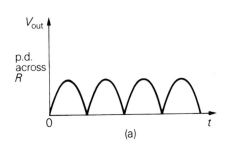
(a)

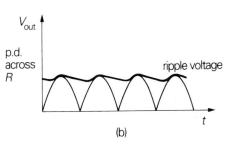
(b)

Figure 6.27

Figure 6.28 Capacitor smoothing

Summary

The potential difference across two parallel conducting plates is directly proportional to the charge on them.

Capacitance is defined by the ratio charge to potential difference.

$$C = \frac{Q}{V}$$

1 farad = 1 coulomb per volt; $1\,F = 1\,C\,V^{-1}$

The energy stored in a capacitor of capacitance C farads, charged to a p.d. of V volts is given by $E = \frac{1}{2}CV^2$ joules.

When a capacitor is charged from a d.c. supply, the current is at first large and gradually reduces to zero; the p.d. across the capacitor rises from zero to a maximum value during this time.

When a capacitor is inserted in an a.c. circuit, the current and voltage across the capacitor are out of phase. The current reaches its maximum value before the voltage reaches its maximum value. The current leads the voltage.

Problems

1 What is the relationship between the charge Q on a capacitor and the p.d. V across its plates? Describe a simple experiment to find this relationship.

2 Define capacitance in terms of charge and p.d. Write an equation which includes units as well as symbols.

3 What quantity of charge is needed to charge a $5\,\mu F$ capacitor to a p.d. of 12 V?

4 A charge of $5 \times 10^{-12}\,C$ transferred to the plates of a capacitor produces a p.d. of 10 mV. What is the capacitance of the capacitor?

5 A parallel plate capacitor is connected to a battery. What happens to its charge and the p.d. across its plates when a slab of dielectric is inserted between the plates?

6 A smoothing capacitor in a low voltage power supply has to store 6 mC of charge when the p.d. across it is 12 V. What capacitance should it have?

7 Draw a circuit which will demonstrate the charge and discharge of a capacitor. Draw a current-time graph for charge and discharge of a capacitor in a d.c. circuit.

8 Draw the p.d.-time graphs for charge and discharge of a capacitor as described in Question 7.

9 Draw current-time graphs for the charging of a large and a small value capacitor for a constant voltage d.c. supply.

10 Draw current-time graphs to illustrate the effect of a large and a small resistor on the charging of a capacitor from a constant voltage d.c. supply.

11 Consider the circuit shown.
   a) What is the maximum charging current?
   b) What is the final p.d. across C?
   c) How much charge is transferred to the capacitor?

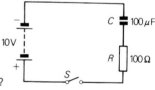

12 A 2000 μF capacitor is connected to a 15 V d.c. supply. Calculate the charge and energy stored in the capacitor.

13 The capacitor C is charged with a steady current of 1 mA by carefully adjusting the variable resistor R.

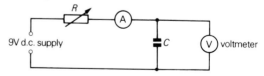

The voltmeter reading is taken every ten seconds. The results are shown in the table.

Time (s)	0	10	20	30	40
Voltmeter reading (V)	0	1.9	4.0	6.2	8.1

Plot a graph of charge against voltage for the capacitor and hence find its capacitance.

SEB

14 To study the charging of a capacitor the circuit shown is used.

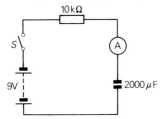

a) Describe the response of the ammeter after switch S is closed.
b) How would you know when the potential difference across the capacitor is at its maximum?
c) Suggest a suitable range for the ammeter.
d) If the 10 kΩ resistor is replaced by one of larger resistance, what will be the effect on the maximum potential difference across the capacitor?

SEB

15 In the circuit below, the neon lamp flashes at regular intervals.

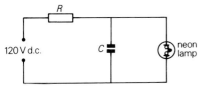

The neon lamp requires a potential difference of 100 V across it before it will conduct and flash. It continues to glow until the potential difference across it drops to 80 V. While it is lit, its resistance is very small compared with R.
a) Explain why the neon lamp flashes regularly.
b) Suggest **two** methods of decreasing the flash rate.

SEB

16 The charging of a capacitor is studied using the circuit shown. The ammeter A is a centre-zero instrument and a constant d.c. supply of 6 volts is used.

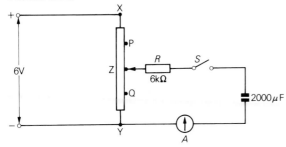

a) The sliding contact Z is set at the mid-point of XY and switch S is closed.
i) Calculate the final charge on the capacitor C.
ii) Sketch a graph showing how the charging current varies with time.
b) With the capacitor fully charged as in **a)** describe how the current through the milliameter changes when the sliding contact Z is moved, in turn, to a new position
i) P (nearer to X)
ii) Q (nearer to Y).
c) At the end of the experiment switch S is opened and a short conducting wire is connected directly across the plates of the capacitor.
Describe what happens to the energy that was stored in the capacitor.

SEB

17 You are given a capacitor, a battery, a resistor, a switch, a cathode ray oscilloscope and connecting wires.
You are asked to set up a circuit which would allow you to look at the variation of current as the capacitor is charged up through the resistor.
a) Draw a diagram of your circuit.
b) Draw a sketch to show the variation of current while the capacitor is charging.

SEB

18 The graph of charge against p.d. for a capacitor is shown below.

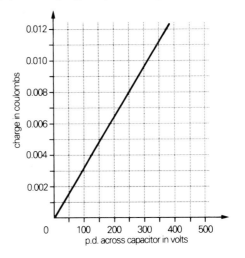

Calculate
i) the capacitance of the capacitor;
ii) the energy stored in the capacitor when the p.d. is 300 V.

SEB

19 The circuit shows an uncharged 470 µF capacitor in series with a 1.2 kΩ resistor. An oscilloscope is connected across the resistor.

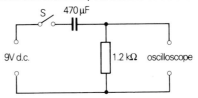

a) Calculate the initial current in the 1.2 kΩ resistor after the switch S is closed.
b) Calculate the final charge stored on the capacitor.
c) Sketch the trace shown on a suitably adjusted oscilloscope during the charging period.

SEB

20 Using modern technology, many electrical components are produced by depositing very thin films of material on insulating bases.
a) A capacitor is constructed by depositing tiny gold plates on either side of a thin layer of insulating material.
i) State how the capacitance of the capacitor will be affected as the thickness of the layer between the plates is increased.
ii) A capacitor produced by the above method has a capacitance of 220 pF. A potential difference of 5.0 V is applied to the plates.
(A) What will be the charge on the capacitor?
(B) How much energy will be stored in the capacitor?
(1 picofarad = 1×10^{-12} farad)

SEB

21 A simplified circuit diagram for a high voltage supply unit is shown below.

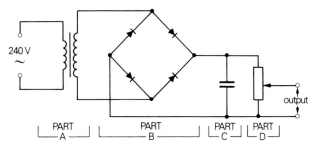

i) State the function of each of the parts of the circuit labelled A, B, C and D.

ii) The capacitor used in the circuit must have a large capacitance. Suggest two ways in which a paper capacitor can be designed to meet this requirement.

iii) Why does this type of capacitor have a maximum working voltage?

SEB

22 A pupil notices the following filter network in the circuit diagram for her new stereo amplifier.

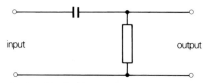

Explain whether this filter is intended to remove low frequency "rumble" or high frequency "hiss".

23 An initially uncharged capacitor is charged using a **constant** current of 90 μA. After 100 seconds the voltage across the capacitor is 12 volts.

i) How much charge is stored on the capacitor after 100 seconds?

ii) How much energy is stored in the capacitor after 100 seconds?

iii) A second capacitor, with a larger capacitance, is charged for the same time using the same current.

(A) How does the voltage across the second capacitor compare with the first?

(B) How does the energy stored in the second capacitor compare with the first?

SEB

7 Analogue electronics

7.1 Introduction

Figure 7.1

Analogue electronics gets its name from the fact that early computers used the behaviour of electronic components to represent numbers. The physical property was 'analogous to' or representative of the numbers. The size of a voltage could represent the size of a number in an equation. Analogue computers did mathematics using the properties of various combinations of resistor, capacitor, inductor or diode. They were able to add, subtract, and even do differentiation! Analogue computers were able to simulate experiments which would take too long to carry out. They can be used to 'model' how a system will behave under a wide range of conditions and thus save having to do expensive (or disastrous!) experiments. For example, before constructing a bridge a design engineer would use an analogue computer program to predict how the bridge should behave under a wide range of conditions. This procedure can help to avoid such disasters as the San Francisco highway, Figure 7.1, which collapsed under earthquake conditions. A computer analysis could have predicted this.

One of the most common analogue circuits in use is the amplifier. The amplifiers in early computers used 'valves', and required a large power consumption when operating. Nowadays we still use amplifiers in analogue electronics applications but we are able to use the 'semi-conductor' variety. This is a single package (or 'chip') called an integrated circuit (I.C.) and uses much less power. Amplifiers have also found many more modern applications.

Figure 7.2

7.2 Properties of amplifiers

Amplifiers are used not only for stereo systems or for boosting the power of pop stars' performances! They 'amplify' electrical signals and must therefore increase the signal in some way. It is convenient to begin by studying an amplifier which can increase the voltage of a signal. The components which make up this amplifier are shown in Figure 7.3. A chip known as an **operational amplifier**, or **op-amp** for short, requires very few extra components to be added to make it amplify.

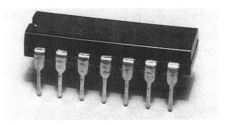

Figure 7.3

The reason why so few extra components are needed is that inside the op-amp chip there may be about 20 transistors, a few capacitors and about a dozen resistors integrated into its silicon slice. The workings of the individual circuit sections inside the chip can remain a mystery, as it is the output from the circuit which is of interest to us in this study!

The symbol for the op-amp, Figure 7.4, is simplified a great deal. There are two 'input' connections and an 'output'. The power supply which operates the circuit is not shown; it is usually indicated by $+V_s$ and $-V_s$. The two input connections are called the 'inverting' and 'non-inverting' inputs.

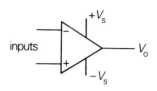

Figure 7.4 Diagram of op-amp with two inputs, one output and power

7.3 Inverting mode

When the op-amp is arranged as shown in Figure 7.5, it is arranged in the 'inverting mode'; a.c. or d.c. voltage signals are fed to the input and they are compared with the resulting output signals. Some examples are shown in Figure 7.6.

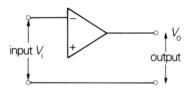

Figure 7.5 An op-amp in 'inverting mode'

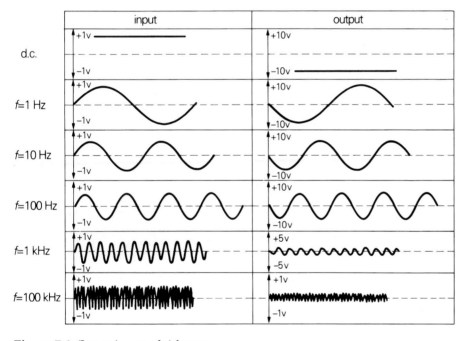

Figure 7.6 'Inverting mode' features

Three features become apparent from Figure 7.6.

1. The 'sense' of the output voltage is the opposite of the input so that a positive input voltage results in a negative output voltage. The signal is '**inverted**' – hence the reason why we call this the 'inverting mode'.
2. The amplitude of the output voltages does not change very much for different frequencies of the same input voltage until the frequency becomes greater than 100 Hz. The amplification does not depend on frequency over a given range (in this case 0–100 Hz).
3. As the frequency of input signal increases beyond 100 Hz, the output voltage tends to reduce; there is less amplification. The amplification is frequency-dependent beyond a certain range.

The ratio of the output voltage V_o to the input voltage V_i is a measure of the **gain** of the amplifier. The frequency dependence of the op-amp is illustrated in the graph of voltage gain versus frequency, Figure 7.7.

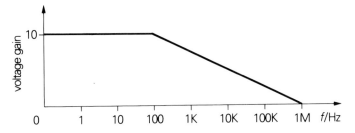

Figure 7.7

The graph shows that the gain of this op-amp is high for a limited range of input signal frequencies. This property would severely restrict the range of applications possible for the op-amp. This restriction can be overcome by the use of negative feedback.

7.4   Negative feedback

Negative feedback involves taking some of the output signal (which is of opposite sense) and feeding it back to the input, Figure 7.8. Since it is of opposite sign, it is 'negative' and reduces the gain. The voltage gain is reduced by negative feedback, but the gain remains constant over a large range of frequencies of input voltage.

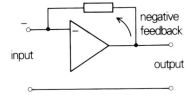

Figure 7.8

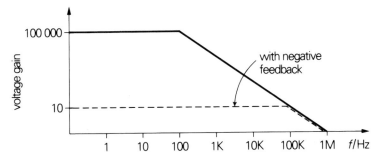

Figure 7.9   Gain with and without negative feedback

7.5   Deriving an equation for the amplifier gain

In dealing with the equations for the inverting mode op-amp circuit, it is important to realise that the basic principle behind this differential amplifier is that it amplifies the **difference** between the two inputs. This can be written quite simply as:

$$V_o = A(V_2 - V_1)$$

where V_o represents the output voltage;

V_1 and V_2 are the input voltages which are amplified by a factor A.

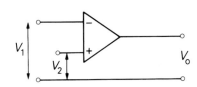

Figure 7.10

In the case of the amplifier operating in the 'inverting mode', the voltage V_2 applied to the non-inverting input terminal is zero and so the expression becomes:

$$V_o = A(0 - V_1)$$
$$= A(-V_1)$$
$$\Rightarrow \quad V_o = -AV_1$$

Notice too that the output voltage V_o must be in the opposite sense (inverted) because the equation has a negative sign.

Table 1 shows typical output voltages V_o obtained from this circuit, Figure 7.11, for a range of input voltages V_i when various sets of resistors are inserted in the R_1 and R_2 slots.

V_i (V)	R_2 (kΩ)	R_1 (kΩ)	$\frac{R_2}{R_1}$	V_o (V)
-1	100	100	1	$+1$
-1	10	2	5	$+5$
$+1$	100	10	10	-10
$+1.5$	2	10	0.2	-0.3
$+1.5$	2	1	2	-3

Table 1

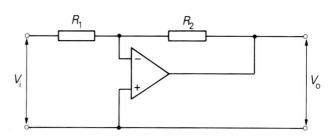

Figure 7.11

Inspection of these results indicates the relationship:

$$V_o = -\frac{R_2}{R_1}V_i$$

Comparing this with $\quad V_o = -AV_1$ as derived above,

it follows that $\quad A = \dfrac{R_2}{R_1}$

The gain of the amplifier depends only on the values of the external resistors R_1 and R_2!

The equations can be verified in the following way.

1. Consider the amplifier without negative feedback.
An amplifier without negative feedback resistor has an 'open loop', Figure 7.12. In this condition the amplifier has an extremely high 'open loop gain' A_o of the order of 100 000 for most practical op-amps. So, if the potential at the inverting input terminal is V_x,

then the output V_o is given by $V_o = -A_oV_x$

$$\Rightarrow \quad V_x = -\frac{V_o}{A_o}$$

If the output voltage V_o is approximately 1 V,

then $V_x = -\dfrac{1}{100\,000}$

$V_x = -10\,\mu V$

$V_x = 0$ volts (approx)

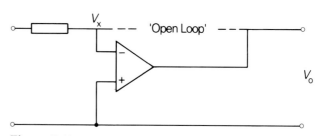

Figure 7.12

V_x is therefore virtually zero and we define earth as 0 volts, so it is called a 'Virtual Earth'.

The amplifier has a very high internal resistance, Figure 7.13, and therefore the input current I is very small.

The voltage across the input resistor R_1 is $V_i - V_x$

$$= V_i - 0$$
$$= V_i$$

Using Ohm's Law, $I = \dfrac{V_i}{R_1}$

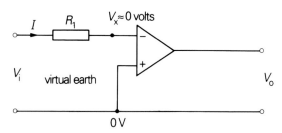

Figure 7.13

2. Now consider the amplifier with resistor R_2 included, Figure 7.14. The internal resistance of the amplifier is so great that we can assume the current which goes through it in this arrangement is negligible.

The voltage across R_2 is $V_x - V_o$

$$= 0 - V_o \quad \text{if } V_x = 0$$
$$= -V_o$$

Once again, using Ohm's Law, $\quad I = \dfrac{V_o}{R_2}$

But from Part 1 above, $\quad I = \dfrac{V_i}{R_1}$

it follows that $\quad -\dfrac{V_o}{R_2} = \dfrac{V_i}{R_1}$

and so $\quad \dfrac{V_o}{V_i} = -\dfrac{R_2}{R_1}$

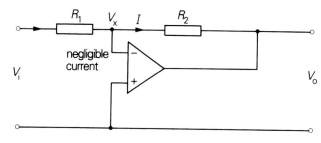

Figure 7.14

Since R_2 is in fact the feedback resistor, it is often identified by a different symbol, R_f. Hence

$$\boxed{\dfrac{V_o}{V_i} = -\dfrac{R_f}{R_1}}$$

Example 1

An op-amp in inverting mode has a $+5\,\mu V$ signal applied to its input. If the feedback resistor R_f is $10\,k\Omega$ and the input resistor R_1 is $1\,k\Omega$, what is the output voltage V_o?

$$V_o = -\left(\dfrac{R_f}{R_1}\right) \times V_i$$

$$\Rightarrow V_o = -\left(\dfrac{10}{1}\right) \times +5$$

$$\Rightarrow V_o = -50\,\mu V$$

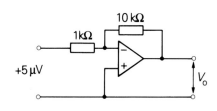

7.6 Making use of the inverting mode

If two voltages are applied via input resistors R_1 and R_2 to an op-amp, Figure 7.15, the circuit can perform addition.

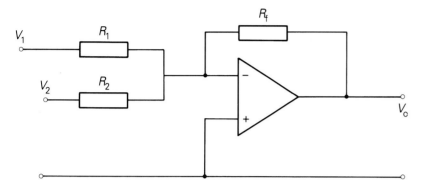

Figure 7.15

Using the usual notation, if V_1 and V_2 are the input voltages and V_0 is the output voltage, the equation is:

$$V_0 = \left(\frac{-R_f}{R_1}\right) \times V_1 + \left(\frac{-R_f}{R_2}\right) \times V_2$$

If $R_1 = R_2 = R_f$

this simplifies to $\qquad V_0 = -(V_1 + V_2)$

The output voltage is equal to the **sum** of the input voltages.

This circuit could form the basis of a simple 'mixer' to combine the output of an electric guitar with that from a microphone. It also has the obvious mathematical ability of being able to add two (voltage) numbers.

This type of circuit arrangement can also be used in the conversion of digital voltages to analogue voltages. Computers are increasingly being used to control analogue systems, but computers deal with 'digital' signals. Sometimes the signals have to be converted from analogue to digital, and at other times from digital to analogue. For example, the digital signals from the autopilot computer on board an aircraft are converted to analogue form in order to operate the rudder or flaps, Figure 7.16.

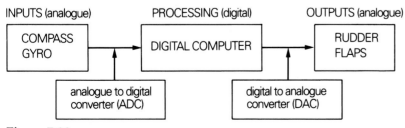

Figure 7.16

The information which it senses is analogue and the tasks it needs to perform are analogue. The computer output needs to be converted to analogue using a digital-to-analogue convertor. Another example is the **compact disc** player; it deals with digital information which must be converted to analogue form for the loudspeakers.

The conversion can be demonstrated using an op-amp as a summing amplifier with four input resistors, Figure 7.17. The values of the resistors are chosen so that they are in the ratio $1:2:4:8$
(in binary notation, $2^0 = 1$, $2^1 = 2$, $2^2 = 4$ and $2^3 = 8$). The set of input resistors is thus called a binary 'weighted' resistor network.

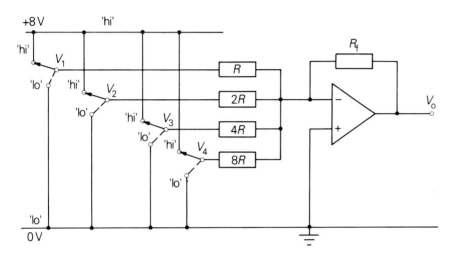

Figure 7.17

The output voltage V_0 is given by:

$$V_0 = -\left[\left(\frac{R_f}{R}\right) \times V_1 + \left(\frac{R_f}{2R}\right) \times V_2 + \left(\frac{R_f}{4R}\right) \times V_3 + \left(\frac{R_f}{8R}\right) \times V_4\right]$$

and if $R = R_f$
$$V_0 = -(V_1 + \tfrac{1}{2}V_2 + \tfrac{1}{4}V_3 + \tfrac{1}{8}V_4)$$

Now if V_1, V_2, V_3 and V_4 are digital, they can only be 'lo' or 'hi', say values 0 volts or 8 volts, and this can result in a large number of output voltages V_0 as shown in Table 2.

V_1	V_2	V_3	V_4	V_1	V_2	V_3	V_4	V_0
lo	lo	lo	lo	0	0	0	0	0
lo	lo	lo	hi	0	0	0	$\frac{8}{8}$	1
lo	lo	hi	lo	0	0	$\frac{8}{4}$	0	2
lo	lo	hi	hi	0	0	$\frac{8}{4}$	$\frac{8}{8}$	3
lo	hi	lo	lo	0	$\frac{8}{2}$	0	0	4
lo	hi	lo	hi	0	$\frac{8}{2}$	0	$\frac{8}{8}$	5
and so on until ...								
hi	hi	hi	hi	$\frac{8}{1}$	$\frac{8}{2}$	$\frac{8}{4}$	$\frac{8}{8}$	15

Table 2

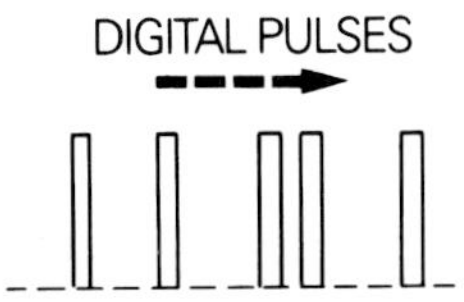

DIGITAL PULSES

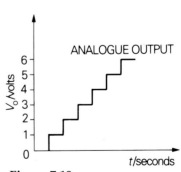

Figure 7.18

Figure 7.19

If the voltage values for V_1, V_2, V_3 and V_4 follow the sequence shown above, the output voltage will show a steadily increasing (but stepped) value.

The graph in Figure 7.19 does not appear to be a particularly continuous or 'analogue' form of output variation.

The same voltage change could be described by eight- or sixteen-bit binary pulses, Figures 7.20 and 7.21, instead of four-bit pulses.

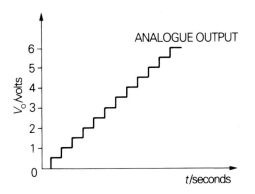

Figure 7.20 8-bit sampling

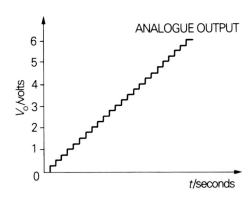

Figure 7.21 16-bit sampling

This results in a much more 'analogue' output. The 'steps' are much smaller and the variation of voltage looks more 'continuous'.

7.7 Saturation

Varying the gain ratio

The inverting mode amplifier has its limitations. From earlier discussion, it would seem that by inserting any pair of resistors R_1 and R_2 in the circuit, it should be possible to provide any gain and thus a very wide range of output voltages from very low to extremely high.
The circuit shown in Figure 7.22 can illustrate the behaviour of an inverting-mode amplifier as the gain is increased.

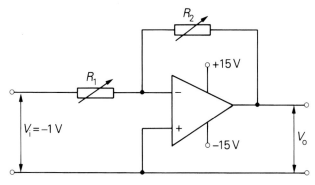

Figure 7.22

R_1 and R_2 are resistance boxes which can be changed to different values quite conveniently. As they are altered, the following set of data results, showing the typical behaviour of such a system, Table 3.

Figure 7.23 shows the graph of output voltage V_o against gain A. It becomes clear that, no matter what value of gain the amplifier is given, the output voltage can go no greater than the positive supply voltage (+15 volts in this case). A

Input voltage V_i (V)	R_1 (kΩ)	R_2 (kΩ)	A	Output voltage V_o (V)
−1	100	100	1	+ 1
−1	50	100	2	+ 2
−1	10	100	10	+ 10
−1	10	150	15	+ 15
−1	10	200	20	+ 15
−1	10	250	25	+ 15

Table 3

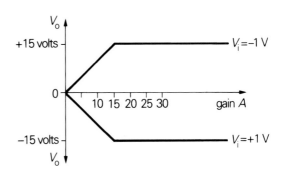

Figure 7.23

similar pattern is observed with a positive input voltage; the output goes no greater than the negative supply voltage (−15 volts).

Varying the input voltage

An investigation into how the output voltage is affected by the input voltage for a given gain factor A can be carried out using the circuit shown in Figure 7.24. The input voltage V_i is varied using a variable voltage power supply, and the corresponding output voltage V_o is measured.

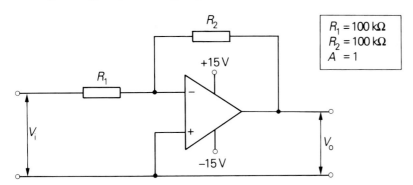

$R_1 = 100\,kΩ$
$R_2 = 100\,kΩ$
$A = 1$

Figure 7.24

Typical results from an experiment of this kind are shown in Table 4.

Input voltage V_i (V)	Output voltage V_o (V)	Input voltage V_i (V)	Output voltage V_o (V)
− 1	+ 1	+ 1	− 1
− 2	+ 2	+ 2	− 2
− 3	+ 3	+ 3	− 3
− 5	+ 5	+ 5	− 5
− 10	+ 10	+ 10	− 10
− 15	+ 15	+ 15	− 15
− 20	+ 15	+ 20	− 15
− 25	+ 15	+ 25	− 15

Table 4

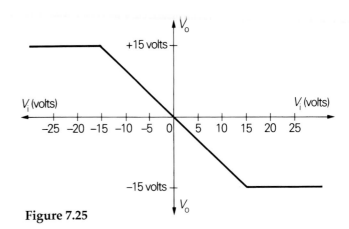

Figure 7.25

A graph of output voltage V_o versus input voltage V_i is illustrated in Figure 7.25. Once again the conclusion is similar. The greater the value of the input, the greater the output voltage also becomes; but the output voltage cannot increase beyond the positive or negative supply voltage value.

For this particular amplifier, in order to obtain an output voltage of magnitude 15 volts, positive or negative, all that is required is an input of value 15 volts or above – any value above 15 will do.

This behaviour of the op-amp is known as **saturation**, and it merely illustrates the inability of the device to output any higher voltage than its supply voltage. This property can be used to advantage in many of its applications – it is not a problem!

7.8   Saturation and a.c. inputs

The effect which saturation has on a.c. signals applied to the input of an op-amp in the inverting mode can be investigated as follows. The circuit is shown in Figure 7.26.

Since 'saturation' means that the output voltage can be no greater than the supply voltage, a stage is reached when the amplified output voltage *should* be greater, but is *unable* to be. This stage can be reached as the 'gain' of the amplifier is gradually increased.

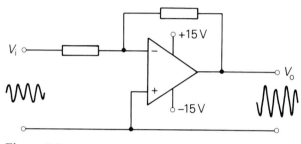

Figure 7.26

When 'gain' multiplied by 'input voltage' is greater than the supply voltage value, the output voltage waveform is **clipped**. The output looks as if it has had the top chopped off. Figure 7.27 illustrates this effect.

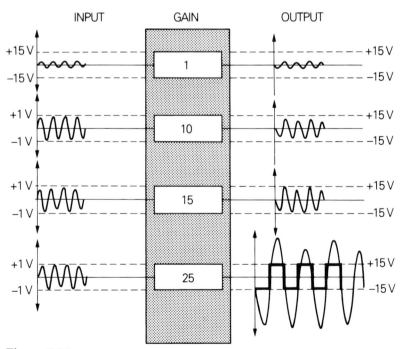

Figure 7.27

When the supply voltage is much smaller than the output voltage, the output waveform becomes approximately a 'square' wave. This is a simple way of generating square waves, with their on-off-on-off voltage variation.

7.9   Differential mode

An op-amp connected as shown in Figure 7.28 is arranged in the differential mode. In this arrangement the amplifier provides an output which depends on the difference between the two inputs V_1 and V_2.

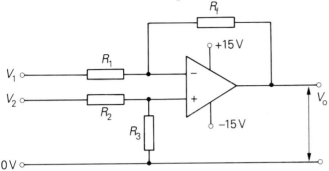

Figure 7.28

The equation governing the behaviour of the amplifier in this mode takes the form:

$$V_o = (V_2 - V_1) \times \frac{R_f}{R_1} \qquad \text{provided that } \frac{R_f}{R_1} = \frac{R_3}{R_2}$$

This equation may look a little familiar – it reverts to the 'inverting mode' form (where $V_2 = 0$):

i.e. $V_o = -V_1 \times \dfrac{R_f}{R_1}$

Now if the resistors R_f and R_1 are equal, implying that R_2 and R_3 are also equal, then the differential mode equation is:

$$V_o = (V_2 - V_1)$$

This is straightforward subtraction.

Results follow the predicted pattern, shown in Table 5.
This circuit can cope with very small differences between two voltages by careful choice of resistors. Remember that the original equation was:

$$V_o = (V_2 - V_1) \times \frac{R_f}{R_1}$$

and in the above case, $\dfrac{R_f}{R_1} = \dfrac{100}{100} = 1$

Supposing that the following voltages were applied:

$V_2 = +1.52$ volts; $V_1 = +1.50$ volts

The output voltage **should** read + 0.02 volts. The measuring instrument used to monitor the voltage difference might not be sensitive enough to register such a small reading.
The solution is to choose resistors R_f and R_1 so that $\dfrac{R_f}{R_1} = 100$, say.

The resulting voltage output will be + 2.0 volts. By choosing this resistor ratio carefully, it is possible to **scale up** the voltage difference to a measurable size, so that the subtraction can be carried out. This could be called **scaled subtraction**.

Another problem might be that the subtraction **should** provide an answer which is greater than the supply voltage, but of course we know that the output voltage

R_1 (kΩ)	R_2 (kΩ)	R_3 (kΩ)	R_f (kΩ)
100	100	100	100
	(values of resistors chosen)		

V_2 (V)	V_1 (V)	V_o (V)
+ 1.5	+ 0.5	+ 1.0
+ 0.5	+ 1.5	− 1.0
− 1.5	+ 1.5	− 3.0
+ 0.5	− 1.5	+ 2.0

Table 5

may not exceed the supply voltage! A solution similar to the last one seems right: use a ratio $\left(\dfrac{R_f}{R_1}\right)$ which **scales down** the output voltage.

Supposing that the following voltages were applied

$V_2 = +1.59$ kilovolts; $V_1 = +590$ volts

$V_2 - V_1 = [(+1590) - (+590)] = 1000$

The output voltage **should** read $+1000$ volts!

If the resistors are chosen such that $R_f = 10\,k\Omega$ and $R_1 = 10\,M\Omega$,

then $\dfrac{R_f}{R_1} = \dfrac{10000}{10000000} = \dfrac{1}{1000}$

and the output voltage for the scaled subtraction would be 1.0 volt.

This **scaling** of the output is useful when the output device being driven by the amplifier is operating within a restricted range of voltages.

The behaviour described above applies to continuously varying (a.c.) input voltages and not just d.c. voltages.

Example 2

Two identical low voltage a.c. power supplies provide the input voltages V_1 and V_2 to an op-amp in the differential mode. The resistors R_f, R_1, R_2, and R_3 and are identical, and equal to $110\,k\Omega$. Two pupils attempt to show that the output voltage $V_o = (V_2 - V_1)$ but they obtain the results shown on the right. Can you explain the different results?

Student A		Student B	
V_1	2.25 volts	V_1	2.25 volts
V_2	2.25 volts	V_2	2.25 volts
V_o	4.50 volts	V_o	0.00 volts

In one case it seems that the voltages are subtracted but in the other it seems that they are added. This can be explained quite simply with reference to the phase of these a.c. supplies.

Student A has subtracted a voltage of the opposite sense (out of phase), which results in an addition.
Student B has used the supplies so that their voltage inputs are in phase and, being identical, subtract to give zero.

Example 3

Which of the following circuits shows an op-amp as a differential amplifier?

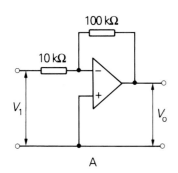

A

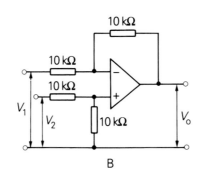

B

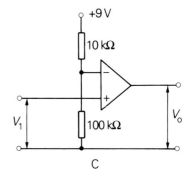

C

Circuit A has only one input voltage and so it is not a differential circuit.
Circuit B has two inputs, so the ratio $R_f/R_1 = R_3/R_2$.
Circuit C has two inputs but no R_f.
Therefore Circuit B shows an op-amp as a differential amplifier.

7.10 Monitoring

The differential amplifier can be used to amplify the output produced by a range of resistive sensors connected in a Wheatstone Bridge arrangement. This allows it to be used in monitoring applications. The circuit shown below in Figure 7.29 can be used to monitor the strain in or on an object.

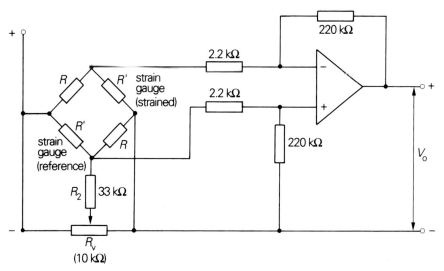

Figure 7.29

Resistors R_2 and R_v are used to adjust the bridge for zero output voltage. An unstrained gauge which acts as a reference is included in the arm opposite the strained one. This allows for any temperature variations in the surroundings which can cause resistance variations and mask the changes in resistance of the strain gauge resulting from the object to which it is attached.

Example 4

The circuit on the right has a number of 1.3 V cells connected as shown.

a) What output voltage would you expect if R_f, R_1, R_2 and R_3 are chosen such that $\dfrac{R_f}{R_1} = \dfrac{R_3}{R_2} = 1$?

b) What value would be obtained if this ratio is 20?

a) The output is given by $\quad V_o = (V_2 - V_1) \times R_f/R_1$
$$V_o = (1.3 - (2 \times 1.3)) \times 1$$
$$V_o = -1.3 \text{ volts}$$

b) If $R_f/R_1 = 20$, then $\quad V_o = (1.3 - (2 \times 1.3)) \times 20$
$$V_o = -26.0 \text{ volts}$$
but the output cannot exceed the supply voltage
so $\quad\quad\quad\quad\quad\quad\quad V_o = -15.0 \text{ volts}$

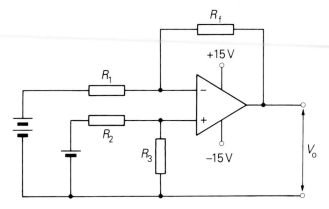

7.11 Driving output devices

If a differential amplifier is to control situations, then it must be able to make something happen at the output of the system of which it forms a part. An output action generally requires a higher current than most op-amps can provide. However, there are some op-amps which do not have this drawback.

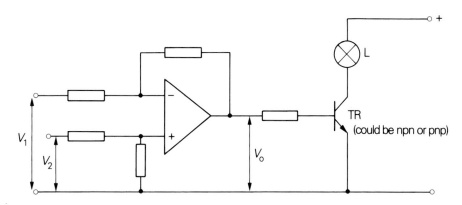

Figure 7.30

If an op-amp is not powerful enough to give the required current, it can use its output voltage to switch on a transistor with a higher current handling capacity, Figure 7.30.

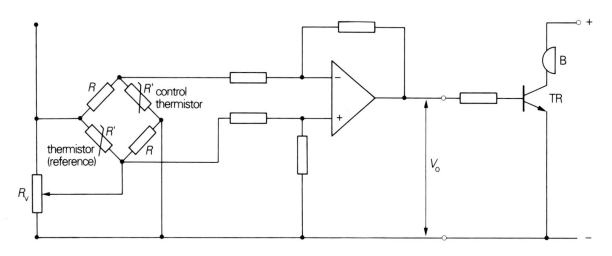

Figure 7.31

In the circuit shown in Figure 7.31, two thermistors R' are placed in a Wheatstone bridge circuit; R_v can be adjusted so that there is zero output voltage while both thermistors are at the same temperature. When the temperature difference between the control thermistor and the reference thermistor reaches a pre-determined value, the op-amp output V_o will be great enough to 'switch on' a transistor. The transistor can then operate a warning buzzer, B. This circuit thus warns of an unacceptable temperature rise.

Figure 7.32 shows a circuit containing a light-dependent resistor (LDR). This will operate a motor (M) when the light level becomes lower than a particular level. The resistor R_v and R_1 adjust zero and switching light level. This system might pull the curtains when it gets dark!

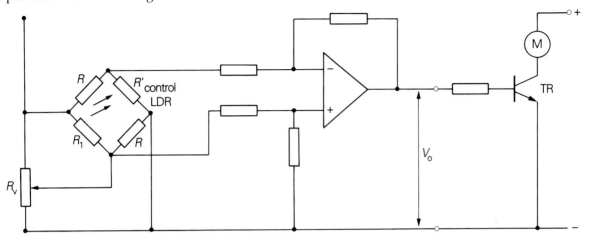

Figure 7.32

There are many physical situations where the op-amp can be used to monitor and control equipment or conditions.

Summary

An op-amp can be used to increase the voltage of a signal.

An op-amp connected in the inverting mode will invert the input signal.

For the ideal op-amp, the input current is zero, i.e. it has infinite input resistance. There is no potential difference between the inverting and non-inverting inputs, i.e. both inputs are at the same potential.

The gain expression for an op-amp in the inverting mode

is $\dfrac{V_o}{V_i} = -\dfrac{R_f}{R_1}$

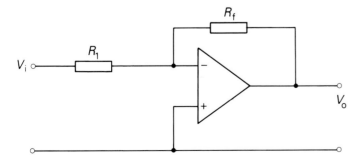

An op-amp cannot produce an output voltage greater than the positive supply voltage or less than the negative supply voltage. The output voltage 'saturates'.

The inverting mode gain equation can be used to 'add'.
$$V_o = -(V_1 + V_2) \text{ when } R_1 = R_2 = R_f$$

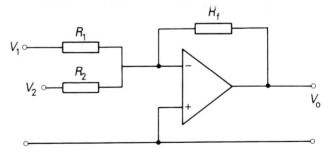

A differential amplifier amplifies the potential difference between its two inputs.

The differential mode gain equation is $V_o = (V_2 - V_1) \times \dfrac{R_f}{R_1}$

Op-amps can be used in monitoring and in control applications.

Problems

1 The diagram shows an operational amplifier connected in the inverting mode.

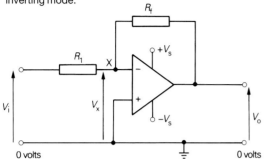

a) R_f and R_1 are the values of the feedback and input resistors. Derive the gain expression for this amplifier.

b) Describe how this circuit could be modified to carry out the following mathematical functions:
(i) multiply by 15   (ii) divide by 20

2 How could this circuit be used to generate square waves from a 20.0 volt sine wave input voltage?

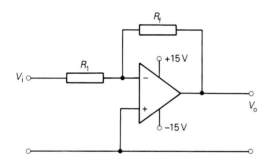

Give suitable values for R_1 and R_f.
What amplitude will the square waves have?

3 Look at the circuit diagram given below and answer the questions which follow.

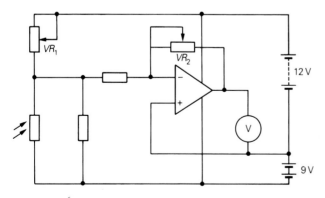

a) What use would the circuit have?
b) What would VR_1 and VR_2 be used for?
c) What will the output voltage V_o be when $V_i = 0$?

4 A physicist designed the circuit shown, to give a voltmeter reading which was dependent on the load applied to the beam on which the strain gauge was attached.

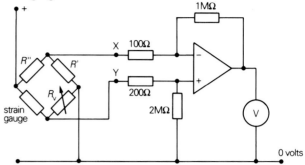

a) In what mode is the op-amp working?
b) Explain the purpose of the variable resistor R_v.
c) For a particular load on the beam the voltage between points X and Y is 0.3 mV. What is the reading on the voltmeter?

5 a) Derive an expression for the gain of an op-amp in the inverting mode.

b) The circuit in Figure 1 represents an operational amplifier used to combine V_1 and V_2.

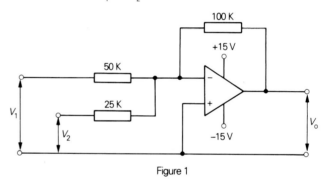

Figure 1

V_1 is maintained at + 1.0 V d.c. The voltage V_2 has the form as shown in Figure 2 with a frequency of 1 kHz.

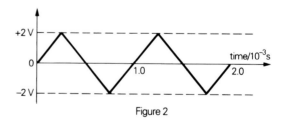

Figure 2

i) Draw to scale the output voltage V_o for the same two cycles shown in Figure 2. Label the axes clearly and show numerical values.
ii) Indicate what modification in V_o occurs if the supply voltages to the operational amplifier are reduced to ± 9 V.
c) i) Describe, with the aid of a suitable circuit diagram, how an operational amplifier can perform the process of subtraction.
ii) Explain how this arrangement can be used in the control of the speed of a motor.

SEB

6 a) Draw the circuit diagram for an operational amplifier connected in the inverting mode.
b) You are asked to design an amplifier using an op-amp connected in the inverting mode.

The following two design points should be taken into account:
the input impedance of the op-amp in this mode is
approximately, the same as the value of the input resistor;
the input impedance of the amplifier should be at least
100 times the output impedance of the device feeding into
it.
Give suitable values for the input and feedback resistors of a
single-stage inverting amplifier taking its input from a
microphone of impedance 600 Ω and having a gain of 1000.

7 The diagrams below, Figures 1 and 2, show the construction and
circuit for a sun-tracker.
The shadow cast by the card divider falls on the LDR changing its
resistance. The motor then turns the tracker until both LDRs are
equally illuminated.

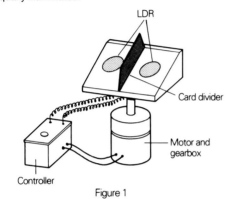

Figure 1

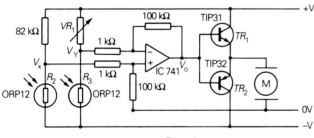

Figure 2

i) Describe what happens when the LDR R_2 is shaded by the card.
ii) What is the function of the variable resistor VR_1?
iii) Why are transistors TR_1 and TR_2 needed?
iv) Derive the relationship between the output potential V_o and the
two input potentials V_X and V_Y.

8 a) Circuit 1 shows an operational amplifier used in the differential
mode.

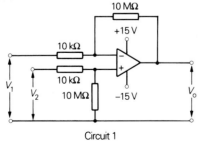

Circuit 1

i) Explain what is meant by the term 'differential mode'.
ii) Calculate the output voltage V_o when $V_1 = 500$ mV and
$V_2 = 510$ mV.

b) Electrical signals from the heart produce pulses of potential
difference of the order of 1 mV between the hands. The body
also picks up 50 Hz signals from the mains supply. This mains
signal is of the order of 20 mV with respect to earth at both
hands and makes the small 1 mV heart signal undetectable.
A biological amplifier may be used to reject the mains signal
and amplify the heart signal only.

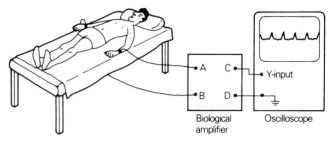

Diagram 2

i) Show how the differential amplifier in Circuit 1 could be
connected to A, B, C and D to amplify the heart signals only.
ii) Explain how your circuit works.

9 a) An ideal operational amplifier has
i) infinite input impedance,
ii) zero output impedance.
Explain why each of these properties is desirable.
b) Figure 1 shows an operational amplifier circuit which uses
a ± 15 V supply (not shown).

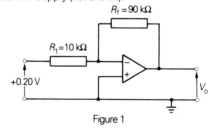

Figure 1

i) What is the purpose of R_f?
ii) Calculate the output voltage V_o for an input voltage
of + 0.20 V.
iii) Draw a circuit, using the same components, to illustrate how
an input of + 0.20 V can produce an output of + 2.0 V.
Show by calculation that the required voltage is obtained.
c) Figure 2 shows the operational amplifier connected in another
circuit.

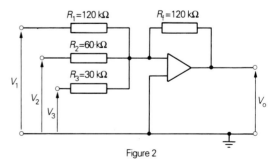

Figure 2

i) Calculate the output voltage V_o when $V_1 = 1$ V, $V_2 = 0$ V, and
$V_3 = 1$ V.
ii) The inputs V_1, V_2 and V_3 can be set to either zero or one volt.
For appropriate inputs, give the magnitudes of the maximum
and minimum output voltages.

10 a) An operational amplifier is used in the circuit as shown. In each case, the amplifier is connected to a power supply with outputs of + 15 V and − 15 V. An a.c. signal of peak voltage 1.0 V is applied to the input.

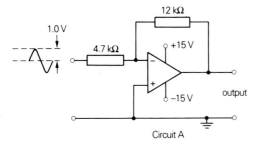

Circuit A

i) How does the phase of the output compare with that of the input?

ii) Calculate the peak output voltage.

iii) Sketch the waveform of the voltage obtained at the output if the input signal remains the same but the gain is changed to 20. Indicate the amplitude of this waveform.

b) An operational amplifier is used in the differential mode, as shown in Circuit B.

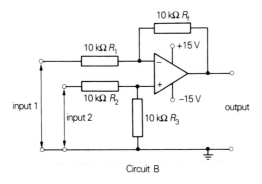

Circuit B

i) What arithmetic operation does this circuit perform?

ii) Calculate the output voltage of Circuit B if the voltage at input 1 is − 0.7 V and the voltage at input 2 is + 3.4 V.

c) The diagram shows the signals received at input 1 (Signal 1) and input 2 (Signal 2) of Circuit B when a microphone is connected to these inputs by means of a long pair of wires.

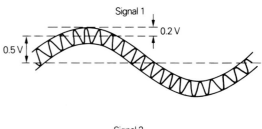

Signal 1

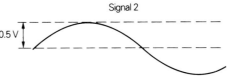

Signal 2

Signal 1 is a sine wave of frequency 1 kHz and amplitude 0.2 V combined with another sine wave of frequency 50 Hz and amplitude 0.5 V. Signal 2 is a sine wave of frequency 50 Hz and amplitude 0.5 V.
Sketch the waveform at the output of Circuit B. Indicate clearly its amplitude and frequency.

d) A temperature sensor has a resistance that varies between 1.0 kΩ at 0°C and 1.6 kΩ at 100° C. It is connected in the bridge circuit shown. The resistance of each of the three fixed resistors in the circuit is 1.0 kΩ.

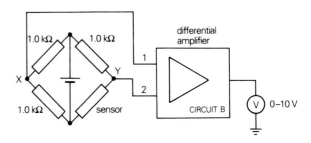

The outputs X and Y of the bridge circuit are connected to inputs 1 and 2 respectively of Circuit B.

i) What is the temperature of the sensor when the potential difference across XY is zero?
In order to change the gain of Circuit B, the values of R_f and R_3 are altered together, so that they remain equal. R_1 and R_2 are unchanged.
When the sensor is placed in boiling water, the potential difference across XY is 0.61 V.

ii) Calculate the values required for R_f and R_3 in Circuit B so that the voltmeter at the output of Circuit B will read 10.0 V. Assume that the values of R_1 and R_2 in Circuit B are unchanged at 10 kΩ.

SEB

8 The wave nature of light

8.1 Early theories of the nature of light

The debate over what light is has continued for many centuries. We have records of this debate as far back as the ancient Greeks. Plato wrote about light as being a fire which flowed out from the eyes. Aristotle argued that this could not be the case as it did not explain why some things could be in darkness. If the eyes were the source of the light all objects could be illuminated by the eyes and nowhere would be dark.

By the start of the seventeenth century it had become generally accepted that light was received by the eye rather than transmitted by the eye. However, at that time, another debate was started about the nature of light. Scientists divided into two groups, one group believing light to be a stream of particles and the other that light was a wave. Towards the end of the seventeenth century, Huygens published his book, *Treatise on Light*. In this book he proposed the theory that light was a wave. Huygens had a formidable opponent to his wave theory. Isaac Newton supported the corpuscular theory which stated that light was a stream of particles. Each side was able to give objections to the theory of the other and these objections could not, at that time, be answered. The biggest objection to the corpuscular theory was its failure to explain how two beams of light could pass through each other without being affected. If light were streams of particles they would be expected to collide. Supporters of the wave theory could easily demonstrate, using water waves, that waves could pass through each other without being affected. Supporters of the corpuscular theory argued that light could not be a wave since it apparently did not demonstrate the property now known as diffraction. Observation of water waves showed that they were able to bend round objects, Figure 8.1. Sound, which was known to be a wave motion, also demonstrated the property of bending round corners. Such bending, however, could not be observed with light, and Newton and his supporters argued that this was proof that light was not a wave.

Figure 8.1 Diffraction of water waves

We now know that light is diffracted round the edges of obstacles but that the amount of bending is so slight that it is not easily observed. The reason for this is that the wavelength of light is very small. Figure 8.2 shows diffraction patterns for water waves of different wavelengths and demonstrates that the wave with the shorter wavelength is diffracted less.

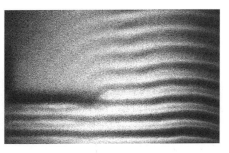

(a) Long wavelength   (b) Short wavelength

Figure 8.2 Diffraction of waves of different wavelengths

123

Light waves have wavelengths of the order of 10^{-6} m, which means that they are of the order of one ten-thousandth of the wavelength of the water waves in a ripple tank. With such a small wavelength the degree of bending is very slight, and not observable by the naked eye.

Because of the status of Newton, who supported the corpuscular theory, and the apparent fact that light did not demonstrate diffraction, the wave theory of Huygens did not receive much support. It was not until the start of the nineteenth century that Thomas Young supplied important new experimental evidence which supported the wave theory, and scientists accepted the idea that light was a wave motion. Young demonstrated that light could form an interference pattern and this could only be explained in terms of the wave theory.

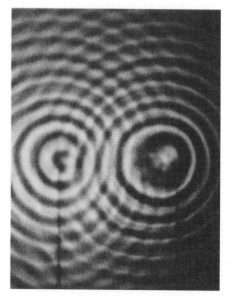

Figure 8.3 Interference of water waves

8.2 Interference of waves

Interference of waves can be demonstrated with water waves in a ripple tank. An interference pattern is produced by two overlapping circular wave patterns from coherent sources, Figure 8.3. Coherent sources generate waves of identical frequencies.

Two coherent sources of circular wave patterns can be produced by passing a plane wave through two narrow slits. If the width of each slit is less than the wavelength of the wave, two circular wave patterns are produced by diffraction of the wave by the slits.

Figure 8.4 shows the interference pattern with lines drawn along areas of uniform illumination. This uniform illumination means that, along these lines, the water is calm.

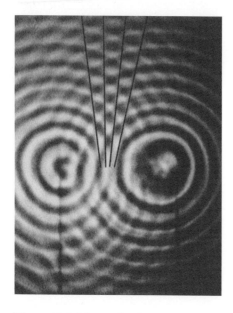

Figure 8.4 Lines of calm in an interference pattern

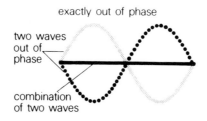

Figure 8.5 Destructive interference

These are lines along which destructive interference occurs. This results from the waves being half a wavelength out of phase and cancelling each other out.

Figure 8.6 shows the interference pattern with lines drawn along areas where the illumination is alternately bright and dark, showing that the water surface has a series of crests and troughs.

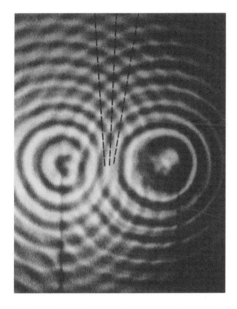

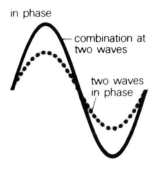

Figure 8.6 Lines of crests and troughs in an interference pattern

Figure 8.7 Constructive interference

These are lines along which constructive interference occurs. This results from the waves being in phase and combining to give a wave of greater amplitude, Figure 8.7.

Thus the interference pattern consists of a series of lines of constructive interference and destructive interference which means that these lines are lines of maximum and minimum wave amplitude, Figure 8.8.

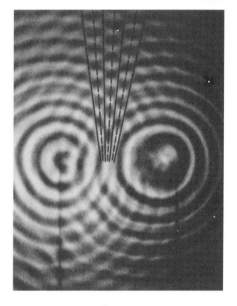

Figure 8.8 Interference pattern

Young's slits experiment

Young demonstrated the interference of light by splitting a narrow beam of sunlight into two beams. He allowed sunlight to pass through a small hole made by piercing a card with a needle. Across the small hole he placed a very thin card, edge on, to divide the beam of light into two narrow beams. When he did this, Young observed a series of bright and dark lines on the wall opposite. These lines are known as interference fringes, the bright lines being produced by constructive interference and the dark lines resulting from destructive interference.

A similar experiment may be repeated in the laboratory to demonstrate the interference of light. Two narrow slits, very close together, are prepared by using a pin point to scratch two fine lines across a glass slide which has been painted black, Figure 8.9. Light is passed through these slits and is viewed on a screen, Figure 8.10.

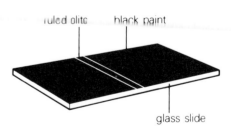

Figure 8.9 Preparation of glass slide for Young's slits experiment

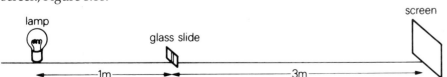

Figure 8.10 Apparatus to demonstrate the Young's slits experiment

A series of fringes is observed on the screen. With a white light source, the central fringe is white but the other fringes have coloured edges. Interference patterns for different colours of light are produced by inserting different filters between the lamp and the glass slide. When this is done, it is observed that the spacing of the fringes varies with the colour of light. The fringes for light nearer the red end of the spectrum are further apart than fringes for light nearer the blue end of the spectrum. Red light has a longer wavelength than blue light and longer wavelengths produce maxima which are more widely spaced, Figure 8.11.

When glass slides with slits of different separation are used, the spacing of the fringes is found to depend on the separation of the slits. The fringes are more widely spaced when the slits are closer together, Figure 8.12

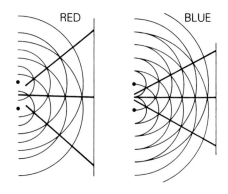

Figure 8.11 Interference patterns for waves of different wavelengths

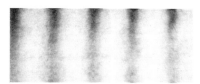 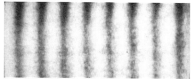

a) Slits close together   **b)** Slits further apart

Figure 8.12 Effect of slit separation on fringe spacing

Another factor which affects the fringe separation is the distance from the slits to the screen. If the screen is moved further from the slits, the fringe separation increases.

The factors found experimentally to affect the fringe separation are listed below.
a) Red light produces fringes of greater separation than those produced by blue light;
b) Smaller slit separation produces greater fringe separation;
c) Greater distance between the screen and the slits produces greater fringe separation.

The way in which fringes are produced can be explained by considering two rays from the slits S_1 and S_2 to the point X on the screen as shown in Figure 8.13.

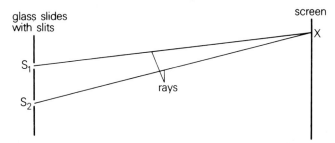

Figure 8.13 Two rays from the slits to a point on the screen

The ray from S_1 has travelled a shorter distance S_1X to the screen than the distance S_2X travelled by the ray from slit S_2.

The difference between these two distances is called the **path difference.**

If the path difference is equal to zero or a whole number of wavelengths, the waves will arrive **in phase**, and constructive interference will occur producing a bright fringe, Figure 8.14. Here the solid lines in the waves indicate wave fronts which left the slits at the same time.

For a path difference of a whole number of wavelengths a bright fringe (maximum brightness) is formed,

   path difference $= n\lambda$ for maxima   where n is zero or an integer.

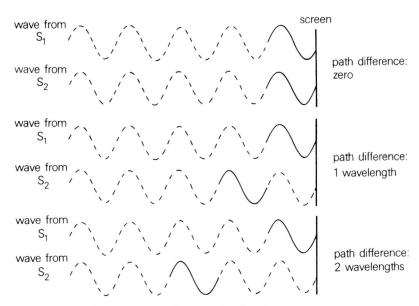

Figure 8.14 Waves from the two slits arriving in phase

Dark bands in an interference pattern are formed by destructive interference between the light from the two different slits S_1 and S_2. Destructive interference occurs when two waves are **out of phase** and this occurs when the path difference between the two rays from the slits is equal to an odd number of half wavelengths, Figure 8.15.

For a path difference of an odd number of half wavelengths a dark band (minimum brightness) is formed,

$$\text{path difference} = (n + \tfrac{1}{2})\lambda \qquad \text{for minima} \qquad \text{where } n \text{ is zero or an integer.}$$

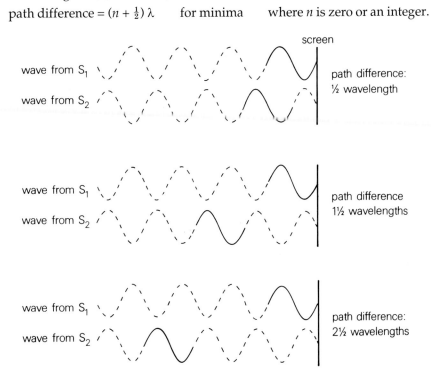

Figure 8.15 Waves from the two slits arriving out of phase

Coloured fringes

White light contains the range of colours in light from violet with a wavelength of 4×10^{-7} m to red light with a wavelength of 7×10^{-7} m. When Young's slits experiment is carried out with white light, multicoloured fringes are formed. How this comes about can be illustrated by producing fringes with light of two different colours. Figure 8.16 is drawn to scale and shows the relative fringe positions for two different colours. The conditions for maxima and minima depend on the number of wavelengths in the path difference for the two rays. Because the wavelengths of red and blue light are different, the separation for the maxima and minima of each colour will be different.

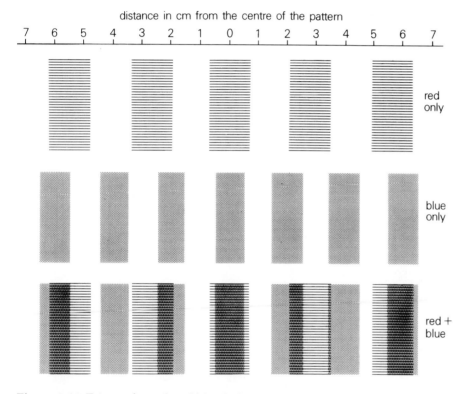

Figure 8.16 Fringes for red and blue light

Multiple slit interference

In Young's slits experiment, light was passed through two very narrow slits and, because the slits were so narrow, the amount of light energy passing through was small and the interference fringes were not very bright. A brighter pattern can be obtained by using a greater number of slits.

In Young's experiment we consider rays from the two slits and how they interfere when they meet at the screen. Since the distance d between the slits (less than 10^{-3} m) is very small compared with the distance D from the slits to the screen (usually several metres), two rays to any point on the screen will be effectively parallel, Figure 8.17.

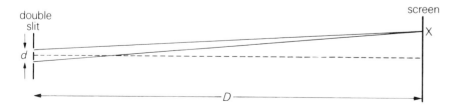

Figure 8.17 Two rays from the slits to a point on the screen

The condition for constructive interference is that the path difference between these rays is a whole number of wavelengths. For the first fringe away from the centre of the pattern, the path difference between the rays is one wavelength, Figure 8.18.

When this is the case, the waves in the two rays arrive in phase at the screen, Figure 8.19, and they produce a bright fringe by constructive interference.

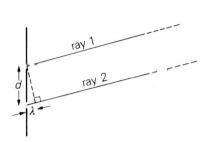

Figure 8.18 Path difference for first fringe away from the centre of the pattern

Figure 8.19 Two waves with a path difference of one wavelength

Consider now what happens when a third slit is introduced at a distance d from one of the other slits. Again, because D is very large compared with d, the rays from the slits to a point on the screen will be effectively parallel. If the path difference between ray 1 and ray 2 is 1λ, the path difference between ray 2 and ray 3 will also be 1λ, Figure 8.20.

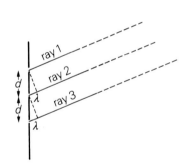

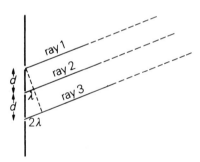

Figure 8.20 Rays from three slits to a point on the screen

Figure 8.21 Path differences between rays 2 and 3 and ray 1

Figure 8.22 Three waves arriving in phase

This means that the path difference between ray 1 and ray 3 is 2λ, Figure 8.21, and the wave in ray 3 will also arrive in phase with ray 1, Figure 8.22.

Thus the addition of a third slit has the effect of adding further to the constructive interference producing the bright fringe. The location of the fringe is the same as it was for two slits but it will now be brighter.

The argument can be extended for any number of slits providing they are all equally spaced.

The **diffraction grating** is the best and most useful example of a multiple slit used for producing an interference pattern. The diffraction grating is made by a machine cutting very fine, equally spaced grooves on the surface of a glass plate. The light is diffracted by this series of grooves. Normal diffraction gratings may have between 10 000 and 20 000 lines per inch (about 400 to 800 lines per mm).

8.3 Diffraction grating and the spectrometer

The spectrometer is an instrument which uses either a prism or a diffraction grating to separate light into its different colours. Figure 8.23 shows a photograph of a spectrometer and Figure 8.24 shows a diagram of how it is set up using a diffraction grating.

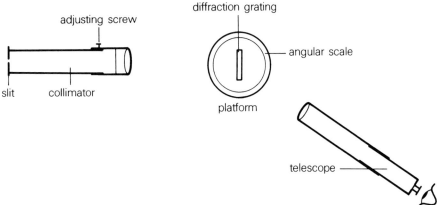

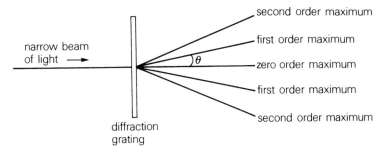

Figure 8.23 Spectrometer

Figure 8.24 Spectrometer with diffraction grating

The collimator is used to form a narrow beam of parallel light. A lamp is placed near the slit in the collimator. The length of the collimator is adjusted so that the slit falls in the focal plane of the collimator lens and this results in the light from the slit emerging as parallel rays from the collimator lens. In practice the telescope is first focused on a distant object so as to receive parallel rays. The telescope is then lined up on the collimator and the collimator length is adjusted until a clear sharp image of the slit is observed through the telescope. Since the telescope is adjusted to focus on parallel rays, the fact that the slit is sharply focused shows that the light emerging from the collimator consists of parallel rays. Once the collimator and telescope have been adjusted in this way, the diffraction grating or prism is placed on the platform. The angular scale on the platform is used for two purposes: first in setting the platform position so that the grating is at right angles to the beam of light from the collimator, and secondly to measure the angle between the telescope and this beam of light from the collimator.

With the interference pattern produced on a screen, the measurements made on the pattern were on fringe positions and spacings. With the spectrometer, the measurements made are the angles between the beams of light forming the fringes. A simple illustration of this is given in Figure 8.25.

Figure 8.25 Measurements of angles between maxima

An equation can be derived to relate the path difference S_2N between rays from two slits to the distance d between the two slits and the angle θ through which the rays are being diffracted, Figure 8.26.

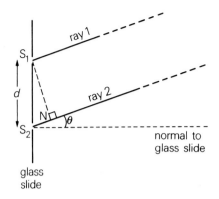

In the triangle, $S_1\hat{N}S_2 = 90°$

$$S_1\hat{S}_2N + S_2\hat{S}_1N = 90°$$
$$S_1\hat{S}_2N + \theta = 90° \text{ (angle between the grating and the normal)}$$
$$S_2\hat{S}_1N = \theta$$

In Figure 8.26 the distance S_2N is the path difference between the two rays. The triangle S_1S_2N is shown in Figure 8.27 with the path difference S_2N, the distance d between the two slits, and the angle θ.

Figure 8.26 Path difference and angle of diffraction

From Figure 8.27

$$\sin\theta = \frac{\text{path difference}}{d}$$

$\Rightarrow$ path difference $= d\sin\theta$

The condition for constructive interference is:

  path difference $= n\lambda$ where $n = 0,1,2,3,...$

$\Rightarrow$ $d\sin\theta = n\lambda$

$\Rightarrow$ $\sin\theta = \dfrac{n\lambda}{d}$

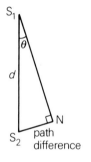

For constructive interference:

$$\sin\theta = \frac{n\lambda}{d}$$

θ = angle of diffraction
n = order of the maximum
λ = wavelength of the light
d = distance between the centres of the slits

Figure 8.27 Path difference between two rays

While this equation has been derived for two slits, it has already been shown that the same conditions apply for any number of slits providing they are equally spaced.

A spectrometer is usually used to measure the wavelength of light; d is known for the grating and the angle θ is measured: θ is the angle through which the telescope is rotated in going from the central maximum ($n = 0$) to the first order maximum ($n = 1$). This angle is greater for light of longer wavelengths, Figure 8.28.

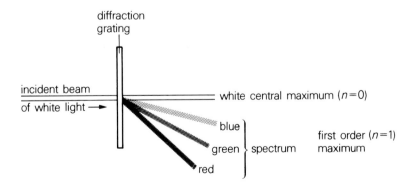

Figure 8.28 First order maxima for different colours

For the central maximum, $n = 0$

$\Rightarrow \ \sin \theta = 0$

$\Rightarrow \quad \theta = 0$

This is independent of wavelength, and is therefore the same for light of all wavelengths. Thus, if the incident beam is white light, the central maximum will be white.

For the first order maximum

$$\sin \theta = \frac{n\lambda}{d} \ \text{ where } n = 1$$

The wavelength, λ_b of blue light is less than the wavelength λ_r of red light.

For blue light the first order maximum will be at an angle θ_b such that

$$\sin \theta_b = \frac{\lambda_b}{d}$$

For red light the first order maximum will be at an angle θ_r such that

$$\sin \theta_r = \frac{\lambda_r}{d}$$

$$\lambda_b < \lambda_r$$

$$\Rightarrow \sin \theta_b < \sin \theta_r$$

$$\Rightarrow \quad \theta_b < \theta_r$$

Example 1

A parallel beam of white light consisting of light of wavelengths from 4×10^{-7} m (violet) to 7×10^{-7} m (red), is passed through a diffraction grating of 10 000 lines per inch (1 inch = 2.54 cm).
Describe the first order maximum and calculate the angle between the extremes of that maximum.

The first order maximum will be a spectrum of colours ranging from violet nearer the central fringe to red at the outer limit.

diffraction grating has 10 000 lines per 2.54 cm

distance between the lines $= \dfrac{2.54}{10\,000}$ cm

$$d = 2.54 \times 10^{-4} \text{ cm}$$

$$d = 2.54 \times 10^{-6} \text{ m}$$

For the first order maximum $\quad \sin \theta = \dfrac{\lambda}{d}$

For violet $\qquad \lambda_v = 4 \times 10^{-7}$

$\Rightarrow \qquad \sin \theta_v = \dfrac{4 \times 10^{-7}}{2.54 \times 10^{-6}}$

$\Rightarrow \qquad \sin \theta_v = 0.157$

$\Rightarrow \qquad \theta_v = 9.1°$

For red $\qquad \lambda_r = 7 \times 10^{-7}$

$\Rightarrow \qquad \sin \theta_r = \dfrac{7 \times 10^{-7}}{2.54 \times 10^{-6}}$

$\Rightarrow \qquad \sin \theta_r = 0.276$

$\Rightarrow \qquad \theta_r = 16.0°$

$\Rightarrow \qquad \theta_r - \theta_v = 16.0 - 9.1$

$\Rightarrow \qquad \theta_r - \theta_v = 6.9°$

The angle between the extremes of the first order maximum is 6.9°

Units for wavelength

Like that for any length or distance, the SI unit for wavelength is the metre. However the wavelength of light is very small, ranging from about 4×10^{-7} m to 7×10^{-7} m. Other smaller units are often used to express wavelengths of light and other electromagnetic radiations with small wavelengths. Three commonly used units are the micron (μ), the ångström (Å) and the nanometre (nm).

$$1\,\mu = 10^{-6}\,m \qquad\qquad 1\,\text{Å} = 10^{-10}\,m \qquad\qquad 1\,nm = 10^{-9}\,m$$

Example 2

A lamp gives off an intense monochromatic green light. When passed through a diffraction grating with 18000 lines per inch, this light gives a first order maximum at an angle of 23°.

a) What is the wavelength of the light?
b) Express this wavelength in nanometres, ångströms and microns.

a) For the first order maximum, $\quad \sin\theta = \dfrac{\lambda}{d}$

The grating has 18000 lines per 2.54 cm

$$d = \frac{2.54 \times 10^{-2}}{18000} = 1.4 \times 10^{-6}$$

$$\Rightarrow \quad \sin 23° = \frac{\lambda}{1.4 \times 10^{-6}}$$

$$\Rightarrow \quad \lambda = 1.4 \times 10^{-6}\sin 23° = 1.4 \times 10^{-6} \times 0.39 = 5.46 \times 10^{-7}$$

Wavelength of the light = 5.46×10^{-7} m

b)
$$\lambda = 5.46 \times 10^{-7}\,m$$
$$\Rightarrow \quad \lambda = 546 \times 10^{-9}\,m$$
$$\Rightarrow \quad \lambda = 546\,nm$$
$$\Rightarrow \quad \lambda = 5460 \times 10^{-10}\,m \quad \Rightarrow \quad \lambda = 5460\,\text{Å}$$
$$\Rightarrow \quad \lambda = 0.546 \times 10^{-6}\,m \quad \Rightarrow \quad \lambda = 0.546\,\mu$$

8.4 Formation of spectra

A diffraction grating can be used to split light into separate colours and this is the result of an interference pattern being formed. A prism may also be used to split light into separate colours. The prism refracts different colours by different amounts. A prism can be used in place of the diffraction grating on a spectrometer.

With a diffraction grating, it is light of longer wavelength that is seen to make a greater angle with the path of the incident ray. This is because the fringe spacing of the interference pattern is greater for longer wavelengths. With a prism, it is the light with the shorter wavelength that makes the greater angle because light of shorter wavelength is refracted more.

X-ray diffraction

Light produces an interference pattern when it passes through a diffraction grating. The spacing between the lines of the grating is of the same order of magnitude as the wavelength of light. The spacing between atoms in a solid is of the same order of magnitude as the wavelength of X-rays. X-rays, like light, are part of the electromagnetic spectrum, but they have a shorter wavelength than light. When X-rays are passed through a crystalline solid, a diffraction pattern is formed, Figure 8.29, and this pattern can be analysed to give information about the arrangement and spacing of the atoms in the solid.

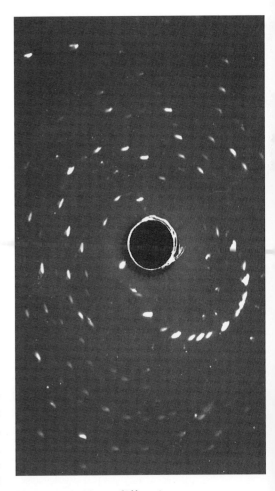

Figure 8.29 X-ray diffraction pattern

8.5   Refraction of light

When a ray of light passes from air to glass, it is bent towards the normal so that the angle θ_a between the normal and the ray in air is greater than the angle θ_g between the normal and the ray in glass, Figure 8.30.

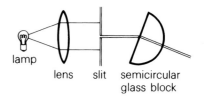

Figure 8.30 Refraction of light

The apparatus shown in Figure 8.31 is used to investigate the relationship between θ_a and θ_g. Since the glass block is semicircular, any beam of light through the centre of the straight face of the block travels along a radius in the glass and will therefore be normal to the curved face. The lens is used to produce a parallel beam of light and the slit is used to produce a narrow beam. By varying the angle between the ray and the glass block, a series of measurements of θ_a and θ_g is made. Table 1 shows a typical set of such measurements. If these results are plotted on a graph, the graph shown in Figure 8.32 is obtained.

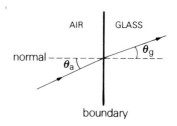

Figure 8.31 Investigation of relationship between θ_a and θ_g

θ_a	θ_g
10°	6°
22°	12°
29°	16°
40°	21°
55°	27°
63°	30°

Table 1

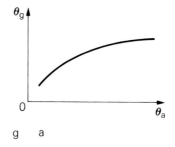

Figure 8.32

Neither the table of results nor the graph shows any obvious mathematical relationship between θ_a and θ_g. However, if we take the sines of the angles (Table 2) and plot a graph of $\sin \theta_a$ against $\sin \theta_g$, we obtain the graph shown in Figure 8.33.

θ_a	θ_g	$\sin \theta_a$	$\sin \theta_g$
10°	6°	0.17	0.10
22°	12°	0.37	0.21
29°	16°	0.48	0.28
40°	21°	0.64	0.36
55°	27°	0.82	0.45
63°	30°	0.89	0.50

Table 2

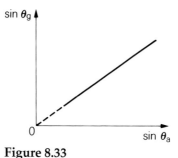

Figure 8.33

Since the graph in Figure 8.33 is a straight line passing through the origin,

$$\sin \theta_a \propto \sin \theta_g$$
$$\Rightarrow \quad \sin \theta_a = \text{constant} \times \sin \theta_g$$
$$\Rightarrow \quad \frac{\sin \theta_a}{\sin \theta_g} = \text{constant}$$

This constant is a property of the glass and is called the **refractive index** of the glass. The symbol for refractive index is n (sometimes the Greek letter μ, pronounced 'mu' is used).

The expression below defines the refractive index n for light passing from a vacuum into a substance.

$$n = \frac{\sin \theta_v}{\sin \theta_s}$$

where θ_v = angle between the ray and the normal in a vacuum
θ_s = angle between the ray and the normal in the substance

Substance	Refractive index
ice	1.31
water	1.33
crown glass	1.51–1.65
flint glass	1.53–1.93
perspex	1.50
diamond	2.42

Table 3

For practical purposes, the difference between the path change for rays passing from air and those passing from a vacuum is so small that we can ignore it: the values given for the refractive index by the two equations are effectively the same.

The refractive indices for some different substances are given in Table 3. The refractive index of a substance can be regarded as a measure of the ability of that substance to bend light: substances having a higher refractive index are those which bend the light more.

Refraction and colour

If we allow narrow beams of light of different colours to pass through a prism, we observe that red light is bent less than blue light. This shows that the refractive index n_R for red light is less than the refractive index n_B for blue light. If a beam of white light is passed through a prism, the white light is split up into a spectrum, Figure 8.34. The white light contains the range of colours red, orange, yellow, green, blue, indigo and violet. Different colours have different wavelengths. Those colours with longer wavelengths (the red end of the spectrum) are refracted less than those with shorter wavelengths. This indicates that the refractive indices are smaller for light of longer wavelengths.

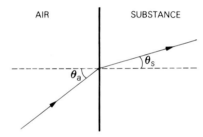

Figure 8.34 Spectrum from white light

Angles of incidence and refraction

For any ray passing from air into a substance, θ_a is the angle of incidence i, and θ_s is the angle of refraction r, Figure 8.35.

Thus, $n = \dfrac{\sin i}{\sin r}$
For a ray passing from air into another substance

where i = angle of incidence
r = angle of refraction for a ray entering the substance from air
(or more accurately from a vacuum)
n = refractive index of the substance.

$$i > r$$
$$\Rightarrow \quad \sin i > \sin r$$
$$\Rightarrow \quad \frac{\sin i}{\sin r} > 1$$

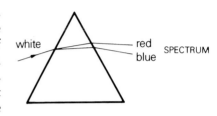

Figure 8.35

Thus the refractive index of any substance must be greater than one.

Changes in wavelength and speed on refraction

We cannot observe light waves, but interference patterns can be produced by light and this is evidence of the wave nature of light. While the wavelength of light is far too small to be observed directly, we can consider what the change in direction of the waves on refraction means in terms of wavelength. Light consists of wavefronts and the wavefronts are at right angles to the wave direction, Figure 8.36.

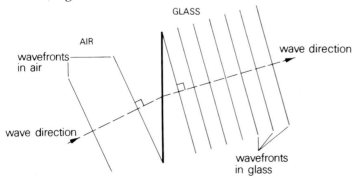

Figure 8.36 Wavefronts in air and glass

Figure 8.37 shows one wavefront AC on the air side of the boundary AB and one wavefront BD on the glass side of the boundary.

In triangle ABC, the wavefront AC is at right angles to BC and BC is one wavelength λ_a in air.

$$\Rightarrow \quad \sin B\hat{A}C = \frac{\lambda_a}{AB} \quad \dots [1]$$

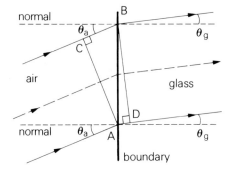

Figure 8.37

The normal at B is at right angles to the boundary AB

$$\Rightarrow \qquad \theta_a = 90° - A\hat{B}C$$

But in the right-angled triangle ABC,

$$B\hat{A}C = 90° - A\hat{B}C \qquad \text{(sum of internal angles} = 180°)$$

$$\Rightarrow \qquad \theta_a = B\hat{A}C$$

So, from equation [1]

$$\sin \theta_a = \frac{\lambda_a}{AB} \quad \dots [2]$$

Similarly, from the right-angled triangle ABD in which $AD = \lambda_g$

$$\sin \theta_g = \frac{\lambda_g}{AB} \quad \dots [3]$$

Dividing equation [2] by equation [3] gives the refractive index n.

$$\frac{\sin \theta_a}{\sin \theta_g} = \frac{\lambda_a}{\lambda_g} = n$$

The wavefronts in the glass are generated by wavefronts in the air, and so the number of wavefronts generated per second is the same in both the glass and the air, and the frequency f is unchanged.

$$\Rightarrow \qquad \frac{\sin \theta_a}{\sin \theta_g} = \frac{f\lambda_a}{f\lambda_g} = n$$

From the wave equation $v = f\lambda$

$$v_a = f\lambda_a \qquad \text{where } v_a = \text{speed of light in air}$$
$$v_g = f\lambda_g \qquad \qquad v_g = \text{speed of light in glass}$$

$$\Rightarrow \qquad \frac{\sin \theta_a}{\sin \theta_g} = \frac{v_a}{v_g} = n$$

For glass:
$$n = \frac{\text{wavelength in air (or a vacuum)}}{\text{wavelength in glass}}$$

$$= \frac{\text{speed in air (or a vacuum)}}{\text{speed in glass}}$$

This is true for any medium of refractive index n:
$$n = \frac{\text{wavelength in a vacuum}}{\text{wavelength in the medium}}$$

$$= \frac{\text{speed in a vacuum}}{\text{speed in the medium}}$$

Total internal reflection

If a ray of light will travel in one direction, it could travel along the same path in the opposite direction. The semicircular glass block can be used to investigate the bending of a ray of light at one surface only, and we can consider what happens to a ray passing from glass to air, Figure 8.38.

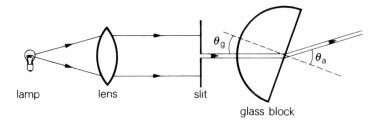

θ_g	θ_a
10°	17°
16°	28°
23°	42°
31°	61°
35°	77°

Figure 8.38 Ray passing from glass to air

Table 4

If θ_g is varied and pairs of values of θ_g and θ_a are measured, a set of values such as those shown in Table 4 might be obtained.

When θ_g is increased above 36°, the ray of light does not emerge from the glass block, but is reflected at the straight face, Figure 8.39. The ray is said to be totally internally reflected.

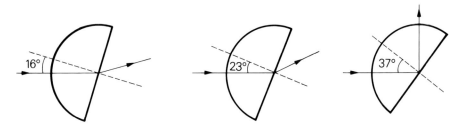

Figure 8.39 Total internal reflection

For the ray to emerge from the glass, θ_a must be less than 90°. Thus the maximum angle of incidence θ_g for the ray passing from glass to air can be calculated using the following equation.

$$n = \frac{\sin \theta_a}{\sin \theta_g}$$

For maximum value, $\theta_a = 90°$

$\Rightarrow$ $\sin \theta_a = 1$

$\Rightarrow$ $n = \dfrac{1}{\sin \theta_g}$

or $\sin \theta_g = \dfrac{1}{n}$

The maximum value of θ_g for which refraction occurs is called the critical angle θ_c.

$$\sin \theta_c = \frac{1}{n}$$

For θ_g greater than θ_c, the ray undergoes total internal reflection.

Summary

The amplitude of a wave is the size of the maximum disturbance, measured from the line of zero disturbance.

The wave speed is the distance travelled by the wave in one second.

Points in a wave separated by a whole wavelength are in phase.

Points in a wave separated by half a wavelength are exactly out of phase.

Two sources are coherent if they have the same frequency and are in phase with each other or have a constant phase difference.

When light is passed through two very narrow slits very close together (Young's slits), it forms an interference pattern.

In an interference pattern:

path difference = $n\lambda$ for a maximum

path difference = $(n + \frac{1}{2})\lambda$ for a minimum

where $n = 0$ or an integer.

A diffraction grating consists of a large number of fine, equally spaced, parallel grooves on the surface of a glass plate, and produces an interference pattern similar to that of two slits, but of greater brightness.

For a diffraction grating, the angle θ through which the rays are diffracted for a bright fringe is given by:

$$\sin \theta = \frac{n\lambda}{d}$$ where n = order of the maximum

λ = wavelength of the light

d = distance between the centre of the slits.

Common units for the wavelength of light are:

1 micron (μ) = 10^{-6}m

1 ångström (Å) = 10^{-10}m

1 nanometre (nm) = 10^{-9}m

X-ray diffraction patterns can be produced by passing X-rays through a crystalline solid, and can be used to give information about the arrangement and spacing of atoms in the solid.

For a ray of light crossing the boundary between air (or vacuum) and a substance, the refractive index n of the substance is given by

$$n = \frac{\sin \theta_a}{\sin \theta_b}$$ where θ_a = angle between the ray in air and the normal to the boundary,

θ_b = angle between the ray in the substance and the normal to the boundary.

The refractive index of a substance is greater for light of higher frequency. For a ray of light passing the boundary between air (or vacuum) and a substance of refractive index n

$$n = \frac{\text{wavelength in air (or vacuum)}}{\text{wavelength in the substance}}$$

$$n = \frac{\text{speed in air (or vacuum)}}{\text{speed in the substance}}$$

Within a transparent substance, a ray undergoes total internal reflection if the angle between the ray and the normal is greater than the critical angle θ_c given by:

$$\sin \theta_c = \frac{1}{n}$$

Problems

1   Which are diffracted least: waves of shorter wavelength or waves of longer wavelength? How does this account for the fact that it was some time before people would accept Huygens' wave theory of light?

2   At the start of the eighteenth century there were two main theories of the nature of light: the Wave Theory and the Corpuscular Theory. What was the experimental evidence, demonstrated by Thomas Young, which strongly supported the Wave Theory?
Explain, with the aid of a diagram, how you would set up apparatus to demonstrate this experimental evidence in the laboratory.

3   A spectrometer has a collimator, a telescope and a platform on which a prism or a diffraction grating is mounted.
State briefly what is the function of:
a)   the collimator;
b)   the telescope;
c)   the prism or diffraction grating.

4   In an experiment to demonstrate the interference of light, red light was passed through two narrow slits ruled in black paint on a glass slide. A pattern of red interference fringes was produced on a screen.
State what effect each of the following changes would have on the spacing between the interference fringes:
a)   Replacing the red light source by a blue light source.
b)   Replacing the glass slide by another on which the two narrow slits are closer together.
c)   Increasing the distance between the screen and the glass slide.

5   White light can be separated to form a continuous spectrum by passing it through a spectrometer using either a prism or a diffraction grating on the platform. What is the main difference between the angles at which the different colours are observed when using a prism or a diffraction grating?

6 Express the following lengths in metres:
a) 0.7 μ; **b)** 25.0 μ; **c)** 7000 Å; **d)** 400 nm.

7 What is 6.6×10^{-7} m when expressed in:
a) microns; **b)** nanometres; **c)** Ångstroms?

8 Why are X-rays rather than light used to produce a diffraction pattern of a crystalline solid?

9 A laser is a device which produces a narrow beam of monochromatic light. One type of laser produces red light. Light from this laser is allowed to strike a blackened glass plate on which there are two narrow parallel slits. The light emerging from the slits is viewed on a screen placed a distance from the slits as shown in Figure 1.
On viewing the screen a series of equally spaced fringes is observed, Figure 2.

Figure 1

Figure 2

a) Explain how the fringe pattern is produced.
b) Suggest how the pattern observed on the screen would be affected if:
  i) blue light from a second laser replaced the beam of red light.
  ii) the beam of red light was allowed to shine on a pair of slits tapering as shown in Figure 3, the beam being gradually moved from X to Y.

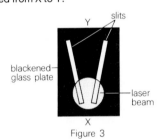

Figure 3

10 A ray of light from a tungsten filament lamp is incident on a glass prism as shown in the diagram.

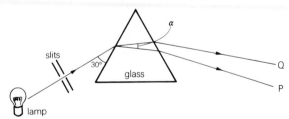

The refractive index of glass is 1.53 for blue light and 1.51 for red light.
a) If P and Q represent the ends of the visible spectrum, which is the blue end?
b) Calculate the angle α
c) From the refractive indices above, deduce whether red or blue light travels faster through the glass. Show your reasoning. *SEB*

11 The diagram shows the path of a ray of red light passing through a glass prism.

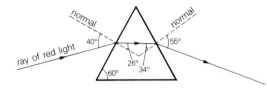

a) Use the information in the diagram to find the refractive index of the glass for the red light.
b) The refractive index of the glass for blue light is 1.58. Draw a diagram similar to the one above to show the path of a ray of blue light through the glass prism. Make the initial angle of incidence 40° as above. *SEB*

12 The diagram shows the ray AOB traced by a pupil investigating the refraction of red light using a semicircular glass block.

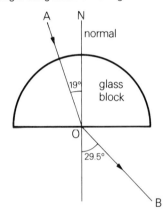

a) Use the information given in the diagram to calculate the refractive index of glass, $_{air}n_{glass}$, for red light.
b) Draw an accurate diagram to show the path of the ray if angle AON is increased to 30°.
c) The speed of red light in air is 3×10^8 ms^{-1}. Calculate the speed of red light in glass. *SEB*

9 Optoelectronics

9.1 Intensity of illumination

When an object is illuminated, it is receiving light energy. The **intensity** of the illumination of a surface is defined as the amount of light energy per second falling on one square metre of the surface. Since energy per second is power, the intensity of illumination is a measure of the power per unit area and is measured in watts per square metre ($W\,m^{-2}$).

The inverse square law

Figure 9.1 shows an experimental arrangement that can be used to investigate the relationship between the intensity of illumination on a surface and the distance of the light source from the surface. The experiment must be carried out in a darkened room so that the lamp is the only source of light.

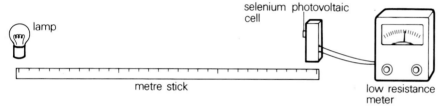

Figure 9.1 Investigation of the variation of intensity with distance

When light shines on the selenium photovoltaic cell, the cell produces an e.m.f. which is proportional to the intensity of illumination on it. The low resistance meter measures this e.m.f. and the meter reading is directly proportional to the intensity of illumination on the cell. The distance from the lamp to the cell is measured and the reading on the meter is noted. If this is repeated for a number of different distances and a graph of the results is plotted, the graph shown in Figure 9.2 is obtained.

The relationship between the meter reading and the distance is not apparent from this graph, but an inverse relationship is indicated by the fact that the meter reading decreases as the distance increases. If a graph of the meter reading against $1/(\text{distance})^2$ is plotted, a straight line is obtained which, when extended, passes through the origin, Figure 9.3.

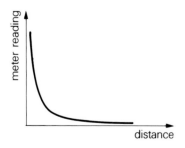

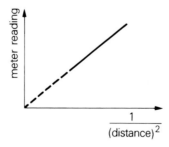

Figure 9.2 Variation of meter reading with distance between the cell and the lamp

Figure 9.3 Results of experiment demonstrating inverse square law

Since the meter reading is directly proportional to the intensity of illumination on the cell, this result shows that

$$\text{intensity} \propto \frac{1}{(\text{distance})^2}$$

This is an expression of the **Inverse Square Law**, which states that the intensity of the illumination is inversely proportional to the square of the distance from the light source.

The Inverse Square Law applies only to radiation from a point source, Figure 9.4.

Figure 9.4 Light radiated from a point source

In the experiment to show the Inverse Square Law, the distances measured are large compared with the size of the lamp filament from which the light is emitted: the lamp is effectively a point source. In a parallel beam of light the energy is not spreading out and the intensity does not decrease with distance from the source, Figure 9.5.

Figure 9.5 A parallel beam of light

9.2 Photoelectric effect

In Chapter 8 we discussed the fact that there were two conflicting theories of light, the Wave Theory and the Particle Theory. Thomas Young's experiments, producing interference patterns for light, provided strong evidence for the Wave Theory. Evidence supporting the Particle Theory was provided by the photoelectric effect.

In 1887 Heinrich Hertz found that when ultraviolet radiation shines onto two metal spheres, the potential difference required to produce a spark between them is reduced. The following year Hallwachs discovered that a negatively charged zinc plate lost its charge when it was exposed to ultraviolet radiation. In 1899 Lenard carried out further experiments which indicated that the ultraviolet radiation ejects electrons from some metals. These experiments were all demonstrations of what is known as 'the photoelectric effect'.

This effect can be demonstrated by a simple laboratory experiment, Figure 9.6. An electroscope with a polished zinc plate on its disc is negatively charged. When ultraviolet radiation is shone onto the zinc plate the electroscope rapidly discharges.

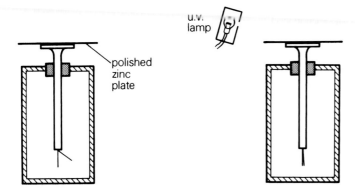

Figure 9.6 Photoelectric effect

At first this may not appear to be very surprising. Electroscopes are discharged by simply bringing a flame near to them. This happens because the energy of the flame ionizes some of the molecules in the surrounding air, forming negative and positive ions. A negatively charged electroscope attracts the positive ions which collect electrons from the electroscope and cause it to discharge, Figure 9.7.

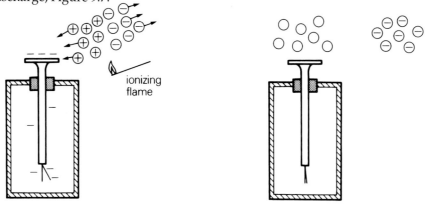

Figure 9.7 Discharge of a negatively charged electroscope

If the electroscope is initially positively charged, it is the negative ions which are attracted to it and cancel out its charge, Figure 9.8.

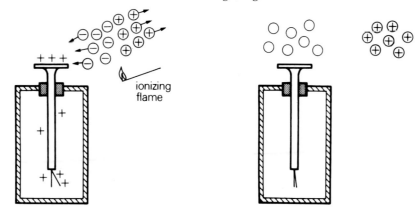

Figure 9.8 Discharge of a positively charged electroscope

Other ionizing sources such as alpha particles or X-rays discharge electroscopes in the same way. Ultraviolet radiation discharges a negatively charged electroscope with a zinc plate but, if the same electroscope is positively charged, the ultraviolet radiation does not discharge it, Figure 9.9.

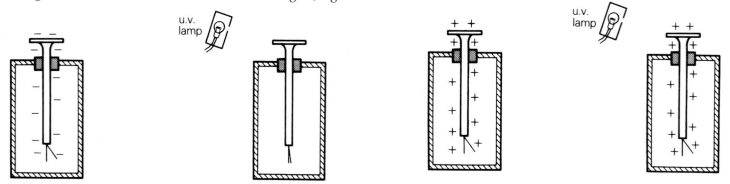

Figure 9.9 Effect of ultraviolet radiation on charged electroscopes

This shows that the ultraviolet radiation does not discharge the electroscope by ionizing the air.

Ultraviolet radiation discharges the negatively charged zinc plate of an electroscope. Light, which is an electromagnetic radiation of a lower frequency than ultraviolet, does not discharge such an electroscope. It seems that ultraviolet radiation has sufficient energy to eject electrons from the zinc, while visible radiation does not. If the case were that simple, increasing the brightness of the light would increase the total energy supplied and, if the light were bright enough, the electroscope would be discharged. This is not the case. No matter how bright the visible radiation, the electroscope is not discharged. However, a relatively small amount of ultraviolet radiation will cause it to discharge.

The explanation of the photoelectric effect was that electromagnetic radiation consists of small particles or corpuscles.

The radiation will eject electrons only if the corpuscles have sufficient energy. The energy of a corpuscle of visible radiation is less than the energy required to remove an electron from zinc and, no matter how many corpuscles of visible radiation are supplied, no electrons are ejected. The energy of a corpuscle of ultraviolet radiation is sufficient to eject an electron from zinc.

The idea that radiation consists of corpuscles rather than continuous waves is support for the corpuscular theory. The simple demonstration with the gold leaf electroscope provides evidence for this theory. The evidence can be summarized as follows:

evidence	conclusion
1 Ultraviolet radiation discharges the zinc plate of an electroscope which is negatively charged but not of one which is positively charged.	Discharge is a result of ejecting electrons and not a result of ionizing the air about the electroscope.
2 Visible radiation, no matter how bright, does not produce the same effect.	It is *not* simply a case of the total energy supplied, but rather a case of whether each 'bundle' of radiation has sufficient energy to eject an electron.

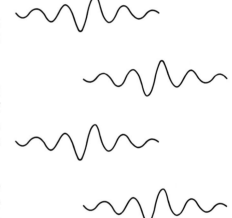

Young's slits experiment provided strong evidence for the wave theory for electromagnetic radiation. The photoelectric effect provided strong evidence for the corpuscular theory. Einstein provided an explanation which embodied both theories. He suggested that the corpuscles could be thought of as bundles of wave energy, called photons, Figure 9.10.

Figure 9.10 Photons of wave energy

The energy E of each photon is proportional to the frequency f of the radiation.

$$E \propto f$$

$$\Rightarrow \quad E = h \times f \quad \text{where } h \text{ is a constant}$$

The constant h is known as **Planck's constant** and was named after Max Planck who first suggested that the frequency of radiation emitted by an atom was directly proportional to the amount of energy radiated by the atom. The value of h is 6.6×10^{-34} J s.

The intensity of light falling on a surface is equal to the power of light per unit area. N photons of light, of frequency f, have an energy of Nhf.
The intensity of illumination on a surface is given by

$$I = Nhf$$

where N = number of photons per second per unit area and
I = intensity of light on the surface

Example 1

The energy required to eject an electron from sodium is 2.9×10^{-19} J. What is the minimum frequency of electromagnetic radiation required to produce the photoelectric effect with sodium?

energy required to eject an electron $= 2.9 \times 10^{-19}$ J

energy of a photon of radiation $\quad = h \times f$

where f = frequency of the radiation
and h = Planck's constant

For the photoelectric effect to occur with sodium

$h \times f = 2.9 \times 10^{-19}$

$\Rightarrow \quad f = \dfrac{2.9 \times 10^{-19}}{h}$

$h = 6.6 \times 10^{-34}$

$\Rightarrow \quad f = \dfrac{2.9 \times 10^{-19}}{6.6 \times 10^{-34}} = 4.4 \times 10^{14}$ Hz

Minimum frequency = 4.4×10^{14} Hz.

Example 2

If the intensity of light of frequency 5×10^{14} Hz falling on a surface of area 1 m² is 10 W m⁻², how many photons of light are incident on the surface every second?

energy of 1 photon $= hf$

Let the number of photons falling on 1 m² each second $= N$

$\Rightarrow \qquad$ total energy per second incident on 1 m² $= Nhf$

$\Rightarrow \qquad$ intensity $I = Nhf$

$\Rightarrow \qquad 10 = N \times 6.6 \times 10^{-34} \times 5 \times 10^{14}$

$\Rightarrow \qquad N = 10 \div (6.6 \times 10^{-34} \times 5 \times 10^{14})$

$\Rightarrow \qquad N = 3.0 \times 10^{19}$

Number of photons incident on the surface per second = 3.0×10^{19}

In 1923, R. A. Millikan won the Nobel prize for his work on the photoelectric effect. He carried out many careful experiments, finding the minimum frequency of radiation required to produce the photoelectric effect in different metals.

Figure 9.11 shows a typical apparatus for finding the minimum frequency of radiation to emit electrons from metals and measuring the rate at which electrons are emitted.

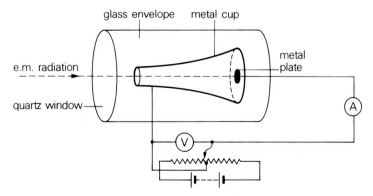

Figure 9.11 Photoelectric effect apparatus

The electromagnetic radiation passes through a hole in the metal cup onto a metal plate. This plate is made of the metal for which the photoelectric effect is being investigated. Any electrons emitted from the metal plate may cross to the metal cup or return to the metal plate, depending on the potential difference between the plate and the cup. A quartz window is used at the end of the glass tube because quartz allows both light and ultraviolet radiation to pass through it while glass absorbs ultraviolet radiation.

When both the frequency and the intensity of the electromagnetic radiation remain constant and the potential difference between the cup and the plate is varied, the current varies as shown by the graph in Figure 9.12.

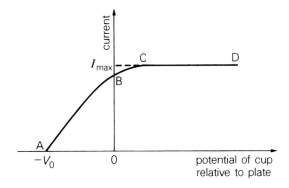

Figure 9.12 Variation of photoelectric current with potential difference

On the graph, negative values of potential difference represent potential differences which oppose the flow of electrons from the metal plate to the metal cup. The minimum value V_0 of the reverse potential which reduces the photoelectric current to zero, is called the stopping potential, Figure 9.13.

For the section AB on the graph, the potential difference between the plate and the cup opposes the flow of electrons from the plate to the cup, but is insufficient to overcome the kinetic energy of all the electrons. Thus the current in this section consists of the flow of electrons which have sufficient kinetic energy to overcome the opposing potential difference, Figure 9.14.

For the section BC on the graph, the potential difference supports the electron flow from plate to cup, but not all of the electrons reach the cup, Figure 9.15.

For the section CD on the graph, increases in the potential difference supporting the electron flow produced no increase in current. This is because all of the photoelectrons reach the plate and an increase in the potential difference does not increase the current because there are no more electrons available, Figure 9.16.

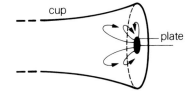

Figure 9.13 Reverse potential stops current

Figure 9.14 Some of the electrons overcome the reverse potential

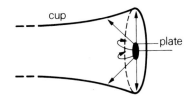

Figure 9.15 Potential supports the flow of electrons

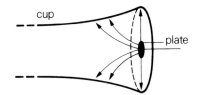

Figure 9.16 All of the photoelectrons reach the plate

Example 3

If the maximum photoelectric current in the apparatus shown in Figure 9.11 is $50\,\mu A$, how many electrons are emitted per second?

current	$= 50 \times 10^{-6}\,A$
charge flow per second	$= 50 \times 10^{-6}\,C$
charge on an electron	$= 1.6 \times 10^{-19}\,C$

$\Rightarrow$ number of electrons emitted per second $= \dfrac{50 \times 10^{-6}}{1.6 \times 10^{-19}}$

number of electrons emitted per second $= 3.1 \times 10^{14}$

Number of electrons per second $= 3.1 \times 10^{14}$.

If the experiment is repeated several times with different intensities of electromagnetic radiation (all with the same frequency), the results produce a set of curves as shown in Figure 9.17.

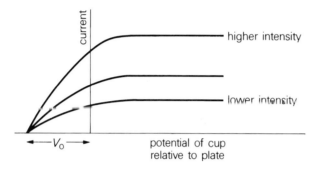

Figure 9.17 Photoelectric current for different intensities of radiation

These results show that the photoelectric current, which is equal to the maximum current in the circuit, depends on the intensity of the radiation. In fact, the photoelectric current is directly proportional to the intensity of the radiation. Increasing the intensity increases the number of photons per second and hence the number of electrons ejected per second.

The results also show that the stopping potential V_0 is independent of the intensity of the radiation; V_0 is the minimum potential difference required to stop all, including the most energetic, of the electrons emitted from the plate. Thus the fact that V_0 is independent of the intensity of radiation indicates that the energy of the electrons emitted is independent of the intensity of the radiation.

When a charge of Q coulombs moves through a potential difference of V volts, the work done on the charge is QV joules. Thus, if V_0 is the potential difference required to overcome the kinetic energy of the electrons which are emitted with most energy, the work done in stopping those electrons is qV_0 (q = charge on an electron). The work done on the electron is equal to the kinetic energy lost by that electron. Thus the maximum kinetic energy of an emitted electron is given by

$$E_{max} = qV_0 \qquad \text{where } V_0 = \text{stopping potential}$$
$$q = \text{charge on an electron}$$

If the experiment is repeated using electromagnetic radiations of different frequencies and V_0 is measured in each case, the results obtained are as illustrated in Figure 9.18.

The frequency f_0 is the minimum frequency for which the photoelectric effect occurs and is known as the threshold frequency for the metal being used. The results shown in Figure 9.18 are those obtained by Millikan for sodium; in that case he found the threshold frequency to be $4.39 \times 10^{14}\,Hz$. For radiations of

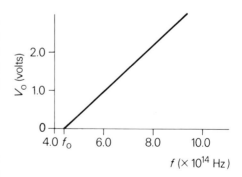

Figure 9.18 Variation of stopping potential with frequency of radiation

frequency less than f_0, the individual photons do not have sufficient energy to eject electrons from the metal. The minimum energy required to eject an electron from a metal is called the work function and is given by:

$$E_{min} = hf_0 \qquad \text{where } h = \text{Planck's constant}$$
$$f_0 = \text{threshold frequency for that metal}$$

From the experiments carried out with this apparatus we know that

1 the minimum frequency of radiation required to eject an electron from a metal is given by

$$E_{min} = hf_0 \qquad \text{where } f_0 = \text{threshold frequency;}$$

2 the maximum kinetic energy of an ejected electron is given by

$$E_{max} = qV_0 \qquad \text{where } V_0 = \text{stopping potential}$$
$$q = \text{charge on an electron.}$$

These two energies may be related to the energy of the photons of radiation producing the photoelectric effect since, when a photon is absorbed, its energy ejects the electron with a certain amount of kinetic energy.

$$\begin{array}{ccccc} \text{energy of} & = & \text{energy needed to} & + & \text{kinetic energy given} \\ \text{1 photon} & & \text{eject electron} & & \text{to that electron} \end{array}$$

The electron which needs least energy to be ejected will gain the most kinetic energy.

$$\begin{array}{ccccc} \text{energy of} & = & \text{minimum energy required} & + & \text{maximum kinetic energy of} \\ \text{1 photon} & & \text{to eject an electron} & & \text{an emitted electron} \end{array}$$

If the frequency of the radiation producing the effect is f,

$$hf = hf_0 + qV_0$$

Example 4

Sodium has a threshold frequency of 4.4×10^{14} Hz. What is the stopping potential when the sodium is irradiated with light of frequency 6.0×10^{14} Hz?

$$f = 6.0 \times 10^{14} \text{ Hz}$$
$$f_0 = 4.4 \times 10^{14} \text{ Hz}$$
$$h = 6.6 \times 10^{-34} \text{ J s}$$
$$q = 1.6 \times 10^{-19} \text{ C}$$
$$hf = hf_0 + qV_0$$
$$\Rightarrow \quad 6.6 \times 10^{-34} \times 6.0 \times 10^{14} = 6.6 \times 10^{-34} \times 4.4 \times 10^{14} + 1.6 \times 10^{-19} \times V_0$$
$$\Rightarrow \quad V_0 = \frac{6.6 \times 10^{-34}(6.0 - 4.4) \times 10^{14}}{1.6 \times 10^{-19}}$$
$$\Rightarrow \quad V_0 = \frac{6.6 \times 1.6 \times 10^{-20}}{1.6 \times 10^{-19}}$$
$$\Rightarrow \quad V_0 = 0.66$$

Stopping potential = 0.66 V.

9.3 Spectra

The photoelectric effect provided evidence for the discrete rather than the continuous nature of electromagnetic radiation. This means that the radiation consists of 'bundles' of energy called photons. In the photoelectric effect, photons are absorbed and give energy to electrons in the atoms. The reverse also occurs. This is when electrons in the atoms lose energy and that energy is given off as electromagnetic radiation. The radiation given off when this occurs can be dispersed by a prism or diffracted by a diffraction grating. The spectrum formed in this way is different from that formed from the light from a filament lamp or the Sun.

Emission spectra

When light is given off from a light source, it is split into its different colours by a prism or diffraction grating and forms a spectrum; such a spectrum is called an emission spectrum. Emission spectra are found to be of two types, continuous spectra and line spectra, Figure 9.19. Examples of these in colour are given on the back cover of the book.

Figure 9.19 Emission spectra

Continuous spectra are produced by light from sources which are solids, liquids or high-pressure gases raised to high temperatures. Common examples of such sources are lamp filaments and the Sun. Line spectra are produced by light from gas discharge tubes, such as those used in neon lights and sodium street lights, or from hot gases and vapours.

Line emission spectra

A line emission spectrum consists of narrow lines of colour, showing that only radiations of specific frequencies are emitted.

The electric current through the gas gives some energy to the atoms in the gas and this energy gives electrons in the atoms extra energy. When this happens the electrons are said to be 'excited' to higher energy levels and the atoms to be in the 'excited state'.

The atoms in the excited state then tend to return to their original more stable state, giving off their surplus energy. It is this surplus energy that is the radiation given off. In any such light source there are millions of atoms absorbing and emitting energy, yet the emission spectrum consists of a limited number of wavelengths. The reason for this is that, for atoms of a particular element, the electrons can have only a limited number of energy values, known as 'energy levels'. Figure 9.20 illustrates how an electron which has been excited to a higher energy level W_3 may return to its more stable energy level W_0 either in one step or by a number of steps through other permitted energy levels, W_1 and W_2.

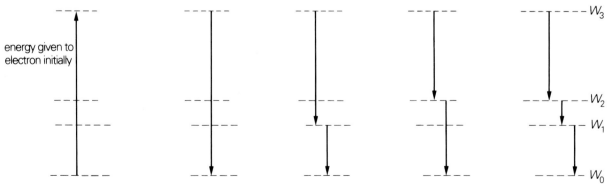

Figure 9.20 Changes in energy levels

The most stable level W_0 is known as the 'ground level'. In the example shown in Figure 9.20, there are four different ways in which the electron can descend from energy level W_3 to the ground level. When an electron descends from one energy level to another, it loses energy and this energy is emitted as a photon of radiation. The energy E of a photon is given by

$E = hf$ where h = Planck's constant
                              f = frequency of the radiation.

Thus, if the electron descends from energy level W_x to W_y the change in energy E is given by

$E = W_x - W_y$

energy of the photon emitted = hf_{xy} where f_{xy} = frequency of the photon

energy of the photon emitted = decrease in the energy of the electron

$$hf_{xy} = W_x - W_y$$
$$\Rightarrow f_{xy} = \frac{W_x - W_y}{h}$$

Figure 9.21 shows the four possible ways in which the electron can descend from level W_3 to W_0 and the frequency of each photon emitted (the higher the wavelength the smaller the frequency).

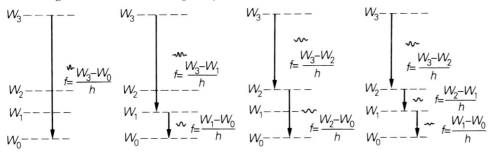

Figure 9.21 Photons of emitted radiation

An electron may descend by one of these ways only, but, with millions of atoms in the light source, electrons in different atoms will descend in different ways and the light emitted will contain the full range of frequencies shown in Figure 9.21. There are six different frequencies in this example. Not all of the frequencies are necessarily in the visible range of the electromagnetic spectrum.

In a line spectrum, the frequency of each radiation corresponds to the frequency of photons emitted by electrons descending between two definite energy levels.

Study of line spectra shows that some lines are brighter than others. This is because the electrons are more likely to occupy some energy levels than others. If in the example illustrated in Figure 9.21, W_1 is an energy level which is less likely to be occupied, the number of atoms in which the electrons descend by steps involving level W_1 will be less. This means that, in the spectrum, the lines produced by these steps would be less bright because there would be fewer photons of the energy corresponding to these steps.

In the example given, the frequencies of the lines that would be less bright if level W_1 is less likely to be occupied are:

$$\frac{W_3 - W_1}{h}; \quad \frac{W_1 - W_0}{h}; \quad \frac{W_2 - W_1}{h}$$

The fact that line spectra are produced by radiations from millions of atoms in the source shows that the permitted energy levels are the same in the many atoms of the element. In fact, these permitted energy levels are a characteristic of an element, and can be used to identify the element. Chemists use this fact to analyse very small samples. The sample is excited by an electric spark or simply by heating in a flame, and the light given off is dispersed to form a spectrum which is photographed. The photograph is compared with those of the spectra of different elements to see which elements are present in the sample.

By studying the spectra produced from the light emitted by stars, astronomers can determine which elements are present in the stars.

When an electron is not attached to an atom, it is said to be at an energy level of zero. When the electron becomes attached to the atom, energy is given off and this means that the energy of the electron is reduced below zero and is, therefore, negative. Since energy levels in an atom are the possible electron energies, energy levels must have negative values.

Example 5

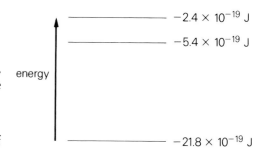

The diagram represents three possible energy levels of an atom of hydrogen.

When the energy of an electron changes from a higher to a lower energy level, a quantum of electromagnetic radiation is emitted. The frequency f of the radiation emitted in a transition between energy levels W_1 and W_2 is given by

$W_2 - W_1 = hf$ where h is Planck's constant.

a) How many lines in the hydrogen spectrum are produced as a result of transitions between the energy levels shown in the diagram?
b) Calculate the wavelength of one of these hydrogen spectrum lines.

$h = 6.63 \times 10^{-34}\,\text{J s}$

a) The possible ways that electrons might descend from the highest energy level to the lowest are shown in the diagram.

This shows that there are three possible changes in energy levels and this means that these changes will produce three lines in the hydrogen spectrum.

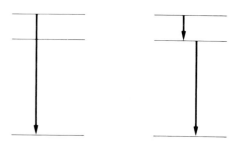

b) For the change from the highest energy level to the lowest,

$$W_2 = -2.4 \times 10^{-19}\,\text{J}$$
$$W_1 = -21.8 \times 10^{-19}\,\text{J}$$
$$h = 6.63 \times 10^{-34}\,\text{J s}$$
$$W_2 - W_1 = hf \quad \text{where } f = \text{frequency of emitted photon}$$
$$\Rightarrow \quad -2.4 \times 10^{-19} - (-21.8 \times 10^{-19}) = 6.63 \times 10^{-34} \times f$$
$$\Rightarrow \quad f = \frac{19.4 \times 10^{-19}}{6.63 \times 10^{-34}}$$
$$\Rightarrow \quad f = 2.93 \times 10^{15}$$
$$v = f \times \lambda$$

For electromagnetic radiation in air $v = 3.0 \times 10^8\,\text{m s}^{-1}$

$$3 \times 10^8 = 2.93 \times 10^{15} \times \lambda$$
$$\Rightarrow \quad \lambda = \frac{3 \times 10^8}{2.93 \times 10^{15}}$$
$$\Rightarrow \quad \lambda = 1.02 \times 10^{-7}\,\text{m}$$

Wavelength of emitted radiation = 1.02×10^{-7} m.

Continuous emission spectra

In a solid, liquid or high-pressure gas, the atoms are much closer than in a normal gas. Under these circumstances, some of the outer electrons in the atoms experience forces from the neighbouring atoms as well as from the nucleus of the atom containing the electrons. At high temperatures the high energy of the atoms combined with these interatomic forces result in some of the electrons being able to take on a wide range of energies rather than being confined to the small number of energy levels within one atom. Since the electrons may now occupy a wide range of energy values, and may therefore undergo a wide range of energy changes, the radiation emitted contains a range of frequencies. In this way, light emitted by hot sources of radiation in which the atoms are relatively close together, contains the range of frequencies that produces a continuous spectrum.

Absorption spectra

White light emitted by a hot source produces a continuous spectrum when viewed through a spectroscope. If the white light is passed through a gas before entering the spectroscope, some dark lines are seen in the spectrum, Figure 9.22. The dark lines show that the gas absorbs some of the light, but only at certain definite frequencies. The spectrum formed in this way is called the absorption spectrum of the gas which absorbed the light.

Figure 9.22 Absorption spectrum of mercury

The frequencies of absorbed light are identical to those in the line emission spectrum of the same gas, Figure 9.23.

The absorption spectrum is a result of photons of energy being absorbed by the atoms and exciting the electrons to higher energy levels. Only those photons with exactly the energy required to excite the electrons are absorbed.

Thus the process that is occurring is the reverse of that described for the production of a line emission spectrum, Figure 9.24.

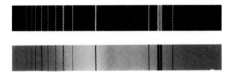

Figure 9.23 Emission and absorption spectra of sodium

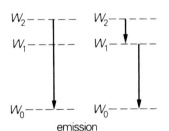
emission

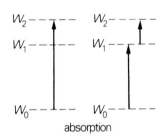
absorption

Figure 9.24 Transitions for line emission and absorption spectra

When an atom has absorbed a photon, it is in the excited state and is likely to return to the stable state by re-emitting the photon. At first sight it might seem that, since the photons are re-emitted, there should be no dark lines and hence no absorption spectrum; yet experiment shows this is not true. The reason for this is that the light beam from which the light is absorbed is directed towards the spectroscope. When the light is re-emitted it is emitted in all directions, and only a small percentage of it will reach the spectroscope.

Absorption spectra can be used to analyse a gas through which light has passed.

Dark lines are observed in the spectrum of light produced from the Sun's rays. These are due to absorption by gases in the outer atmosphere of the Sun and study of these spectra has enabled astronomers to analyse the composition of this outer atmosphere. Similarly, absorption spectra of light which has passed through the atmospheres of some of the planets have produced evidence of the compositions of these atmospheres.

9.4 Lasers

Lasers are one of the more modern applications of physics, of great importance with uses ranging from delicate eye surgery to navigation in aircraft and the guidance of missiles. The absorption of photons, raising electrons to higher energy levels, and the emission of photons when the electrons return to lower energy levels, are important processes in the production of laser beams.

Spontaneous emission of radiation

Different energy levels in atoms have different stabilities. If an electron is raised to an unstable level, it will immediately descend to a lower level with the emission of a photon. On average, the time for which the electron remains in the higher energy level is in the order of a one hundred millionth of a second (10^{-8} s). This is called **spontaneous emission** of radiation.

Stimulated emission of radiation

Other upper energy levels are more stable, and the electron may stay there for a short time before descending. Electrons in these levels may stay there on average for in the order of 1 s, and they are said to be in the metastable state. The length of time for which the electron remains in the higher level varies from one atom to another, and there is no way of predicting how long it will do so. Some may descend just as rapidly as those in unstable energy levels, while others may stay in the higher level for well over 1 s. This can be compared with the process of radioactive decay, when nuclei of radioactive atoms emit radiation. In this case, some atoms will emit radiation immediately while others may remain unchanged for some time.

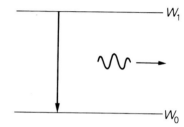

Figure 9.25 Emission of radiation

When an electron is in a relatively stable energy level, it may be 'encouraged' or stimulated to descend to a lower level, Figure 9.25.

If an electron in a higher energy level W_1 falls down to the ground state energy level W_0 a photon of radiation is emitted of frequency f and

$$hf = W_1 - W_0$$

If an atom in the excited state that has an electron in the energy level W_1 receives a photon of energy hf equal to the difference between the energy levels, it causes the electron to descend to the lower energy level with the emission of a photon of the same energy, Figure 9.26. This is called **stimulated emission** of radiation; the first photon stimulates the electron to descend to the lower level, emitting the second photon.

The emitted photon in stimulated emission of radiation has important properties. It is emitted **in phase** with, and **parallel** to the stimulating photon. If this occurs in a substance with a large number of excited atoms, the process starts a chain reaction. Emitted photons become stimulating photons, the number of photons rapidly increases, and the amount of radiation in the beam is amplified. In this way a concentrated beam of photons, all in phase and all moving parallel to each other is produced. This amplification of the beam of photons as a result of the stimulated emission led to the naming of the **laser** which stands for 'Light Amplification by the Stimulated Emission of Radiation'.

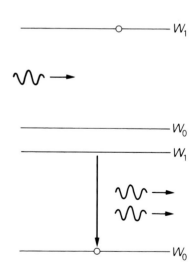

Figure 9.26 Stimulated emission of radiation

Amplification in the laser

In a laser, the substance containing the excited atoms is held in a tube with a mirror at one end and a half-silvered mirror at the other end. The half-silvered

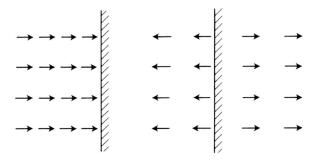

Figure 9.27 Half-silvered mirror

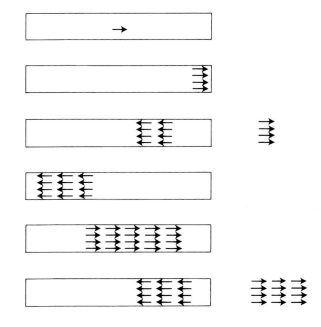

Figure 9.28 Amplification of the radiation

mirror is one with a very thin layer of silvering so that half of the light striking its surface is reflected and half passes through, Figure 9.27.

The light is reflected backwards and forwards between the ends, causing a rapidly increasing number of photons to be produced, Figure 9.28. In this way the intensity of the beam increases until the beam escaping through the half-silvered mirror is very intense.

Since the light travels at a speed of over $2 \times 10^8 \, \mathrm{m \, s^{-1}}$ through the material in the laser tube, this build-up takes well under a ten millionth of a second. The transmitted light is the laser beam consisting of a narrow, parallel beam of photons which are all in phase. The fact that the photons are all in phase results in the laser delivering high energy, since all the photons reinforce each other. The fact that all the photons move parallel to each other results in another important laser property that the beam does not spread out and does not, therefore, decrease in intensity over large distances.

Exciting the atoms

In a laser, the photons of light have energy exactly equal to the difference between two permitted energy levels in the atoms of the substance. When a photon meets one of these atoms, one of two things may happen.

If the atom is in the ground state, the photon of light may be absorbed, resulting in an electron being raised to the higher energy level. Whenever this happens, a photon is absorbed and the intensity of the beam is decreased, Figure 9.29.

If the atom is already in the excited state, the photon of light may stimulate the emission of a second photon, causing the electron to descend to the ground state. Whenever this happens, there is an increase in the number of photons and hence in the intensity of the beam, Figure 9.30.

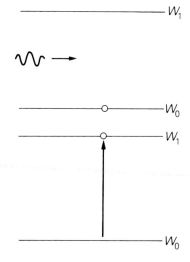

Figure 9.29 Absorption of radiation

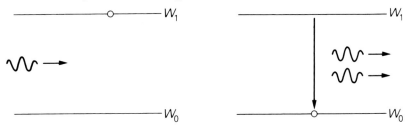

Figure 9.30 Stimulated emission

If the laser is to amplify the radiation, there must be a greater number of photons meeting excited atoms than meeting atoms in the ground state. If this is so, the amplification of radiation by stimulated emission will be greater than the decrease in radiation by the absorption of photons.

One way of exciting electrons from energy level W_0 to energy level W_1 would be to radiate the atoms with light of frequency f so that

$hf = W_1 - W_0$.

This is not a practical way of creating large numbers of atoms in the excited state, because these photons are also of the correct energy to stimulate the electrons to descend back to the lower energy level. Other ways of building up the number of excited atoms are needed, and different methods are used with different laser materials.

The ruby laser

Artificial ruby is one material used in lasers. The ruby is illuminated with flashes of yellow-green light from a flash tube surrounding the ruby rod. The photons of this light have the correct energy to excite the electrons in the ruby atoms to a higher energy level W_2. This is an unstable energy level, and the electrons immediately descend to a lower energy level W_1 between W_2 and the ground state energy level W_0. In this way a large number of atoms with electrons in energy level W_1 is built up, and these are the excited atoms necessary for the production of the laser beam.

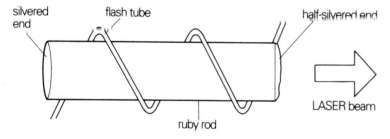

Figure 9.31 Ruby laser

In the ruby laser, a rod of artificial ruby is surrounded by a flash tube. The mirrors are made by silvering the ends of the rod, one end with a thick layer of silver to provide total reflection, and the other end with a thin layer to provide partial reflection, Figure 9.31. A flash of light from the flash tube provides a population of excited atoms in the ruby rod, Figure 9.32.

Some of the atoms will emit photons by spontaneous emission. These photons will then go on to cause stimulated emission in other excited atoms, and the laser process takes place. Photons which are not moving parallel to the sides of the rod will soon pass through the sides of the rod. Only beams of photons which are moving parallel to the sides will continue to move to and fro between the mirrors, without being lost.

In this way a pulse of radiation results from the population of excited atoms produced by the flash of light from the surrounding tube. Another flash of light from the tube starts the process again. The ruby laser is a pulsed laser, producing a large number of pulses of radiation.

The helium-neon laser

In a helium-neon laser, a mixture of the two inert gases helium and neon, at a very low pressure, is held in a sealed glass tube with two electrodes in contact

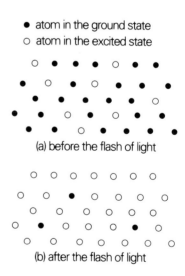

Figure 9.32 Excitation of the atoms

with the gases. When a high voltage is placed across these electrodes, a current flows through the gases producing light. This is the way in which the more familiar neon lights work. This flow of electricity through the gases produces ions (charged particles produced by removing electrons from atoms) and atoms in excited energy states. When helium atoms which have been excited to a metastable state collide with neon atoms, they transfer energy to electrons in the neon atoms. In this way a population of excited neon atoms is produced, and the laser action can take place.

The power of the laser

The power output of lasers can range from 0.1 mW to several million watts. The effectiveness of the laser results largely from its ability to deliver energy in a concentrated form. This can be demonstrated by considering the intensity of radiation delivered by a 100 W bulb with that delivered by a 0.1 mW laser at a range of 1 m.

If the light from the 100 W light bulb is radiated in all directions, at a range of 1 m the power output will be spread over an area represented by a sphere of radius 1 m. The surface area of such a sphere is approximately 12 m², Figure 9.33.

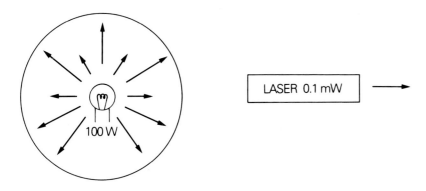

Figure 9.33 Light bulb and laser

$$\text{intensity} = \frac{\text{power}}{\text{area}}$$

$$= \frac{100}{12}$$

$$= 8.3$$

At a range of 1 m the light intensity delivered by a 100 W bulb is about 8 W m^{-2}.

The radiation from a laser is in a parallel beam which is very narrow and has a cross section in the order of 1 mm². Since it is parallel, the laser beam does not spread out, and the energy is just as concentrated 1 m from the source, as it is very close to the source. For a 0.1 mW laser with a beam of cross-section 1 mm²

$$\text{power} = 0.1 \times 10^{-3} \, \text{W}$$
$$\text{area} = 1 \times 10^{-6} \, \text{m}^2$$
$$\text{intensity} = \frac{0.1 \times 10^{-3}}{1 \times 10^{-6}}$$
$$= 10^2 \, \text{W m}^{-2}$$

At a range of 1 m the light intensity delivered by a 0.1 mW laser is about 100 W m^{-2}.

The laser is using one millionth of the power of the light bulb, but, at a range of 1 m, delivers ten times the intensity of light.

Safety with lasers

The properties of lasers which make them useful in a wide range of applications also contribute to the dangers that can result from their use. The laser supplies a concentrated beam of light, in which the photons are in phase. The energy of this light is capable of burning and, if it should enter the eye it will damage the sensitive material at the back of the eye. For this reason, even with the least powerful lasers, the laser beam should never be allowed to shine directly into the eye. Care should also be taken to ensure that the beam is not reflected into the eye. Operators should always wear laser safety goggles to reduce the intensity of the laser beam should it happen to be directed towards the eye. The goggles act in much the same way as sun glasses in that they only allow a very small part of the light to pass through, Figure 9.34.

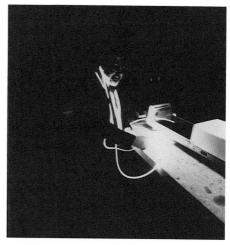

Figure 9.34 Safety goggles with a laser

9.5 Uses of lasers

Lasers in medicine

Lasers can be used by surgeons to perform very delicate operations. The fact that the laser beam can be very concentrated means that it can be used to deliver energy to a very small area. An example of such use is in operations on the inside of the eye. Where the sensitive lining in the back of the eye comes adrift from the inside of the eyeball, a laser can be used to fuse the retina back in place. The

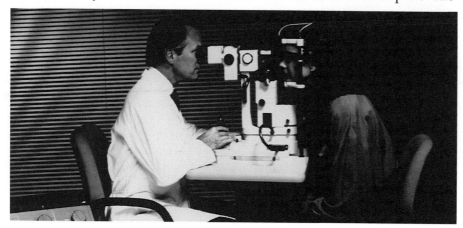

Figure 9.35 Photograph of surgeon operating on eye

beauty of this operation is that it can be carried out inside the eye without having to cut into the eye. The laser beam can be directed through the lens into the eye, to supply the energy needed to fuse the retina into place. Another similar use is in treating burst blood vessels on the inside lining of the eye. The heat from laser light directed onto such blood vessels seals them and prevents further bleeding, Figure 9.35.

Another example of the use of lasers in carrying out delicate surgery is in operations inside the body using an endoscope. Since a laser beam is a beam of light, it can be directed along an optical fibre. An endoscope is a bundle of optical fibres and controls, less than 1 cm across.

It can be fed into a patient via the mouth and throat, and directed through the internal vessels to the area where surgery is needed. The controls are used to guide and direct the fibres inside the body of the patient. Ordinary light fed through the optical fibres illuminates the inside of the body and reflected light

Figure 9.36 An endoscope

transmitted back through other fibres allows the surgeon to see inside the patient. When the endoscope reaches the diseased part inside the patient, the surgeon sends pulses of laser light down a separate optical fibre system. The energy of the beam is sufficient to cut away diseased parts. Such operations avoid having to cut open the patient to reach the diseased areas; therefore much less damage is caused and recovery time after the operation is considerably reduced.

Not all medical use of lasers is for internal operations. Laser light of different colours is absorbed in different amounts by different colours of skin. Laser light of a colour absorbed by coloured skin can be used to burn off birthmarks, warts and tattoos from the skin. Since the laser light does not penetrate the skin, only a thin layer of skin is burnt off, and it is quickly replaced by new skin growing over the area.

Lasers and metals

The ability of a laser to deliver a concentrated beam of energy has several uses in engineering when working with metal. A high-powered laser beam provides a very efficient cutting tool which will cut through thick pieces of metal. It has the added advantage over more traditional cutting tools and drills that it does not throw up pieces of metal as it cuts, Figure 9.37.

Figure 9.37 Photographs of laser and drill cutting

As well as cutting metal, lasers can be used to join pieces of metal together by welding. The heat produced by the concentrated laser beam is used to melt the edges of two pieces of metal in contact with each other. When the metal is allowed to cool, it solidifies and the two pieces of metal are welded together, Figure 9.38.

Another use of lasers in treating metal is the hardening of metal. If the surface of a metal is heated with a high power laser and then rapidly cooled, the surface is hardened. This makes it more resistant to wear and tear, and is useful for metal used to make moving parts of machinery.

The laser and other materials

Lasers are not only used for cutting metal where high power is needed. The laser beam is easily manipulated, either by moving the laser, by reflecting it with mirrors or by directing it down flexible optical fibres. The beam can be moved easily and with great precision by computer controlled mirrors or optical fibres. An example of such use is in the clothing trade. Lasers are used to cut several layers of cloth to a pattern. An added benefit is that the laser beam cuts the cloth with a neat edge. The heat from the laser seals off the cloth. This makes the cloth less likely to fray than cloth cut by scissors.

Similar benefits are obtained by using lasers for cutting other materials such as plastics.

Figure 9.38 Photograph of welding by laser

The laser as a distance measuring instrument

The laser beam is used in the measurement of great distances. Light travels at a speed of $3 \times 10^8 \, \text{m s}^{-1}$. If the time taken for a laser beam to travel to a certain object is measured, the distance to that object can be calculated using the equation

distance = speed × time

Perhaps the most spectacular example of this is in the measurement of the distance to the Moon. Apollo II astronauts placed a mirror on the Moon. Scientists are able to shine a laser beam onto this mirror and time how long it takes the light to travel to the Moon and back, Figure 9.39. Using this method, they have been able to calculate the distance to the Moon to an accuracy of 5 cm. It is the fact that the laser beam is perfectly parallel that enables it to travel such great distances without spreading out and becoming too faint to be detected.

Meteorologists are able to measure the height of clouds by reflecting laser beams off the water droplets in the clouds. Inspectors can monitor the smoke output of factory chimneys by reflecting laser beams off the smoke. Surveyors use laser beams when measuring distances on the Earth's surface, by reflecting the beam off conveniently placed mirrors.

As well as measuring these very large distances, lasers are used in the measurement of very small distances. If a laser beam is split by mirrors, the two parts of the beam can be brought together again to form an interference pattern, Figure 9.40.

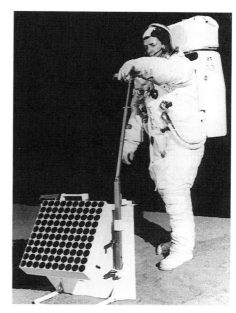

Figure 9.39 Mirror on the Moon for reflecting a laser beam

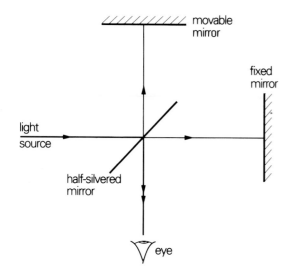

Figure 9.40 Interferometer

If one of the mirrors is then moved a very small distance, this can cause a change in the interference pattern which can be used to measure distances in the order of 10^{-5} m. One use of this method is in measuring small shifts in the surface of the Earth, a valuable aid in monitoring and predicting earthquakes.

Military uses of lasers

Lasers have a wide and increasing range of uses in weaponry and guidance systems. Their use for measuring distances makes them useful rangefinders for setting missiles and guns on target. Targets can be pinpointed by laser beams. If the laser beam is directed onto the target, detectors on a missile can pick up the reflected laser light and home in on the target. Not only can lasers be used to direct and aim other weapons, they can be powerful weapons in themselves. The concentrated energy in a laser beam can be enough to shoot down missiles or aircraft.

Lasers in communications

Information can be transmitted by directing laser beams along optical fibres. This has a number of advantages over radio and telephone. The laser beam is confined to the optical fibre until it reaches the receiver. The only way to tap into the signal is to cut the fibre; this is immediately detectable, making it a much safer method of sending confidential information than the radio or the telephone which can be 'tapped'.

In order to transmit information using a laser beam, sound, electronic output from a computer or T.V. signals are converted into electric signals which control pulses sent out by the laser. At the receiving end, these pulses of laser light are converted back into electrical signals which then reproduce the original signal at the other end.

Optical fibres are much cheaper to make than telephone wires, and a single fibre is capable of carrying much more information than a telephone wire.

In space, where there are no clouds or objects to get in the way, lasers are used for communicating with astronauts and for sending control signals to the equipment contained in the satellites.

Lasers in the future

Lasers have many and varied uses. It is likely that scientists will continue to find further uses for the laser. One exciting development is in the field of nuclear fusion. If hydrogen nuclei are made to fuse together, vast amounts of energy are released. This is the power which makes the hydrogen bomb such an awesome weapon. The difficulty in using this potentially great source of energy is the problem of controlling it and the fact that large amounts of energy are required to start the fusion process. Scientists are experimenting with controlled thermonuclear explosions, using lasers to produce the high temperatures needed to start the fusion process.

9.6 Semiconductors

Conductors, semiconductors and insulators

If a potential difference is set up across a conductor, a current will flow in the conductor. If a potential difference is set up across an insulator, no current will flow.

However, if the potential difference across the insulator is increased sufficiently, a point will be reached where the insulation breaks down and a current will flow. A dramatic example of this is lightning, Figure 9.41. Air is an insulator, but friction on the clouds can build up the potential difference between earth and the cloud sufficiently for a current to flow as shown by a flash of lightning.

Generally speaking, conductors are substances which require only a small potential difference across them to cause a current to flow, while insulators are substances which do not normally allow a current to flow unless very high potential differences develop across them.

A group of substances, called **semiconductors**, fall into a category between conductors and insulators. When a potential difference is set up across a semiconductor, a current will flow but this current will be less than for the same potential difference across a conductor of the same dimensions, Figure 9.42.

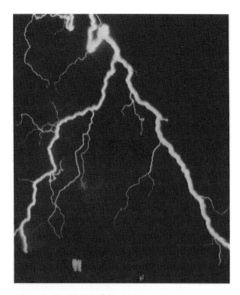

Figure 9.41 Lightning

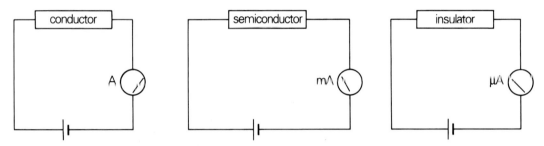

Figure 9.42 Conductors, semiconductors and insulators

What determines whether a substance is a good conductor, a semiconductor or an insulator is the ease with which the electrons in the substance can be made to move. In a good conductor, the outer electrons in the atoms of the substance are easily removed from the atom. A potential difference placed across the conductor will result in these easily moved electrons moving towards the more positive end of the conductor, and a flow of current is produced. In a semiconductor, more energy is required to release the outer electrons from the atom, and this means that the current flow produced is less than in a conductor. In insulators, the electrons are tightly bound to the atoms and only very high potential differences can release the electrons to produce a current flow.

Comparison of the resistance of conductors, semiconductors and insulators can be made by measuring the resistance of samples of different materials. Since the resistance depends on the length of the sample and the area of cross section, then samples used must be of the same dimensions. Table 1 shows some typical resistances of samples of different substances of length 1 m and area of cross section 0.01 mm^2.

conductor	resistance (Ω)	semiconductor	resistance (Ω)	insulator	resistance (Ω)
copper	1.72	carbon	3.5×10^3	glass	1.0×10^{20}
steel	20	germanium	6.0×10^7	wood	1.0×10^{18}
nichrome	100	silicon	2.3×10^{11}	sulphur	1.0×10^{23}

Table 1

In a semiconductor there are electrons that are relatively free to move, allowing current to flow when a potential difference across the semiconductor sets up an electric field in it. Additions of very small amounts of certain impurities can increase the conductivity of the semiconductor. For example, the addition of 1 part of the impurity arsenic to 10^{10} parts of the semiconductor germanium increases its conductivity greatly. The reason for this is based on the electronic structure of the atoms of the two substances.

The germanium atoms form a lattice structure bonded together by a sharing of their outer electrons. Each germanium atom has four outer electrons which take part in the bonding, so that each atom is linked to four neighbouring atoms, Figure 9.43.

While all of the electrons are bound in this way, the energy required to release them is not very great, and an electric field in the semiconductor will release some of them to flow as an electric current. The introduction of a minute quantity of arsenic greatly increases the conductivity, because it increases the number of electrons which are free to move. The arsenic atom has five outer electrons. When it replaces a germanium atom in the lattice, only four of these electrons are used to bond to neighbouring atoms, and the fifth outer electron is easily removed by an electric field. Thus the conductivity is increased by the availability of free electrons which can be made to flow by the application of an electric field. A semiconductor which has its conductivity increased by the addition of a small amount of impurity is said to have been **doped**. When the doping increases the conductivity by releasing electrons, which are negatively charged, the semiconductor is called an **n-type semiconductor**.

Doping a semiconductor with an impurity which has only three outer electrons in each atom can also increase the conductivity. For example, germanium can be doped with gallium. The gallium atom has only three outer electrons to bond with the four neighbouring germanium atoms in the lattice. Thus one of the four bonds is not complete, but an electron from another germanium atom can easily be moved in to complete this bond. The germanium atom that has lost an electron in this way can then readily accept an electron from its neighbour and the process is repeated. In this way, atoms with only three outer electrons act as if they are short of electrons and are called **positive holes**. When an electric field is applied, electrons are made to move into these holes and the effect is that the hole moves in the opposite direction to the movement of the electrons as if a positive charge is flowing towards the negative side of the electric field, Figure 9.44.

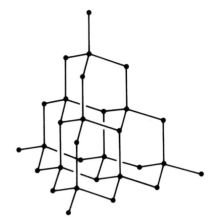

Figure 9.43 Model of a germanium lattice

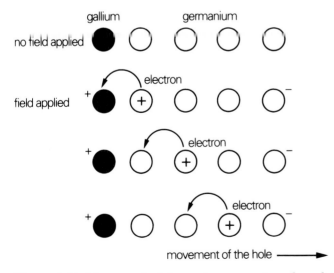

Figure 9.44 Movement of charge in germanium doped with gallium

The apparent effect of the movement of electrons through a semiconductor doped with an impurity with less outer electrons than the semiconductor is the movement of positive holes. A semiconductor in which this occurs is called a **p-type semiconductor**.

When the temperature of a semiconductor is increased, the heat energy excites the atoms so that more electrons are released, creating pairs of electrons and positive holes. This increase in the number of charge carriers decreases the resistance of the semiconductor.

p-n junctions

A semiconductor diode consists of a small semiconductor, part of which is n-type and part p-type. The boundary between the two types is called a junction. The effect of such a junction can be demonstrated by the experiments illustrated in Figure 9.45.

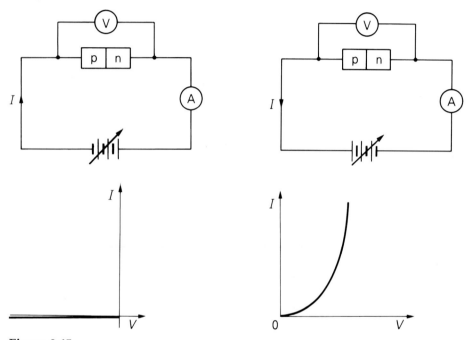

Figure 9.45

The results of these two experiments can be summarised as in Figure 9.46.

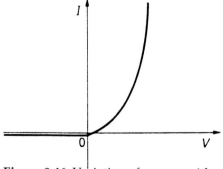

Figure 9.46 Variation of current with potential difference across a p-n junction

The p-n junction is a good conductor when the p-type semiconductor is more positive than the n-type. In this case the junction is said to be **forward-biased**. When the p-type is more negative than the n-type, the junction is a poor conductor, allowing a negligible current to flow, and the junction is said to be

reverse-biased. The overall effect is that the p-n junction allows current to flow in one direction only. A device which allows current to flow in one direction only is called a **diode**, and this type of diode is called a **junction diode**, Figure 9.47.

The p-type semiconductor conducts mainly by the movement of positive holes while the n-type conducts by the movement of electrons. In a junction between the two types, free electrons from the n-type cross the boundary and occupy positive holes in the p-type. This creates a layer at the junction where the effective availability of charge carriers is depleted. This is called the **depletion layer**. The movement of the charge carriers between the n-type and the p-type semiconductor sets up a small potential difference, called the junction voltage, across the depletion layer. The junction voltage is about 0.1 V for germanium and 0.6 V for silicon.

When the junction is reverse biased, the applied voltage is in the same direction as the junction voltage, increasing its effect, and widening the depletion layer. In this state the junction will not conduct.

When the junction is forward biased, the applied voltage opposes the junction voltage, reducing the width of the depletion layer. When the applied voltage exceeds the junction voltage, the charge carriers are able to cross the junction and the junction conducts.

The p-n junction diode is one of the basic electronic components. Its main use is in the rectification of alternating current, based on its property of only allowing an appreciable current to flow in one direction, Figure 9.48.

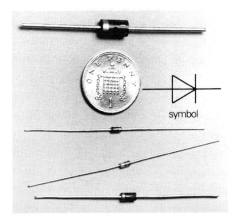

Figure 9.47 Junction diodes

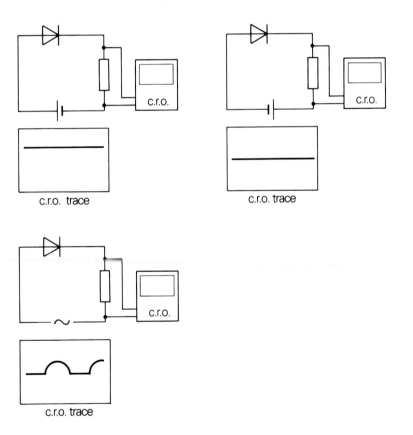

Figure 9.48 Rectification of a p-n junction diode

Rectification converts alternating current, which flows alternately in two directions, into direct current which flows in one direction only. While a simple diode converts alternating current into direct current, the current still varies between 0 and the peak value.

Often, when supplying direct current, a steady current is required. A capacitor can be used to reduce the variations of the current. The capacitor used to reduce the variations in current is called a **smoothing capacitor**. The capacitor is connected in parallel across the load in the circuit, Figure 9.49.

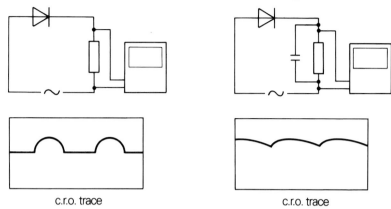

c.r.o. trace   c.r.o. trace

Figure 9.49

Light emitting diodes

When a current flows in a forward-biased junction diode, electrons are continually combining with and being separated from positive holes. Energy is required to separate the electrons from positive holes. This energy is supplied by the power supply which sets up the potential difference across the diode. When an electron combines with a positive hole, a photon of energy is released. In a light emitting diode, the energy W of this photon is such that its frequency f falls in the range of the frequencies of visible light, given by the equation:

$$W = hf$$

In this way, a current flowing through this diode causes electrons and positive holes continually to recombine, giving off photons: the diode gives off light. Whether or not a diode emits light when forward biased depends on the semiconductor from which the diode is made, and on the impurity with which it is doped.

Example 6

In a junction diode, made from the semiconductor gallium arsenide phosphide, the energy released when an electron combines with a positive hole is 2.8×10^{-19} J. Calculate whether this diode is a light emitting diode.

Energy of photon released is given by $W = hf$

$\Rightarrow$ $\qquad\qquad\qquad 2.8 \times 10^{-19} = 6.6 \times 10^{-34} \times f$

$\Rightarrow$ $\qquad\qquad\qquad\qquad f = \dfrac{2.8 \times 10^{-19}}{6.6 \times 10^{-34}}$

$\Rightarrow$ $\qquad\qquad\qquad\qquad f = 4.2 \times 10^{14}$ Hz

This frequency is the frequency of red light, which means that the diode will emit red light when it is forward biased.

The diode is a light emitting diode.

Light emitting diodes are often used for digital displays on electronic equipment, Figure 9.50. They have the advantage over normal light bulbs that they require very little energy to cause them to light; choice of the right semiconductor and doping impurities can give different colours, as required.

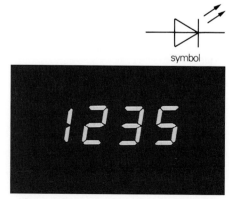

symbol

Figure 9.50 Light emitting diodes in digital displays

Photodiodes

Common practice has been to use a light dependent resistor (LDR) for the measurement of intensity of light. An LDR is normally constructed of cadmium sulphide whose electrical resistance varies with the intensity of light falling on the material. Modern practice is now to use a photodiode having a p-n junction.

Figure 9.51 shows an example of a photodiode and the symbol used to represent it. The p-n junction is connected in the **reverse bias** in a circuit; if no light is falling on the junction, there is negligible current in the circuit. With an increase in the light falling on the p-n junction, this **leakage** current from the n-type layer to the p-type layer increases in direct proportion to the intensity of the light.

symbol

Figure 9.51 Photodiode

The photons of light cause electrons to be released in the depletion layer of the junction; this has the effect of changing the number of positive holes and electrons in the p-type and n-type layers on either side of the depletion layer, so creating more charge carriers. The device is then said to be in the **photoconductive mode**.

Because the leakage current depends only on the number of charge carriers created, this current is independent of the voltage across the diode. The creation of charge carriers in a photodiode by the light falling on it is virtually instantaneous.

This device therefore has immense advantages over the LDR in that variations of current with light intensity are also instantaneous. The photodiode may be regarded as an extremely fast electrical switch. As such, the device, connected in a reverse bias circuit, finds many uses in high speed timing applications. It is also used for measuring the intensity of light in the light meter of a camera where a cell is required for other purposes such as automatic focusing.

One of the most significant developments is the use of the device in fibre optics applied to telecommunications. Here a digital light signal containing the message is sent along an extremely thin glass fibre. The message itself is secure because the signals produce no electromagnetic field and any break in the fibre is immediately detectable.

The photovoltaic cell

In this device, no outside source of electricity is required. The photovoltaic cell contains photodiodes; light falls on the p-n junction of these and produces an e.m.f. in the circuit. The p-type layer of the junction is thin enough to allow light energy to reach the junction. The light energy separates electrons from atoms in the depletion layer, creating positive holes in the p-type side and extra electrons in the n-type side. Thus a potential difference is set up across the cell; if a circuit is connected between its sides, a current will flow from the n-type to the p-type layer. The photodiode used is said to be in the **photovoltaic mode**.

Photovoltaic cells are used to convert sunlight to electrical energy. Solar powered calculators, Figure 9.52, use such cells to avoid the need for batteries. On a larger scale, the solar panels on satellites, Figure 9.53, are constructed of a number of photovoltaic cells which convert the energy from the Sun's rays into electrical energy to power the electrical and electronic equipment in the satellites.

Figure 9.52 Solar calculator

Figure 9.53 Satellite solar panels

Summary

The intensity of illumination of a surface is the amount of light energy falling on one square metre of the surface in one second, and is measured in watts per square metre ($W\,m^{-2}$).

The intensity of illumination on a surface is given by

$$I = Nhf$$

where N = number of photons per second per unit area
h = Planck's constant
I = intensity of light on the surface

The Inverse Square Law states that the intensity I produced on a surface by a point source of light is inversely proportional to the square of the distance d between the surface and the light source.
This can be written

$$Id^2 = \text{a constant.}$$

The photoelectric effect is demonstrated by the fact that ultraviolet light discharges a negatively charged zinc plate on an electroscope.

Electromagnetic radiation is made up of photons of wave energy and the energy E of a single photon of light is given by:

$$E = h \times f \qquad \text{where } h = \text{Planck's constant}$$
$$f = \text{frequency of the radiation.}$$

In the photoelectric effect the maximum kinetic energy of an emitted electron is given by:

$$E_{\max} = qV_0 \qquad \text{where } V_0 = \text{stopping potential}$$
$$q = \text{charge on an electron.}$$

In the photoelectric effect, the minimum frequency of

radiation required to eject an electron from the metal is given by:

$$E_{min} = hf_0 \qquad \text{where } f_0 = \text{threshold frequency}$$
$$h = \text{Planck's constant.}$$

A line emission spectrum consists of lines of specific frequencies of light. Each frequency corresponds to the energy of a photon equal to the energy emitted by an electron descending from one permitted energy level to another.

For an electron descending from energy level W_x to W_y the frequency f_{xy} of the emitted photon is given by:

$$f_{xy} = \frac{W_x - W_y}{h}$$

An absorption spectrum is formed when white light is passed through a gas or vapour and lines of specific frequencies of light are absorbed. Each frequency absorbed corresponds to the energy of a photon equal to the energy of an electron ascending from one permitted energy level to another.

In a laser, the light beam gains more energy by stimulated emission than it loses by absorption.

In stimulated emission, the incident radiation and the emitted radiation are in phase and travel in the same direction.

Materials can be divided into three broad categories according to their electrical properties: conductors, insulators and semiconductors.

Adding atoms of another element to a pure semiconductor increases its conductivity. This process is called **doping**.

The conductivity of a semiconductor increases with temperature rise.

In a light emitting diode (LED), positive and negative charge carriers recombine to give quanta of radiation.

In a photodiode, the action of light on the p–n junction causes electrons to be released in the depletion layer. This changes the leakage current in a reverse bias circuit in proportion to the intensity of illumination.

A photovoltaic cell is a p-n junction which can convert light energy into electrical energy. When light falls on the junction, an e.m.f. is set up across the cell.

Problems

1 A light meter gives a reading of 64 units when placed 1 metre from a small light source.
What readings would it give at distances of **a)** 80 cm **b)** 40 cm?

2 A set of readings I on a light meter at various distances d from a point source of light is shown in the table.

I/units	15	48	116	249	442	761
d/cm	114	64	41	28	21	16

Using these results, develop a relationship between I and d.

3 A boy decides to raise the lamp above his work table from 1 m to 2 m above the surface.

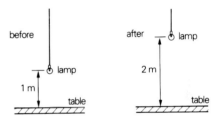

How does the new intensity of light at the surface of the table compare with the original value?

4 An experimenter investigated the effect of shining different electromagnetic radiations on the polished zinc plates of charged electroscopes. He found that ultraviolet radiation discharged the negatively charged electroscope but not the positively charged electroscope. Visible radiation, no matter how bright, did not discharge any electroscope.

a) How does this experimental evidence support the following statements?

   i) The process by which the ultraviolet radiation discharges the electroscope is not the ionization of the surrounding air.

   ii) Whether or not the electroscope is discharged does not depend on the total amount of energy supplied by the electromagnetic radiation.

b) What is the name of the 'effect' by which ultraviolet radiation can eject electrons from zinc?

c) For which theory did this effect provide strong support?

5 For a certain metal, the energy required to eject an electron from an atom is 3.3×10^{-19} J.

a) What is the minimum frequency of electromagnetic radiation required to produce the photoelectric effect with this metal?

b) Would the photoelectric effect occur when this metal is illuminated with light of:

   i) frequency 4×10^{14} Hz;   **ii)** wavelength 5×10^{-7} m?

(Planck's constant $= 6.63 \times 10^{-34}$ J s)

6 Radiation from various lamps is directed at a clean zinc plate in the apparatus shown below.

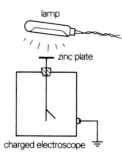

The results of these experiments are summarised in the table below.

	positively charged electroscope	negatively charged electroscope
ultra-violet lamp	(1) remains charged	(4) is discharged
yellow lamp	(2) remains charged	(5) remains charged
infra-red lamp	(3) remains charged	(6) remains charged

i) Explain why the electroscope is discharged in case (4) but not in case (1)

ii) Explain why the electroscope is not discharged in cases (5) and (6).

SEB

7 Energy level diagrams for two atoms A and B are shown to the same scale.

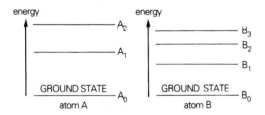

Electrons are excited to levels A_2 and B_3.
Explain which transition, in which atom, would give rise to the emission of radiation with

a) the shortest wavelength;

b) the longest wavelength.

SEB

8 The diagram represents four possible energy levels of an atom of a metal.

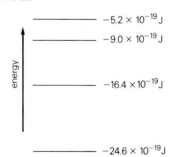

a) How many lines in the spectrum of this metal are produced as the result of transitions between the energy levels shown in the diagram?

b) Calculate the wavelengths of the spectrum lines representing the greatest and the least energy transitions.

(Planck's constant $= 6.63 \times 10^{-34}$ J s)

9 How does the line emission spectrum of an element compare with its absorption spectrum?

10 A beam of ultraviolet radiation falls on a suitable metal plate Y, which lies on the axis of a hollow metal cylinder X. X and Y are connected in an electric circuit including a battery and a milliammeter as shown in the diagram.

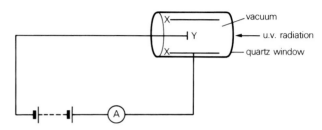

a) Explain why a small current is registered.

b) What would happen to the current if the intensity of the light were increased?

SEB

11 The diagram shows part of the emission spectrum of an element.

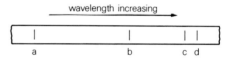

Light of frequency corresponding to each of the above spectral lines is allowed to strike a metal plate in turn and in some cases electrons are ejected from the metal.

i) Light from which of the above spectral lines is most likely to eject electrons from the plate? Give a reason for your answer.

ii) Light of frequency 5.08×10^{14} Hz, corresponding to one of the above lines, can eject electrons with a kinetic energy of 0.45×10^{-19} J from the metal plate. How much energy is required just to release electrons from the metal?

iii) Show whether light of frequency 4.29×10^{14} Hz, corresponding to line c, is capable of ejecting electrons from the metal.

(Planck's constant $h = 6.63 \times 10^{-34}$ J s)

SEB

12 In Planck's Quantum Theory of Light, the energy E of a quantum of light (photon) is given by the equation $E = hf$ where f is its frequency and h is Planck's constant, the value of which is 6.63×10^{-34} J s. The minimum energy required to eject an electron from a certain metal is 3.00×10^{-19} J. Explain whether you would expect light of wavelength 5.00×10^{-7} m to eject electrons from the metal. What is the name given to this phenomenon?

SEB

13 Certain metals are observed to emit electrons when irradiated with ultraviolet light. (The photoelectric effect.)

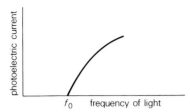

a) The graph indicates that there is no photoelectric current if the frequency of the light is below a certain value f_0. How can this be explained?

b) Discuss **briefly** the consequences of the interpretation of the photoelectric effect on the theory of the nature of light held at the time of its discovery.

SEB

14 a) Explain what is meant by the photoelectric effect. Indicate how it depends on
  i) the frequency of the light;
  ii) the intensity of the light.
  Explain how your answers to **i)** and **ii)** are related to a theory of the nature of light.

b) A clean zinc plate is mounted in an ionization chamber, just below a wire mesh as shown below. The chamber is connected in series with a d.c. supply and a sensitive current meter. The current meter amplifies any small current in the circuit by a factor of 10^6 and displays the amplified current on a microammeter. The zinc plate is illuminated by an ultraviolet lamp.

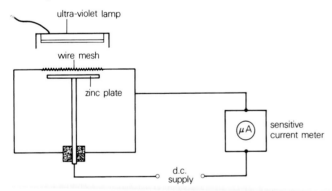

Describe how you would use the apparatus to show that any small current in the circuit was due to the photoelectric effect.

SEB

15 Describe how stimulated emission takes place in a laser.

16 Explain the function of the half-silvered mirrors at the ends of a laser.

17 Explain why a laser beam from a 1 mW laser would be harmful if it entered the eye whereas the light from a 150 watt bulb is safe.

18 Describe one medical and one industrial use of lasers.

19 The diagram below shows a new technique for removing a deposit of fat blocking an artery leading to the heart.
Laser light is transmitted along an optical fibre inserted into the artery as shown.
The energy of this light heats up a tiny metal probe to a temperature sufficiently high to vaporise the fatty deposit.

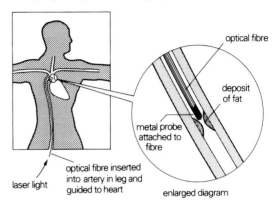

The light from the 8 W argon laser used is of 490 nm wavelength.
a) If the metal probe has a mass of 2.5×10^{-4} kg and specific heat capacity 441 J kg^{-1} K^{-1}, calculate the time required to supply a pulse of energy necessary to raise its temperature from body temperature of 37° C up to 400° C.
(Assume that all the light energy is given as heat to the probe.)

b) Calculate how many photons are required to provide this pulse of energy from the 8 W laser.
(energy of a photon, $E = hf$)

SEB

20 Describe how pure silicon is treated to increase its conductivity.

21 Explain why a rise in temperature increases the conductivity of a semiconductor.

22 Describe how a depletion layer is formed across the p-n junction.

23 Explain what is meant by doping and state which elements would be suitable for producing n-type and p-type silicon.

24 A slab of p-type material is connected to a battery. Describe how conduction takes place in the material.

25 Explain how a semiconductor diode rectifies alternating current.

26 Draw a typical current against voltage graph for a silicon diode.

27 With the aid of a diagram describe the construction of a photodiode and describe what happens to the junction when light falls on it.

28 Draw the circuit of a light meter using a light dependent resistor. Explain how it operates.
What is the difference between this type of light meter and a photovoltaic cell instrument?

10 Radioactivity

10.1 Introduction

At the beginning of the nineteenth century John Dalton put forward a theory which assumed that matter consisted of solid indivisible particles called atoms. At the start of the twentieth century, experimental evidence had suggested the existence of even smaller particles. It was recognized that atoms contain positive and negative charges; J.J. Thomson suggested a model in which the positive charge is distributed evenly throughout the volume of the atom with negative charges fixed at various points, like 'currants in a plum pudding'. On the basis of this model, a stream of charged particles fired at the atom would be deflected through only fairly small angles.

In 1908 Geiger and Marsden, two assistants of Ernest Rutherford, started to investigate the deflection of alpha particles which they fired at a thin metal foil, Figure 10.2.

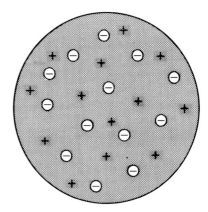

Figure 10.1 Model of the atom suggested by J.J. Thomson

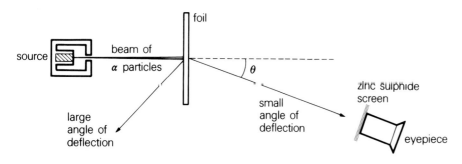

Figure 10.2

In 1909 they made the surprising discovery that a few of the particles bounced back from the foil. When Geiger reported to Rutherford, he expressed his surprise by saying that 'it was almost as incredible as if you had fired a 15-inch shell at a piece of tissue paper and it came back and hit you'.

Rutherford showed that these results could only be explained if the positive charge was concentrated into a very small volume. Making this assumption Rutherford applied the rules of electrostatic force between charges and predicted the number of particles which would be deflected along a given direction.

Geiger and Marsden then tested Rutherford's theory using the apparatus shown in Figure 10.3.

In the experiments, a beam of alpha particles from a radon source was fired at a metal foil. After deflection the particles were observed through the eyepiece which was set at different positions round the rotating table. The presence of the alpha particles was detected by a zinc sulphide screen. Every time an alpha particle hit the screen, a minute flash of light (a scintillation) was seen through the microscope. By counting the number of flashes, it was possible to determine the number of particles arriving at the screen. The screen could be moved to detect alpha particles which had been deflected at various angles. The chamber was evacuated to prevent the absorption of the particles by the air.

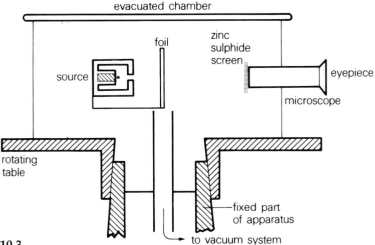

Figure 10.3

In his theory Rutherford predicted four factors upon which the number of particles hitting the zinc sulphide screen would depend.

1   the magnitude of the positive charge on the nucleus
2   the angle of deflection θ
3   the velocity of the particles
4   the thickness of the metal foil.

The experimental results confirmed that these four factors determined the number of particles hitting the screen. On the basis of these findings Rutherford proposed a model of the atom in which the mass and positive charge are concentrated in the nucleus surrounded by a space containing the negative charge.

To appreciate the relative sizes, if the diameter of the nucleus were a few millimetres the whole of the atom would be about the same size as a football stadium. It is not possible to draw this to scale but Figure 10.4 gives a simple picture of the model.

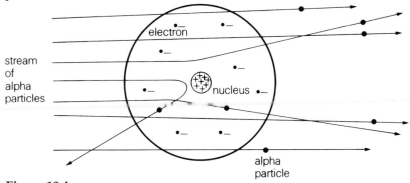

Figure 10.4

The particles in the nucleus were called protons by Rutherford (after the Greek *protos* meaning 'first'). This was taken up by Niels Bohr (among others) who proposed that the negative charges, the electrons, were confined to strictly defined orbits round the nucleus. The charge on an electron is -1.6×10^{-19} C and the charge on a proton is $+1.6 \times 10^{-19}$ C. Since the atom is electrically neutral, the total negative charge is equal to the total positive charge. Thus, for a neutral atom, the total number of electrons must be the same as the total number of positive charges. All the atoms of any one element contain the same number of protons; this number is called the **atomic number**.

10.2   Isotopes

A mass spectrometer is used to determine accurately the mass of the atoms of an element. A simplified diagram of the apparatus is shown in Figure 10.5.

Positive ions of the element under test are produced at an anode and accelerated through a hollow cathode. They then pass through an electric field which produces a deflection away from the positive plate (plate A in Figure 10.5).

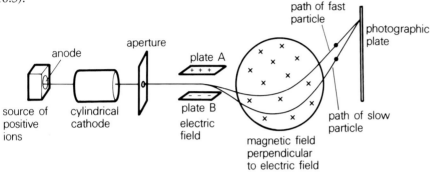

Figure 10.5

The positive ions are then deflected by a magnetic field which causes the particles to hit a photographic plate and form an image. By using these two fields, it is possible to eliminate the effects of varying speeds in the particle stream so that all particles of the same mass are focused at one point only on the screen. It is possible to determine accurately the mass of any particle by measurements taken from the mark on the photographic plate.

Data obtained on the mass of atoms indicated that atoms of the same element can have different masses. Such atoms are called isotopes. It is possible for an atom to have more than one isotope; for example, the element tin has as many as ten isotopes. An explanation for the existence of isotopes was finally provided in 1932 by James Chadwick. He bombarded a beryllium target with alpha particles, Figure 10.6.

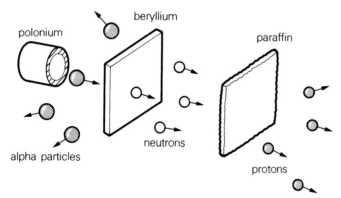

Figure 10.6

The beryllium target gave off radiation which was found to be able to penetrate several centimetres of lead. If however, this radiation is used to bombard paraffin wax the radiation is absorbed and protons are ejected from the slab. By considering conservation of momentum and energy, Chadwick was able to show that a neutral particle was emitted by the beryllium. He called this particle a neutron, symbol $_0^1n$, which has the same mass as a proton but no charge. It is the presence of the neutron in the nucleus which accounts for isotopes. Isotopes of an element have the same number of protons but different numbers of neutrons.

Most elements have several isotopes; many isotopes occur naturally, but others can be made artificially. Often isotopes are stable, but those that are unstable are radioactive and are known as **radioisotopes**, Table 1.

Protons and neutrons are known collectively as **nucleons**.
When specifying an atomic nucleus, it is necessary to give some numbers.

A = mass number or nucleon number
    = number of nucleons (protons + neutrons) in nucleus
Z = atomic number or proton number
    = number of protons in the nucleus
N = neutron number
    = number of neutrons in the nucleus

These are related by $N = A - Z$

For example:

$$_{Z}^{A}\text{Pb} \quad _{82}^{208}\text{Pb}$$

$$N = 208 - 82 = 126$$

For example a beryllium nucleus has the symbol $_{4}^{9}\text{Be}$ where the number of protons is 4 and the number of neutrons is 5.
   These symbols are used in an equation to describe a nuclear reaction. For example, when an alpha particle bombards a beryllium nucleus, a neutron and a carbon nucleus are formed.

$$_{4}^{9}\text{Be} \; + \; _{2}^{4}\text{He} \; \longrightarrow \; _{6}^{12}\text{C} \; + \; _{0}^{1}\text{n}$$
beryllium   alpha particle   carbon   neutron

A specific nucleus of an element is termed a **nuclide**. If the nuclide is radioactive it is called a **radionuclide**. For nuclei of greater mass, greater numbers of nucleons are packed together. For example, the hydrogen nucleus $_{1}^{1}\text{H}$ contains 1 proton and no neutrons, but a uranium nucleus $_{92}^{238}\text{U}$ contains 92 protons and 146 neutrons. Since protons are positive, they exert an electrostatic force of repulsion on each other, yet are contained tightly packed together in the nucleus without flying apart. Part of the reason for this lies in the presence of the neutrons.

	stable isotope	radioactive isotope
carbon	$_{6}^{12}\text{C}$	$_{6}^{14}\text{C}$
strontium	$_{38}^{88}\text{Sr}$	$_{38}^{90}\text{Sr}$
iodine	$_{53}^{127}\text{I}$	$_{53}^{131}\text{I}$
gold*	$_{79}^{197}\text{Au}$	
einsteinium	–	$_{99}^{254}\text{Es}$

* has no naturally occurring isotopes

Table 1

10.3 Nuclear radiation

When a nucleus disintegrates forming the nucleus of a new element, it emits radiation.

The emissions can be alpha, beta or gamma radiation.

Alpha particles

Alpha (α) particles are nuclei of helium and contain two protons and two neutrons.

$_{2}^{4}\text{He}$

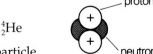

Figure 10.7 Alpha particle

They have a mass number of 4 and a charge of +2e.

Beta particles

Beta (β) particles are high energy electrons which have a very small mass and a charge of $-e$.

$$_{-1}^{0}e$$

Figure 10.8 Beta particle

Gamma-rays

Gamma-rays (γ-rays) are bursts of electromagnetic radiation.

When a nucleus disintegrates emitting either an α-particle or a β-particle, the resulting nucleus is often in a highly excited state. In a very short time, usually less than a microsecond, the nucleons re-arrange themselves into a more stable configuration and energy is released in the form of gamma radiation.

The properties of each of these radiations is given in Table 2.

Name	Nature	Velocity	Ionisation in air	Cloud chamber tracks	Absorption	Deflection
alpha	helium nucleus	5% of speed of light	produces a large number of ions	dense tracks	can be stopped by paper	deflected by a magnetic field
beta	high energy electron	90% of speed of light	produces some ions	less dense tracks than alpha particles	can be stopped by aluminium	deflected by a magnetic field
gamma	electro-magnetic radiation	speed of light	produces very few ions	very few tracks	not easily absorbed even by lead	not deflected by a magnetic field

Table 2

10.4 Equations of decay

When a nucleus disintegrates, it usually undergoes several stages before a stable nucleus is formed.

This series of disintegrations is termed a **radioactive decay** series. At each stage, radiation is emitted and a new nuclide is formed.

An example is the decay of uranium to protactinium during which alpha, beta and gamma radiation is emitted.

Uranium-238 decays to thorium-234 emitting alpha particles and gamma radiation. The thorium-234 decays to protactinium-234 emitting beta particles and gamma radiation.

These processes are taking place at the same time within the same sample of original uranium-238.

The disintegrations can be described using equations of nuclide symbols.

α emission $_{92}^{238}U \longrightarrow {}_{90}^{234}Th + {}_{2}^{4}He + \gamma$

When alpha particles are given out the mass (nucleon) number decreases by 4 and the proton (atomic) number decreases by 2.

β emission $_{90}^{234}Th \longrightarrow {}_{91}^{234}Pa + {}_{-1}^{0}e + \gamma$

When beta particles are given off the mass (nucleon) number is unchanged, but the proton number increases by 1. This occurs because a neutron in the nucleus of thorium-234 splits up into a beta particle which is radiated and a proton which forms the nucleus of protactinium-234.

The process can also be described by omitting the gamma rays and writing the symbols α and β above the arrow.

$$^{238}_{92}U \xrightarrow{\ \alpha\ } {}^{234}_{90}Th \xrightarrow{\ \beta\ } {}^{234}_{91}Pa$$

Example 1

The symbol $^{194}_{78}Pt$ represents an isotope of platinum.

What is the neutron number?

neutron number N = nucleon number − proton number
$$= 194 - 78 = 116$$

There are 116 neutrons in the nucleus.

Example 2

An isotope of lead disintegrates as shown below.

$$^{212}_{82}Pb \xrightarrow{\ \beta\ } {}^{212}_{83}Bi \begin{array}{c} \xrightarrow{\ \alpha\ } X \\[6pt] \xrightarrow{\ \beta\ } Y \end{array}$$

Find the nucleon and proton number for the nuclides X and Y and from the Periodic Table find which elements they represent. Write the symbols for each of these nuclides.

When bismuth decays emitting an alpha particle, the nucleon number decreases by 4 giving

$$212 - 4 = 208$$

The proton number decreases by 2 giving

$$83 - 2 = 81.$$

From the Periodic Table, this represents the element thallium.

Nuclide X is therefore $^{208}_{81}Tl$.

When bismuth decays emitting a beta particle, the nucleon number remains the same but the proton number increases by 1 giving

$$83 + 1 = 84.$$

From the Periodic Table this represents polonium.

Nuclide Y is therefore $^{212}_{84}Po$.

10.5 Radioactive series

When a nuclide disintegrates, it forms a daughter nucleus which in turn disintegrates forming another nucleus. This process continues and a series of new nuclei is formed.

This can be illustrated by using a diagram listing elements in boxes. Each box has a nucleon number on the vertical axis and a proton number on the horizontal axis. These correspond to the numbers A and Z in the nuclide symbol $^A_Z X$. This is shown in the diagram, Figure 10.9.

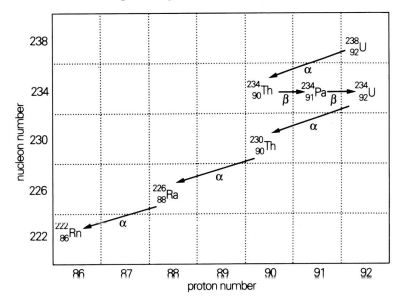

Figure 10.9

Notice that, when uranium-238 decays emitting an alpha particle, the arrow indicates the new nuclide, thorium-234; this is one row down and two columns to the left.

In a similar way, beta emission is indicated by a movement of one column to the right in the same row. Thorium-234 becomes protactinium-234.

Example 3

The diagram shows part of a radioactive decay series.

a)   Give two examples of pairs of isotopes.
b)   Write down in equation form one example of alpha decay.
c)   Write down in equation form one example of beta decay.

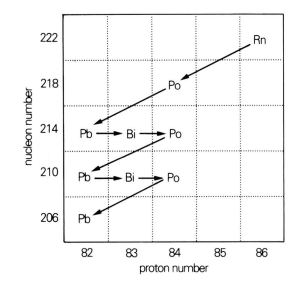

a)   Isotopes have the same proton number but different nucleon numbers.
   From the diagram, examples are $^{218}_{84}$Po and $^{214}_{84}$Po; $^{214}_{82}$Pb and $^{210}_{82}$Pb

b)   Radon decays to polonium emitting an α-particle.
$$^{222}_{86}\text{Rn} \xrightarrow{\ \alpha\ } {}^{218}_{84}\text{Po}$$

c)   Lead decays to bismuth emitting a β-particle.
$$^{210}_{82}\text{Pb} \xrightarrow{\ \beta\ } {}^{210}_{83}\text{Bi}$$

10.6 Hazards

Serious damage can occur when living cells are exposed to ionising radiation such as X-rays, alpha, beta or gamma radiation. The energy absorbed by the cell tissue may remove electrons in the organic molecules of the tissue so that ionisation takes place.

The main serious effect is ionisation of the water in the cells. This upsets the chemical reactions taking place and can lead to injury or death.

Exposure to radiation increases the incidence of cancer in cells.

Doses of radiation cause nausea, vomiting, radiation burns, changes in blood cells, loss of weight and loss of hair. Death can follow within hours or days of a massive exposure.

Henri Becquerel first discovered radioactivity in 1897, and since then a large amount of data on the effects of radiation on the human body has been collected. Various quantities and units relating to radiation exposure are in use, described below.

Activity

The activity A of a sample of radioactive material is the number of disintegrations of nuclei which occur per second. It is measured in becquerels (Bq) where

    1 Bq = 1 disintegration per second

1 gram of radium has an activity of 3×10^{10} Bq while the activity of sea water is about 11Bq per litre. The radioactive sources which are used in schools have activities of around 185 kBq.

Absorbed dose

Damage can result due to the transfer of radiation energy to a body. The greater the transfer of energy, the more likely it is that damage will occur.

The absorbed dose D is the energy absorbed per kilogram and is measured in grays (Gy).

    1 Gy = 1 joule per kilogram

Absorbed dose rate

The absorbed dose rate $\dot{D}$ (pronounced D dot) is the absorbed dose divided by the time during which it is absorbed.

It is measured in grays per hour or grays per minute.

    absorbed dose = absorbed dose rate × time

$$D = \dot{D} \times t$$

Dose equivalent

In biological systems, the damage depends on the radiation type and how it is distributed. To take account of this a quality factor is introduced; this is a number and indicates the ability of the particular radiation to cause damage. Table 3 gives some typical figures for quality factor Q.

Having defined the quality factor Q, the dose equivalent H is given by

    dose equivalent = absorbed dose × quality factor

$$H = D \times Q$$

The dose equivalent is measured in sieverts (Sv).

    sieverts = grays × quality factor.

type of radiation	quality factor Q
X-rays	1
γ-rays	1
β-particles	1
thermal neutrons	3
fast neutrons	10
α-particles	20

Table 3

Example 4

A worker operates in a workplace over a whole year where he receives the following

25 mGy from beta radiation $Q = 1$

300 µGy from fast neutrons $Q = 10$

Calculate his dose equivalent for the year.

dose equivalent = absorbed dose × quality factor

for betas $H = 25 \times 10^{-3} \times 1 = 2.5 \times 10^{-2}\,Sv$

for neutrons $H = 300 \times 10^{-6} \times 10 = 3.0 \times 10^{-3}\,Sv$

total $H = 2.5 \times 10^{-2} + 3.0 \times 10^{-3} = 28 \times 10^{-3}\,Sv$

The dose equivalent for the year is 28 mSv.

Dose equivalent rate

The dose equivalent rate $\dot{H}$ (pronounced H *dot*) is the dose equivalent absorbed divided by the time during which it is absorbed.
It is measured in sieverts per hour or sieverts per minute.

dose equivalent = dose equivalent rate × time

$$H = \dot{H} \times t$$

Also the dose equivalent rate = absorbed dose rate × quality factor

$$\dot{H} = \dot{D} \times Q$$

Example 5

A person spends 5 hours in an area where the absorbed dose rate for thermal neutrons is 36 µGy per hour; the quality factor is 3.
What is the dose equivalent rate and the dose equivalent?

dose equivalent rate = absorbed dose rate × quality factor

$$\dot{H} = 36 \times 10^{-6} \times 3$$
$$= 108 \times 10^{-6}$$

The dose equivalent rate is 108 µSv per hour

dose equivalent = dose equivalent rate × time
$$= 108 \times 10^{-6} \times 5$$
$$= 540\ \mu Sv$$

The dose equivalent received in 5 hours in 540 µSv.

10.7   Background radiation

Everyone is exposed to radiation from natural sources and from man-made radioactive material.

cosmic rays – the earth is bombarded by very high energy particles, mostly protons, from outer space

rocks – soil and rocks contain traces of radioactive material

buildings – building materials are radioactive and the gas radon accumulates in buildings due to seepage from the ground. Insulating a house by reducing the ventilation and flow of air causes a build up of radon gas.

industrial – many industries use radioactive material for monitoring purposes – nuclear reactors contribute to the amount of radiation received

medical – X-rays and radioactive tracers are used in diagnosis

human body – the human body is itself radioactive. This is due to the presence of potassium-40 in all cells and traces of radioactive material from fruit, vegetables and meat which have been eaten.

The average dose equivalent received over a period of one year by members of the public is shown in Table 4.

source	dose equivalent
cosmic rays	0.3 mSv
rocks, soil, buildings	0.3 mSv
present in body	0.4 mSv
industry	1.0 mSv
dental X-ray	0.3 mSv
chest X-ray	2.0 mSv
one flight over the Atlantic	50 µSv

Table 4

A maximum dose equivalent for members of the public has been established at 5 mSv. Radiation workers and those working in certain parts of industry are allowed much higher amounts; this is set at 50 mSv.

The dose equivalent rate for a person standing 1 metre away from a typical school experimental source (185 kBq strontium-90 source) is approximately 130 µSv h^{-1}.

In cancer therapy, the radiation is used to kill the cancer cells so that very high doses are used. A typical cobalt-60 treatment will involve a dose equivalent of 30 000 mSv.

Example 6

A radiation worker receives a total dose equivalent of 450 µSv during a working week of 30 hours.
Calculate the average dose equivalent rate.

$$\text{dose equivalent rate} = \frac{\text{dose equivalent}}{\text{time}}$$

$$\dot{H} = \frac{450 \times 10^{-6}}{30} = 15 \times 10^{-6}$$

The dose equivalent rate is 15 µSv per hour.

Example 7

A monitoring device aboard an aircraft registers a dose equivalent rate of 16 µSv h^{-1}.
Calculate the dose equivalent during a 7-hour flight.

$$\text{dose equivalent} = \text{dose equivalent rate} \times \text{time}$$

$$H = 16 \times 10^{-6} \times 7 = 112 \times 10^{-6}$$

The dose equivalent is 112 µSv.

10.8 Absorption of gamma-rays

Lead is a very effective absorber of gamma-rays. An experimental arrangement to show this is given in Figure 10.10. As greater thicknesses of lead are used, the count rate decreases. Throughout the experiment, the distance between the source and the detector is kept constant.

A graph of a typical set of results is shown in Figure 10.11. This shows count rate N in counts per minute against the thickness of lead t in millimetres.

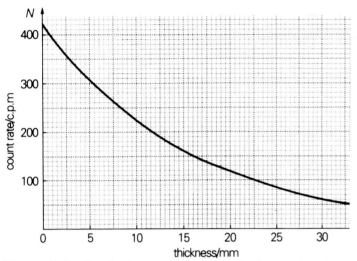

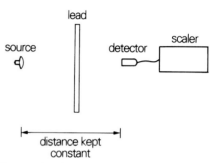

Figure 10.11 Graph of count rate against thickness of lead absorber

Figure 10.10

The thickness of lead required to reduce the count rate to half its original value is known as the **half-value**, $t_{1/2}$. This can be determined from the graph above and shown more clearly in Figure 10.12.

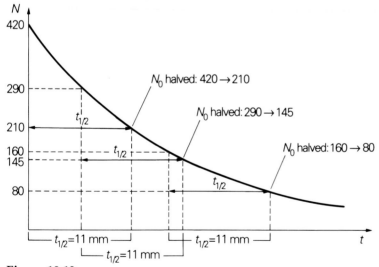

Figure 10.12

It can be seen that the value of $t_{1/2}$ remains constant each time the count rate is halved fron N_0 to $\frac{1}{2}N_0$. The half-value thickness is about 11 mm.

The half-value thickness for absorption depends on the activity of the source and on the energy of the particles emitted. When storing or transporting radioactive material, use is made of the absorption properties of lead, concrete and other materials to reduce the risk of exposure to personnel. These materials have a shielding effect.

Example 8

The dose equivalent rate due to a gamma source is 12 Sv per hour.
If the half-value thickness of lead for this source is 16 mm, what would be the dose equivalent rate with the source placed behind 48 mm of lead shielding?

half-value thickness = 16 mm

thickness = 0 $12 \, \text{Sv} \, \text{h}^{-1}$

thickness = 16 mm $\frac{1}{2} \times 12 = 6.0 \, \text{Sv} \, \text{h}^{-1}$

thickness = 32 mm $\frac{1}{2} \times 6 \ = 3.0 \, \text{Sv} \, \text{h}^{-1}$

thickness = 48 mm $\frac{1}{2} \times 3 \ = 1.5 \, \text{Sv} \, \text{h}^{-1}$

The 48 mm of lead will reduce the dose equivalent rate to 1.5 Sv per hour.

Example 9

A cobalt-60 source emits gamma-rays and, at a point some distance away, produces a dose equivalent rate of 6 μSv per hour.
If the half-value thickness of lead for this source is 11 mm, what thickness of lead would reduce the dose equivalent rate to 1.5 μSv per hour?

     desired rate = $1.5 \, \mu\text{Sv} \, \text{h}^{-1}$

     initial rate = $6 \, \mu\text{Sv} \, \text{h}^{-1}$

The rate has to be cut to one quarter of the original.
One half-value thickness will reduce the rate to $\frac{1}{2}$ of the original; this means that two half-value thicknesses are required $(\frac{1}{4} = \frac{1}{2} \times \frac{1}{2})$

A thickness of 22 mm will reduce the dose equivalent rate to 1.5 μSv per hour.

10.9   Inverse Square Law for γ-radiation

Just as with other sources of radiation like light or heat, we would expect the intensity of radiation from a gamma source to reduce as the distance from it is increased. To investigate this, a source is placed in line with a Geiger-Müller tube which measures the count rate at various distances, Figure 10.13.

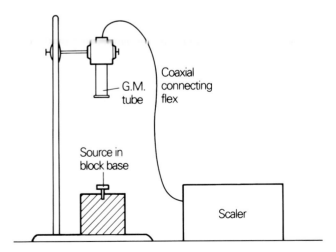

Figure 10.13

A graph of results from a typical experiment is shown in Figure 10.14.

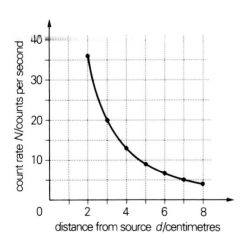

Figure 10.14 Graph of count rate against distance from source

If, as is expected, the count rate is inversely proportional to the distance squared, then

$$N = k \times \frac{1}{d^2} \qquad \text{where } N = \text{count rate}$$
$$d = \text{distance}$$
$$k = \text{constant}$$

$$\Rightarrow \quad N \times d^2 = k$$

When this is done with the results, a constant value is not obtained, Table 5.

distance d (cm)	count rate N (counts per second)	$N \times d^2$
2	36	144
3	20	180
4	13	208
5	9	225
6	7	252
7	5	245
8	4	256

Table 5

The non-constant results arise because there is an uncertainty in the distance measurement, Figure 10.15.

The exact position of the source is not known and the point at which the Geiger-Müller tube detects the radiation is also uncertain. The correct distance should be increased by a small constant amount because of this.

The extra distance can be found by drawing a suitable graph.
When this is done for the results given in Table 5, a length of 1 cm is added to each distance to give the corrected value.

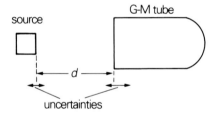

Figure 10.15

Table 6 gives the corrected results which produce a constant value for the product $N \times d^2$.

d (cm)	N (c/s)	$N \times d^2$
3	36	324
4	20	320
5	13	325
6	9	324
7	7	343
8	5	320
9	4	324

Table 6

These results show that $N \times d^2$ gives a constant value for all the readings.
It can therefore be concluded that the intensity of radiation from a gamma-ray source is inversely proportional to the square of the distance from the source.

For a given source, if the dose equivalent rate is $\dot{H}_1$ at a distance d_1 from the source and $\dot{H}_2$ at a distance of d_2, the inverse square law means that:

$$\dot{H}_1 \propto \frac{1}{d_1^2} \quad \text{and} \quad \dot{H}_2 \propto \frac{1}{d_2^2}$$
$$\Rightarrow \quad \dot{H}_1 \times d_1^2 \quad = \quad \dot{H}_2 \times d_2^2$$

Example 10

The dose equivalent rate at a distance of 3 m from a source of gamma radiation is 750 μSv per hour.
What is the dose equivalent rate at 5 m from the source?

The inverse square law gives

$$\dot{H}_1 \times d_1^2 = \dot{H}_2 \times d_2^2$$
$$\Rightarrow \quad 750 \times 10^{-6} \times 3^2 = \dot{H}_2 \times 5^2$$
$$\Rightarrow \quad \dot{H}_2 = 750 \times 10^{-6} \times \frac{9}{25} = 270 \times 10^{-6}$$

The dose equivalent rate is 270 μSv h^{-1} at a distance of 5 m from the source.

Example 11

A detector is placed 10 cm from a point source of gamma rays.
A count rate of 600 c.p.m. is recorded.
What count rate would be obtained at a distance of 20 cm from the source?

The distance has doubled, therefore the count rate will be $\frac{1}{2^2}$ of the original reading.

The new count rate is $600 \times \frac{1}{2^2} = \frac{1}{4} \times 600 = 150$

The new count rate will be 150 counts per minute.

10.10   Carbon dating

When a radionuclide decays, the activity falls with time. A graph of activity against time is a curve, Figure 10.16, so that the activity does not decrease at a constant rate. There is one quantity which remains the same; this is the half-value period or **half-life** $t_{1/2}$ which is the time taken for any activity to drop to half.
On the graph, the original activity A_0 falls to $\frac{1}{2}A_0$ after one half-life, and to $\frac{1}{4}A_0$ after two half-lives.

In general, after N half-lives the activity will be A_N.

$A_N = (\frac{1}{2})^N A_0$

This principle is used to date archaeological specimens which are hundreds or thousands of years old.
Carbon-14 is an isotope of carbon which is formed in a nuclear reaction when neutrons ejected by cosmic rays collide with atmospheric nitrogen.

$$^{14}_{7}N + ^{1}_{0}n \longrightarrow ^{14}_{6}C + ^{1}_{1}H$$

This isotope forms radioactive carbon dioxide which is taken in by plants and trees. The normal activity from a living plant is about 250 Bq per kilogram.

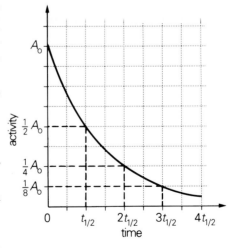

Figure 10.16

When the plant dies, no fresh carbon dioxide is taken in and the carbon-14 present in the plant starts to decay by beta emission with a half-life of approximately 5600 years.

By measuring the residual activity, the age of any material containing carbon, such as wood or linen, can be estimated.

In principle this is straightforward, but the activity is very small so special highly sensitive methods must be used to measure this activity. Corrections also have to be built in to the calculation because of two factors which affect the proportion of carbon present. Since the Industrial Revolution, the burning of fossil fuels has increased the amount of carbon dioxide present in the atmosphere, so altering the proportion of carbon-14. Nuclear tests have been conducted in the atmosphere since 1945, and these have increased the amount of carbon-14. The method of dating is accurate to within about plus or minus 70 years.

Example 12

A section of the decay graph for carbon-14 is shown.
How old is a sample of wood which has an activity
of 226 Bq per kilogram?

From the graph, the activity is 226 Bq kg^{-1} at 800 years.

The sample is 800 years old.

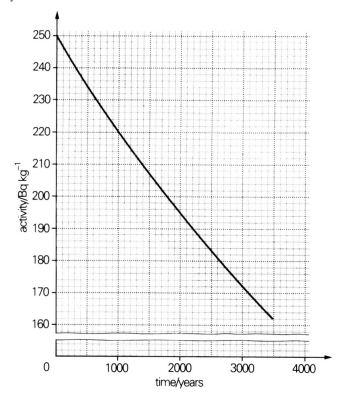

10.11   Binding energy

Neutrons play a part in holding protons together within the nucleus. The force which holds the nucleons together is not completely understood. It appears to be some kind of exchange force which binds protons and neutrons together by means of a continuous exchange of a third particle that moves backwards and forwards between them. We can relate this to everyday experience by imagining two boys representing a proton and a neutron; they remain close to each other because they are playing a game which involves throwing a ball backwards and forwards to each other, Figure 10.17.

The particle is the π-meson and the mass is about 275 times that of an electron. The meson can exist independently for only very short periods of approximately 10 nanoseconds.

Figure 10.17

Mass defect

Although we are not certain of the exact nature of the binding force, we can very accurately determine the binding energy of a nucleus. It is found that when protons and neutrons are packed in a nucleus, the mass of the assembled nucleus is less than the sum of the masses of the individual particles. In his theory of special relativity, Einstein showed that mass and energy were equivalent and connected by the equation

$$E = mc^2 \qquad \text{where } E = \text{energy in joules}$$
$$m = \text{mass in kg}$$
$$c = \text{velocity of light in m s}^{-1}$$

The deficit in mass which occurs when nucleons are packed together into a nucleus is equivalent to the energy needed to bind them together. This deficit is known as the **mass defect**.

The masses involved in nuclei are very small, so a much smaller unit than the kilogram is used. This unit is the average mass of a particle in the nucleus of a carbon-12 atom. Since this nucleus contains 12 particles and has a mass of 1.992×10^{-26} kg, the mass of this unit (known as the unified atomic mass unit, u) is as follows.

$$1\,u = \frac{1.992 \times 10^{-26}}{12}$$
$$= 1.660 \times 10^{-27} \text{ kg.}$$

Example 13

Find the binding energy of a helium nuclide ^4_2He if the mass is 4.0015 u.
The helium nuclide ^4_2He contains 2 protons and 2 neutrons

Individually 2 protons have a mass of $2 \times 1.0078 = 2.0156$ u

2 neutrons have a mass of $2 \times 1.0087 = 2.0174$ u

the total mass of the nucleons is therefore 4.0330 u

However the mass of a helium nuclide is 4.0015 u

There is therefore a deficit in mass, called a mass defect, which is equivalent to the binding energy.

$$\text{This mass defect} = 0.0315\,u$$
$$= 0.0315 \times 1.660 \times 10^{-27}$$
$$= 5.23 \times 10^{-29} \text{ kg}$$

Using Einstein's equation $E = mc^2$

$$\Rightarrow \quad \text{energy} \quad = 5.23 \times 10^{-29} \times (3 \times 10^8)^2$$
$$= 4.71 \times 10^{-12} \text{ J}$$

The binding energy is 4.71×10^{-12} joules.

The binding energy of a nucleon is very small so that it is common practice to state its value in terms of the electron-volt (eV). This is the energy required to move 1 electron through a potential difference of 1 volt.

$$\text{energy} = \text{charge} \times \text{p.d.}$$
$$\Rightarrow \quad 1\,eV = 1.6 \times 10^{-19} \times 1$$
$$= 1.6 \times 10^{-19} \text{ J}$$

The larger unit the mega-electron-volt (MeV) which is 1 million electron-volts is normally used.

$$1\,MeV = 1.6 \times 10^{-19} \times 10^6$$
$$\Rightarrow \quad 1\,MeV = 1.6 \times 10^{-13} \text{ J}$$

If Einstein's equation $E = mc^2$ is applied to the unified atomic mass u and the energy converted to MeV, it is found that

1 u is equivalent to 931 MeV of energy.

10.12 Binding energy per nucleon

When the nucleons in a nucleus are bound together, some of the mass is changed into binding energy. The exact amount of mass which is converted into binding energy varies with the mass number of the element involved.

It is useful to calculate average binding energy per nucleon where

$$\text{average binding energy per nucleon} = \frac{\text{total binding energy of nucleus}}{\text{number of nucleons in nucleus}}$$

A graph of average binding energy per nucleon plotted against mass number (Figure 10.18) provides useful information about the stability of a particular nucleus.

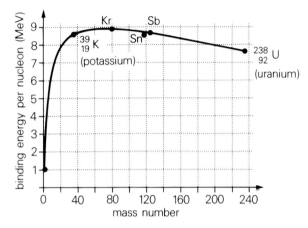

Figure 10.18

It can be seen that the nuclei at each end of the graph, (i.e. those with small and large mass numbers), have smaller average binding energies per nucleon than nuclei with medium mass numbers. Those elements with the highest average binding energy per nucleon are the most stable nuclei.

To see how the graph is constructed consider the following examples.

Example 14

Find the average binding energy per nucleon for uranium-238. ($^{238}_{92}U$)
(proton mass = 1.0078 u; neutron mass = 1.0087 u;
mass of uranium-238 nucleus = 238.0003 u)

$$\text{mass of 92 protons} = 1.0078 \times 92 = 92.7176 \text{ u}$$

$$\text{mass of 146 neutrons} = 1.0087 \times 146 = 147.2702 \text{ u}$$

$$\text{total mass of individual particles} = 239.9878 \text{ u}$$

$$\Rightarrow \qquad \text{mass defect} = 239.9878 - 238.0003 = 1.9875 \text{ u}$$

but 1 u releases 931 MeV of energy.

$$\Rightarrow \qquad \text{binding energy} = 1.9875 \times 931 = 1850.3625 \text{ MeV}$$

and since there are 238 nucleons present

$$\text{binding energy per nucleon} = \frac{1850.3625}{238} = 7.8$$

The average binding energy per nucleon is 7.8 MeV.

Since $\quad$ 1 MeV = 1.6×10^{-13} J

$$\Rightarrow \quad 7.8 \text{ MeV} = 7.8 \times 1.6 \times 10^{-13} = 1.24 \times 10^{-12}$$

The binding energy can also be expressed as 1.24 × 10^{-12} joules.

Example 15

Find the average binding energy per nucleon for potassium-39. ($^{39}_{19}$K)
(proton mass = 1.0078 u; neutron mass = 1.0087 u;
mass of potassium-39 = 38.9533 u)

mass of 19 protons = $1.0078 \times 19 = 19.1482$

mass of 20 neutrons = $1.0087 \times 20 = 20.1740 \, u$

total mass of individual particles = $39.3222 \, u$

$\Rightarrow$ mass defect = $39.3222 - 38.9533 = 0.3689 \, u$

but 1 u releases 931 MeV of energy

$\Rightarrow$ binding energy = $0.3689 \times 931 = 343.4459 \, MeV$

and since there are 39 nucleons present

$$\text{binding energy per nucleon} = \frac{343.4489}{39} = 8.8$$

The average binding energy per nucleon is 8.8 MeV.

10.13   Unstable nuclei

When the number of protons in a nucleus is small, an equal number of neutrons results in a stable nucleus. For example helium has 2 protons and 2 neutrons; oxygen has 8 protons and 8 neutrons. As the number of protons increases, a greater proportion of neutrons is required to ensure stability. This can be seen with iron (26 protons, 28 neutrons), tin (50 protons, 62 neutrons), lead (82 protons, 126 neutrons), and bismuth (83 protons, 126 neutrons). In fact, no nucleus with 84 protons or more is stable. These massive nuclei disintegrate producing radiation.

The disintegration of uranium results in the following radioactive series. In the series each element is formed when the preceding one disintegrates.

element	isotope	radiation		element	isotope	radiation	
uranium	$^{238}_{92}$U	α	γ	lead	$^{214}_{82}$Pb	β	γ
thorium	$^{234}_{90}$Th	β	γ	bismuth	$^{214}_{83}$Bi	β	γ
protactinium	$^{234}_{91}$Pa	β	γ	polonium	$^{214}_{84}$Po	α	
uranium	$^{234}_{92}$U	α	γ	lead	$^{210}_{82}$Pb	β	γ
thorium	$^{230}_{90}$Th	α	γ	bismuth	$^{210}_{83}$Bi	β	
radium	$^{226}_{88}$Ra	α	γ	polonium	$^{214}_{84}$Po	α	
radon	$^{222}_{86}$Rn	α		lead	$^{210}_{82}$Pb	STABLE	
polonium	$^{218}_{84}$Po	α					

The disintegration of the nuclei in such a series will continue until a stable nuclide (usually lead or bismuth) is produced and no more disintegrations take place. Although nuclei with more than 83 protons are unstable, they do exist because all of the nuclei do not disintegrate at the same time.

10.14   Nuclear fission

Nuclear fission is the splitting of a nucleus of large mass into two nuclei of smaller mass. The process may be accompanied by the release of energy, and of neutrons or gamma-rays, or both.

Fission is usually caused by neutron bombardment and this is known as **induced** fission; however it is possible for fission to be **spontaneous**, particularly in the case of the heavier elements.

Nuclear fission was first discovered in 1938 by two Germans, Hahn and Strassman. They bombarded uranium with neutrons and found that the products of reaction had a proton number of about 56. A number of different reactions are possible, including the following.

$$\,^{1}_{0}n + \,^{238}_{92}U \longrightarrow \,^{145}_{56}Ba + \,^{94}_{36}Kr$$

$$\,^{1}_{0}n + \,^{235}_{92}U \longrightarrow \,^{138}_{56}Ba + \,^{95}_{36}Kr + 3\,^{1}_{0}n + energy$$

The reaction with the production of neutrons and energy is shown diagrammatically in Figure 10.19.

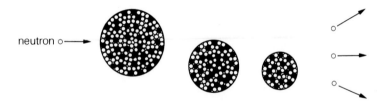

Figure 10.19

To describe how the nucleus splits in this way George Gamow, a Russian working in America, proposed a liquid drop model, Figure 10.20. First the neutron penetrates the 'nuclear liquid' to form the isotope uranium-239. The extra energy causes the nucleus to oscillate. If the energy is sufficient the drop becomes elongated and eventually splits into two separate parts.

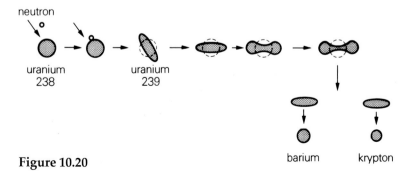

Figure 10.20

If the energy is not sufficient the nucleus vibrates but eventually settles down again releasing a neutron and returning to its original form, Figure 10.21.

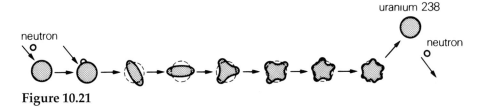

Figure 10.21

Energy release

The amount of energy released in a fission reaction can be found from Einstein's equation of mass-energy equivalence:

$E = mc^2$ where E = energy released (J)
    m = mass defect, or loss in mass after the reaction (kg)
    c = velocity of light (m s^{-1})

Example 16

Consider the fission reaction of uranium-235 that results in the formation of the stable elements molybdenum and xenon.

$$^{235}_{92}U + ^{1}_{0}n \longrightarrow ^{98}_{42}Mo + ^{136}_{54}Xe + 2^{1}_{0}n + 4^{0}_{-1}\beta$$

before		after	
$^{235}_{92}U$	234.993 u	$^{98}_{42}Mo$	97.883 u
$^{1}_{0}n$	1.009 u	$^{136}_{54}Xe$	135.878 u
		$2^{1}_{0}n$	2.018 u
		$4^{0}_{-1}\beta$	0.002 u
total mass	236.002 u	total mass	235.781 u

$$\text{mass defect} = 0.221\,u = 0.221 \times 1.660 \times 10^{-27}$$
$$= 0.369 \times 10^{-27}\,kg$$

energy equivalence: $E = mc^2 = 0.369 \times 10^{-27} \times (3 \times 10^8)^2$
$$= 3.32 \times 10^{-11}$$

Energy released = 3.32 × 10^{-11} J.

Chain reactions and the atomic bomb

Uranium-238 does not easily undergo fission, but the isotope uranium-235 is suited to the capture of a neutron and the production of two, or sometimes three further neutrons. These neutrons in turn are able to continue the fission process, given the right conditions. Under these conditions, a reaction known as a **chain reaction** is started; this provides its own conditions for continuation with the additional neutrons released and enables the rapid release of an enormous amount of energy.

However, the isotope uranium-235 comprises only 0.7% of the total naturally occurring uranium. It is possible to concentrate the isotope in one sample by a process of enrichment and this was made possible in 1945, resulting in the explosion on 16 July of the first atomic bomb at Alamogordo in New Mexico, Figure 10.22.

Figure 10.22

When the nucleus of uranium splits up, it releases further neutrons which are capable of bombarding neighbouring nuclei producing further fission. If there are sufficient nuclei of uranium-235 available there is a build-up of nuclei being split until there is a large release of energy all at once. In order for this to happen a critical mass must be present and when this happens the chain reaction goes ahead and an atomic explosion takes place releasing a huge amount of energy, equivalent to thousands of tonnes of conventional explosive. This is shown diagrammatically in Figure 10.23.

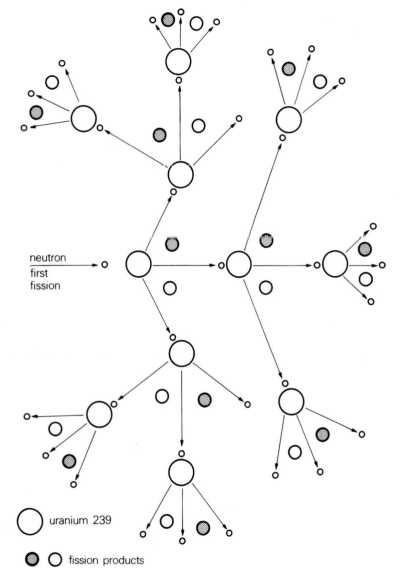

Figure 10.23

When an atomic explosion takes place there are three damaging effects.

Blast – the explosion forces air outward in huge shock waves and the earth trembles. This combination of wind and earthquake has a devastating effect on houses and structures

Heat – a huge release of heat produces very high temperatures and sets up widespread fires

Radiation – very energetic rays, gamma-rays and X-rays, are released which can damage living tissue.

The products of the explosion which are highly radioactive are released and carried by wind and air currents and spread over a large area. These products are known as fallout and are highly dangerous. One of the most dangerous is strontium-90 which does not occur naturally but can be absorbed into the body in much the same way as calcium. This radioactive material persists throughout the lifetime of a human being and increases the risk of cancer.

10.15 Nuclear reactors

In an atomic explosion a chain reaction occurs and a huge uncontrollable release of energy takes place. Fortunately the fission reaction can be controlled so that it produces useful heat energy without the explosion.

For a fission process to continue the following conditions must be satisfied.

1 There are enough heavy nuclei of the fuel material packed together to capture released neutrons. There must be enough fissions to start the reaction.

2 These neutrons must have the correct energy to cause fission in other nuclei before they escape from the material.

There are three essential parts in a reactor.
a) the rods of fuel which provide heavy nuclei and neutrons
b) control rods which absorb some of the neutrons and so regulate the number of neutrons in the system
c) a moderator which slows down the neutrons.

The first type of operating reactor used natural uranium as the fuel, in the form of rods, with rods of cadmium or boron fitted to control the number of neutrons. Graphite was used as the moderator, all three parts forming the **core** of the reactor.

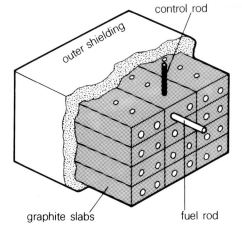

Figure 10.24 Reactor core

The fuel, containing the isotope uranium-235, captures the neutrons and releases a large amount of energy. In order for this to happen, the fast neutrons which are released during fission must be slowed down to increase the chance of capture by the nuclei. Graphite does not capture neutrons but successive collisions with the graphite nuclei result in loss of energy which slows the neutrons down.

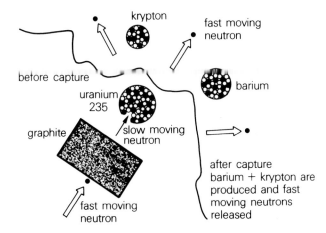

Figure 10.25

The speed of the neutrons must be correct to ensure efficient capturing. Another important aspect is the means of controlling the number of neutrons; this is achieved by using control rods to absorb the neutrons. The control rods are let down into the core and contain a material, such as boron, which has a strong affinity for neutrons. Boron captures neutrons, forming the stable elements helium ($^{4}_{2}$He) and lithium ($^{7}_{3}$Li) so that the captured neutrons are lost for ever.

In practice, the number of neutrons produced in the reaction is monitored continuously and when it rises above a predetermined level, the control rods are pushed a little further into the core. This additional absorption of neutrons causes the reaction to proceed at a lower rate. If the rods are withdrawn slightly, the reaction proceeds at a higher rate.

The nuclear reactor produces heat. This heat raises the temperature of a liquid or gas which circulates round the reactor core. The hot liquid or gas is then used to produce steam which operates a turbine generating electricity, Figure 10.26.

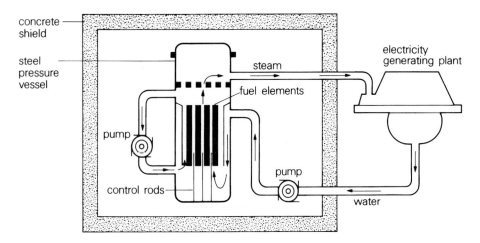

Figure 10.26 Boiling water reactor (BWR)

10.16   Fast breeder reactor

The original reactors used natural uranium (0.7% uranium-235) or slightly enriched fuel (3% uranium-235) but the next generation of reactors may use plutonium as the fuel. This is a man-made element produced as a by-product in the original reactors. The process takes place because of the action of neutrons on uranium-238.

$$^{238}_{92}U + ^{1}_{0}n \rightarrow ^{239}_{92}U + 2^{1}_{0}n$$

followed by

$$^{239}_{92}U \rightarrow ^{239}_{93}Np + ^{0}_{-1}e(\beta)$$
$$\text{neptunium}$$

followed by

$$^{239}_{93}Np \rightarrow ^{239}_{94}Pu + ^{0}_{-1}e(\beta)$$
$$\text{plutonium}$$

The plutonium decays to uranium-235 and the half life of plutonium is very long, about 24 000 years.

$$^{239}_{94}Pu \rightarrow ^{235}_{92}U + ^{4}_{2}He$$

Plutonium undergoes fission in a similar manner to uranium but captures fast neutrons and hence requires no moderator, only control rods to control the rate of the reaction. A typical reaction forms tellurium and molybdenum.

$$^{239}_{94}Pu + ^{1}_{0}n \rightarrow ^{137}_{52}Te + ^{100}_{42}Mo + 3^{1}_{0}n$$

Plutonium has been produced in large quantities as a by-product of some reactors and when used in fast breeder reactors (so called because fast neutrons are used), it is possible to convert natural uranium into additional plutonium which can be used as fuel. It thus 'breeds' additional fuel for use in reactors. The fast breeder reactor holds out the possibility of producing large amounts of nuclear fuel. From the known resources of uranium it is estimated that fast breeder reactors could produce the equivalent of 400 years of coal supplies.

The core of the Dounreay prototype reactor

Figure 10.27 Fast breeder reactor at Dounreay

Radioactive materials can cause cancer and produce genetic damage so they must be safely stored in an isolated place. The storage and disposal of the waste from power stations is a major problem and has not yet been adequately solved.

10.17   Nuclear fusion

We have seen that when a heavy nucleus such as uranium splits up forming two new elements, energy is released either in an uncontrolled manner in the atomic bomb or in a carefully controlled process in a nuclear reactor.

It is also possible to release energy by joining two light nuclei together to form a new nucleus in a process known as nuclear fusion.

In order to explain how energy is released by fusion, the average mass per nucleon, measured in unified atomic mass units, must be considered. This is found by dividing the mass of the nucleus by the number of nucleons in the nucleus.

$$\text{average mass per nucleon} = \frac{\text{total mass of nucleus}}{\text{number of nucleons in the nucleus}}$$

Table 7 shows the calculations for some elements.

element	mass of nucleus (u)	No. of nucleons	average mass per nucleon (u)
hydrogen	1.008	1	1.0080
helium	4.002	4	1.0005
potassium	38.953	39	0.9988
tin	119.875	120	0.9990
platinum	193.920	195	0.9945
uranium	234.993	235	1.0000

Table 7

If similar calculations are carried out for all elements, a graph of average mass per nucleon against number of nucleons can be drawn, Figure 10.28.

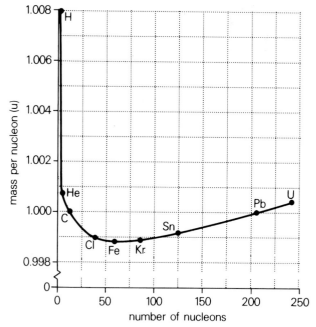

Figure 10.28

^1_1H

hydrogen

^2_1H

deuterium

^3_1H

tritium

Figure 10.29

From the graph it can be seen that if two nuclei of hydrogen are combined to form a helium nucleus, the average mass per nucleon of the single helium nucleus is less than the average mass per nucleon for the original hydrogen nuclei. This deficit in mass is converted into energy.

A number of possible fusion reactions exist and many involve two isotopes of hydrogen, deuterium and tritium, Figure 10.29.

Deuterium, usually called heavy hydrogen, contains an additional neutron and can be written either ^2_1H or ^2_1D. It is in plentiful supply existing in 'heavy water' which makes up about 1 part in 5000 of all water. Another isotope, tritium, contains two additional neutrons and can be written ^3_1H or ^3_1T.

In one possible reaction, two nuclei of deuterium combine to form a single nucleus of an isotope of helium plus one neutron.

$$^2_1D + {}^2_1D \rightarrow {}^3_2He + {}^1_0n$$
$$2.013\,u + 2.013\,u \qquad 3.015\,u + 1.009\,u$$

There is a mass defect which releases energy

mass defect = 4.026 – 4.024

= 0.002 u

But 1 u releases about 931 MeV

Therefore the energy released = 0.002 × 931

= 1.9 MeV

A fusion reaction requires very high temperatures in order to provide enough kinetic energy to overcome the forces of electrostatic repulsion between the positive nuclei. Temperatures of one hundred million degrees Celsius are necessary to fuse a large number of nuclei together at the same time so that a thermonuclear explosion can take place: this is the principle of the hydrogen bomb. In the H-bomb the high temperatures are provided by an atomic explosion which is used to initiate the reaction. The high temperatures produce a stream of positive ions and electrons called a plasma.

One possible reaction which can take place in the plasma is described by the following equation

$$_1^2D + _1^3T \rightarrow {}_2^4He + {}_0^1n + 17.6\,MeV$$

The energy released, 17.6 MeV, is very much less than that obtained by a fission reaction (200 MeV) but it must be remembered that the nucleus of uranium has a mass of about 235 u whereas the mass of one deuterium nuclei is about 2 u. The energy yield per kilogram for a fusion reaction is very much larger than the energy per kilogram for a fission reaction. There is also no requirement for a critical mass as there is for a fission reaction.

The possibility of producing energy from a controlled fusion reaction is very attractive because of the plentiful supply of deuterium and also because the radioactive waste produced is small.

In order to achieve a controlled thermonuclear (fusion) reaction four conditions must be satisfied.
a) suitable material which will undergo fusion must be available
b) material must be heated to the required high temperature
c) hot plasma must be contained sufficiently long to allow the energy produced by fusion to exceed the input energy
d) fusion energy must be converted into electricity

A possible practical arrangement is illustrated in Figure 10.30. This shows the Tokamak system first developed in the USSR in the late 1960's.

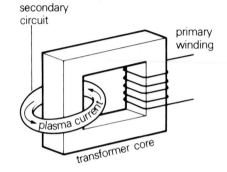

Figure 10.30

A current is produced in the primary circuit, usually by some kind of discharge. Transformer action causes a very large current to be induced in the secondary. This current heats the plasma and temperatures of 70 million degrees have been attained.

The most difficult problem is to contain the plasma because if the plasma touches the walls of the container the high temperatures would destroy the container material. Present methods use strong magnetic fields which are designed to confine the stream of plasma. The magnetic field produced by the plasma current itself tends to hold the particles of the plasma together. The streams of ions moving in the same direction produce magnetic fields which tend to draw the streams together in the same way that two conductors lying side by side will be pulled towards each other by the magnetic fields (Figure 10.31). This is known as the **pinch effect** (Figure 10.32).

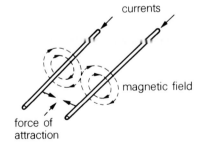

Figure 10.31

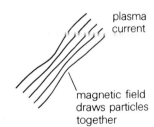

Figure 10.32

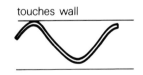

Figure 10.33

Unfortunately the plasma does not remain stable and starts to twist and eventually touches the walls, Figure 10.33.
The plasma can be stabilized for short periods by applying a large magnetic field by means of a coil wrapped round the container walls, Figure 10.34.
This and other methods are not entirely satisfactory and a great deal of further research is needed to produce a working system. The first attempt at a

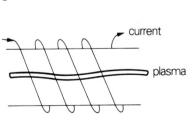

Figure 10.34

Figure 10.35

thermonuclear reactor in the United Kingdom was completed at Harwell in 1958, Figure 10.35. It was known as ZETA.

A circular aluminium tube, known as a torus, contains deuterium. The tube has a diameter of about 1 metre and the circle is about 4 metres across, Figure 10.36.

To start up the process a radio frequency oscillator is used to produce a spark discharge inside the torus which ionizes the deuterium gas. This oscillator is turned off and a large bank of capacitors is discharged through the primary winding of a transformer. This causes a large pulse of deuterium ions to flow round the torus which forms the secondary winding of the transformer. Currents of 250 000 amperes existing for 2 milliseconds have been recorded.

However the plasma cannot be easily stabilized in the circular-shaped torus and research is at present progressing using different methods. Eventually a commercially successful thermonuclear reactor may be built but it will not provide cheap power. There are formidable engineering difficulties and the capital cost of such a reactor is high because of the equipment needed for magnets, cooling systems and ancillary equipment. As supplies of conventional fuel begin to run out the cost of a thermonuclear reactor will become competitive. The exciting aspect of the system is the fact that the deuterium fuel is in such plentiful supply in the oceans of the world.

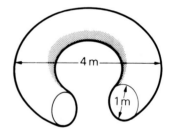

Figure 10.36

Summary

Rutherford's model of the atom assumes that the mass and positive charge are concentrated in the nucleus surrounded by a space containing the negative charge. The volume of the nucleus is extremely small compared with the total volume of the atom.

The nucleus of an atom contains protons and neutrons.

A nucleus can be described using a symbol such as $^A_Z X$ where X denotes the element and

A = number of nucleons
Z = number of protons
$A - Z$ = number of neutrons

Isotopes contain the same number of protons but different numbers of neutrons.

An element can have more than one isotope.

1 unified atomic mass unit $1\,u = 1.66 \times 10^{-27}\,kg$.

1 electron-volt is equal to $1.6 \times 10^{-19}\,J$.

Particles can be represented by symbols.

particle	symbol	rest mass
electron	$^0_{-1}e$	0.00055 u
neutron	$^1_0 n$	1.0087 u
proton	$^1_1 H$	1.0078 u
alpha	$^4_2 He$	4.0026 u

Radiation from a radioactive source can damage cells. The units used to monitor radiation are listed below.

quantity	unit
activity A	becquerel Bq
absorbed dose D	gray Gy
absorbed dose rate $\dot{D}$	gray per hour $Gy\,h^{-1}$
dose equivalent H	sievert Sv
dose equivalent rate $\dot{H}$	sievert per hour $Sv\,h^{-1}$

The dose equivalent received from a point source of radiation is inversely proportional to the square of the distance from the source.

When radiation is absorbed, the half-value thickness of the absorber is the thickness which reduces the dose equivalent to half of its original value.

Einstein showed that mass and energy are related by the equation $E = mc^2$.

In nuclear fission a nucleus splits forming two new elements and releasing energy.

A critical mass is required before a chain reaction can take place.

In nuclear fusion two nuclei join together forming a single nucleus and releasing energy.

Problems

1 Two assistants of Rutherford, Geiger and Marsden, conducted an experiment in order to investigate the nature of the atom. Draw a diagram showing the experimental arrangements used and describe how they collected data from the experiment. What model of the atom did this experiment confirm?

2 Explain the meaning of the following: electron, proton, neutron, isotope.

3 Define mass number and atomic number.

4 Describe a simple form of mass spectrometer.

5 Einstein put forward the relationship $E = mc^2$. Use this equation to calculate the energy released when 1 milligram of mass is converted into energy.

6 Energy is released when a nucleus splits up forming two new nuclei but energy can also be released when two nuclei combine to form one single nucleus. Explain why each of these processes can produce energy.

7 In a nuclear reactor a controlled fission process releases energy. Draw a diagram showing the stages in the reactor leading up to the generation of electricity.

8 A neutron undergoes decay forming a proton. The equation of the reaction is

$$^1_0 n \rightarrow {}^1_1 H + {}^0_{-1}e$$

Determine the energy released during this reaction.
(mass of $^1_0 n$ = 1.0087 u;
mass of $^1_1 H$ = 1.0073 u; mass of $^0_{-1}e$ = 0.0005 u).

9 Calculate the binding energy in MeV of the $^7_3 Li$ nucleus.
(mass of nucleus = 7.0144 u; mass of a proton = 1.0073 u; mass of $^1_0 n$ = 1.0087).

10 Two deuterium nuclei fuse together to form a helium nucleus. The equation of this reaction is

$$^2_1 H + {}^2_1 H \rightarrow {}^3_2 He + {}^1_0 n$$

Calculate the energy released.
(mass of $^2_1 H$ = 2.0136 u; mass of $^3_2 He$ = 3.0149 u; mass of $^1_0 n$ = 1.0087 u).

11   Determine the binding energy of a helium $_2^4$He nucleus if the mass of the nucleus is 4.0015 u.

12   How much energy will be released when 0.5 kg of uranium is completely transformed into energy?

13   Explain briefly the function of a moderator in a fission reactor.

14   In a fission reaction the average energy released is 175 MeV per fission. How many such fissions are required per second in order to provide a power of 1 MW?

15   Plutonium undergoes fission producing tellurium and molybdenum.

$$_{94}^{239}\text{Pu} + _0^1\text{n} \rightarrow _{52}^{137}\text{Te} + _{42}^{100}\text{Mo} + 3_0^1\text{n}$$

Calculate the energy released from this reaction. The mass of $_{52}^{137}$Te is not accurately known but can be taken as 137.0000 u. (mass of $_{94}^{239}$Pu = 239.0006 u; mass of $_{42}^{100}$Mo = 99.8850 u).

16   The carbon-12 nucleus $_6^{12}$C has a mass of 11.9967 u. Calculate the binding energy of the nucleus. What is the binding energy per nucleon?

17   Explain why some types of reactor do not require a moderator.

18   What is spontaneous fission? What isotope is known to be spontaneously fissionable?

19   Why is the controlled fusion of hydrogen into helium such a difficult problem?

20   Uranium splits up forming molybdenum and xenon which are stable. The equation describing this reaction is

$$_{92}^{235}\text{U} + _0^1\text{n} \rightarrow _{42}^{98}\text{Mo} + _{54}^{136}\text{Xe} + 2_0^1\text{n}$$

Calculate the energy released. (mass of $_{42}^{98}$Mo = 97.8830 u; mass of $_{54}^{136}$Xe = 135.8776 u; mass of $_{92}^{235}$U = 234.9934 u).

21   In 1932 Cockroft and Walton produced nuclear disintegrations by accelerating protons with a high voltage machine. The reaction can be written

$$_3^7\text{Li} + _1^1\text{H} \rightarrow _2^4\text{He} + _2^4\text{He}$$

Calculate the energy released. (mass of $_3^7$Li = 7.0144 u; mass of $_2^4$He = 4.0015 u; mass of $_1^1$H = 1.0073 u).

22   Explain the function of the control rods and the moderator in a nuclear reactor.

23   State the conditions necessary for a chain reaction to take place.

24   A proton and a neutron combine to form deuterium $_1^2$H.

$$_1^1\text{H} + _0^1\text{n} \rightarrow _1^2\text{H}$$

Calculate the binding energy of deuterium. (mass of $_1^2$H = 2.0136 u).

25   Calculate the total energy released during the following reaction.

$$_{92}^{238}\text{U} \rightarrow _{90}^{234}\text{Th} + _2^4\text{He}$$

(mass of $_{92}^{238}$U = 238.0003 u; mass of $_{90}^{234}$Th = 233.9942 u; mass of $_2^4$He = 4.0015 u).

26   A worker spends 5 hours in an area where absorbed dose rates are:

thermal neutrons 36 mGy h^{-1}
fast neutrons   20 μGy h^{-1}

Calculate the dose equivalent rates for each type of neutron. What is the total dose equivalent for the 5 hours?

27   In a year a fitter working in a nuclear power station receives:

20 mGy of gamma radiation
300 μGy of thermal neutrons.

Determine the dose equivalent for the year.

28   In the course of a 35-hour week an industrial worker receives a dose equivalent of 400 μSv. Determine the dose equivalent rate for this week.

29   The dose equivalent rate from a source is 1200 μSv h^{-1} at a distance of 2 m. Calculate the distance at which this will fall below a rate of 600 μSv h^{-1}.

30   A businessman receives radiation at the rate of 12 μSv h^{-1} while flying in an aircraft. His total flying time per annum is 250 hours. Calculate his total dose equivalent for the year.

31   At the end of a year a worker has received a dose equivalent of 45 mSv. If she is at work for a total of 2500 hours, determine the average dose equivalent rate while she is at work.

32   A spent fuel rod has a dose equivalent rate of 8 Sv h^{-1}. If the half-value thickness of water for this source is 200 mm, find the dose equivalent rate at the surface of water in a tank if the rod lies 2 metres below the surface.

33   The half-value thickness of a radium-226 source is 27 mm. If the dose equivalent rate 4 μSv h^{-1} with a thickness of 5 mm what additional thickness will reduce this to below a rate of 0.3 μSv h^{-1}?

34   A decay series is shown. Fill in the missing nuclide.

$$_{90}^{232}\text{Th} \rightarrow _{88}^{228}\text{Ra} \rightarrow X \rightarrow _{90}^{228}\text{Th} \rightarrow _{88}^{234}\text{Ra}$$

35   Polonium $_{84}^{218}$Po decays emitting an alpha particle. Write down the symbol of the daughter nuclide produced.

36   Carbon-14 is formed when a neutron bombards a nitrogen nucleus. The equation can be written in the form:

$$_7^{14}\text{N} + _0^1\text{n} \rightarrow X \rightarrow _6^{14}\text{C} + _1^1\text{H}$$

Write down the symbol for nuclide X.

37   Carbon-14 decays emitting a beta particle. Write down the equation for this decay.

38   The nuclide $_{92}^{238}$U decays emitting one alpha particle and then two beta particles. What is the final nuclide formed?

39   A section of a radioactive series is shown in the diagram. Fill in the radiations given out at each stage and name the missing nuclides lettered X and Y.

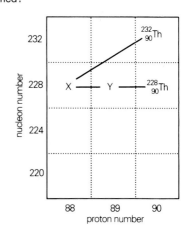

40 a) A radioactivity kit includes three closed sources made up as shown.

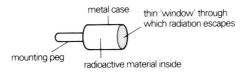

metal case   thin 'window' through
which radiation escapes

mounting peg   radioactive material inside

Description of closed sources

Type of radiation given out	Name of radioactive nucleus	Number of protons	Number of neutrons
alpha	americium 241	95	146
beta	strontium 90	38	52
gamma	cobalt 60	27	33

  i) Describe how to find out, experimentally, which is the alpha source.
  ii) When an alpha particle is emitted from an americium nucleus, state the number of protons and the number of neutrons in the new nucleus formed.
  iii) Cobalt 60 emits beta and gamma radiations. Explain how the case is designed so that the closed source gives out gamma rays only.

b) The discharge of waste solutions from a factory into a bay is to be investigated.
  i) Describe how a radioactive liquid could be used to map the spread of the solution in the bay.
  ii) Suggest whether a liquid would be chosen with a half-life of a few seconds, a few minutes, a few days, a few years or many years.
  Justify your choice.

SEB

41 a) In the symbol X_n^m what do m and n signify?
b) The nuclide X_n^m is radioactive, decaying by emitting in succession alpha, gamma, beta, gamma, beta radiation. What symbol would denote the nuclide at this stage in its decay?
c) In an experiment involving plants, a radioactive isotope is to be used as a tracer. Which type, or types, of isotope radiation would be suitable?
  Justify your choice very briefly.

time in days	total count rate in counts per min.
0	66
3	57
6	49
9	43
12	39

From the data:
  i) determine which of the following isotopes had been used in the experiment:-

    Na^{24} — half life 5.6 days
    I^{131} — half life 8.1 days
    P^{32} — half life 45 days
    Sr^{89} — half life 53 days

  ii) Find when the sample can be safely thrown away, if this is possible, when its activity is less than that which would give a count rate of 10 counts per minute in the apparatus used. The apparatus used has a background count of 23 counts per minute.

SEB

42 a) A girl sets up a Geiger-Müller tube and scaler in front of a radioactive source which emits two types of radiation. Pieces of aluminium, of different thicknesses, are placed between the source and detector and the count rate determined in each case.

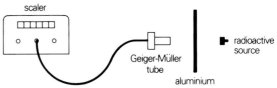

scaler

Geiger-Müller tube

aluminium

radioactive source

The results obtained were used to plate a graph of count rate, corrected for background, against thickness and this is shown below.

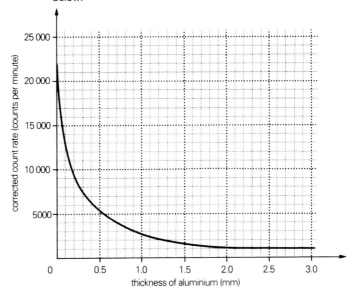

This source is to be stored in an aluminium box and the count rate, measured outside the box, must not be greater than 2000 counts per minute.
Use the graph to estimate
  i) the minimum thickness of aluminium required for the box,
  ii) the count rate when the thickness of aluminium is 3 mm.
  What types of radiation are emitted from the source? Give reasons for your answer.
b) A water engineer wishes to locate leakage from a long sewage pipe buried under a field.
Suggest how he could do this using a Geiger counter and a radioactive liquid.
Which of the liquids listed on the right would be most suitable for use? Why?

Liquid	Half-life	Type of emission
A	10 ms	alpha
B	6 hours	gamma
C	10 hours	beta
D	24 days	alpha
E	1000 years	gamma

SEB

43 The following reaction takes place in the Sun:

$${}_1^3H + {}_1^2H \rightarrow {}_2^4He + {}_0^1n.$$

a) State the name given to this type of reaction.
b) Calculate the energy available from the above reaction, given the following information.
Any other data required will be found in the Science Data Booklet.
Rest mass of ${}_1^3H = 5.005 \times 10^{-27}$ kg
Rest mass of ${}_1^2H = 3.342 \times 10^{-27}$ kg
Rest mass of ${}_2^4He = 6.642 \times 10^{-27}$ kg
Rest mass of ${}_0^1n = 1.674 \times 10^{-27}$ kg

SEB

44 a) Rutherford directed Geiger and Marsden in an investigation into the structure of the atom using the apparatus shown.

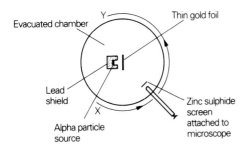

- Evacuated chamber
- Y
- Thin gold foil
- Lead shield
- X
- Zinc sulphide screen attached to microscope
- Alpha particle source

i) Describe what the experimenters observed as the microscope was moved from X to Y and explain the results they obtained.

ii) Geiger and Marsden investigated the effect of using elements other than gold.
By imagining the passage of a single alpha-particle near to the nucleus of an atom with an atomic number less than gold, suggest how the deflection might compare with an alpha-particle passing at the same distance from the nucleus of a gold atom. Explain your answer.

b) The equation for a nuclear fusion reaction involving the release of energy is given below.

$$^2_1H + ^2_1H = ^3_1H + ^1_1H$$

i) State the structure of each of the nuclides in the equation.

ii) A table of nucleon and nuclide masses is reproduced below.

Nuclide/nucleon	Mass in kg × 10⁻²⁷	Nuclide/nucleon	Mass in kg × 10⁻²⁷
^1_0n	1.674	^3_1H	5.005
^1_1H	1.672	^3_2He	5.004
^2_1H	3.342	^4_2He	6.642

(A) Calculate the loss in mass which occurs when the reaction takes place.

(B) Find the energy released in the reaction given the equation $E = mc^2$

c) Astrophysicists believe that the mass of the sun is decreasing at a rate of four million tonnes per second.
Give an explanation.

SEB

45 a) It is stated in a nuclear physics text book that
'The most probable mode of decay of $^{252}_{98}Cf$ is by *spontaneous fission* whereas for $^{235}_{92}U$ in a nuclear reactor the decay is by *induced fission*'

i) What information is conveyed by the symbol $^{252}_{98}Cf$?

ii) Distinguish between *spontaneous fission* and *induced fission*.

b) i) Various thermonuclear reactions take place in the Sun involving the fusion of nuclei.
One possible reaction is

$$^2_1H + ^1_1H \rightarrow ^3_2He + energy.$$

Use Einstein's equation, $E = mc^2$, and the information in the table below, to calculate the energy released per fusion reaction.

nuclide	^1_1H	^2_1H	^3_2He
mass in kg	1.672×10^{-27}	3.342×10^{-27}	5.004×10^{-27}

ii) Einstein's equation may also be applied in other cases, for example, when a γ-ray photon changes into an electron and a positron.

$$\gamma \rightarrow ^0_{-1}e + ^0_{+1}e$$

	electron	positron
symbol	$^0_{-1}e$	$^0_{+1}e$
mass in kg	9.11×10^{-31}	9.11×10^{-31}

(A) Calculate the energy of a photon ($E = hf$) of frequency 2.80×10^{20} Hz.

(B) Show that this photon has sufficient energy to account for the combined mass of the electron and positron.

SEB

46 Various atomic models have been proposed and rejected on the evidence of later experiments.
The figure illustrates the Thomson 'plum pudding' model.

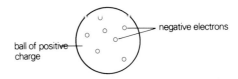

- ball of positive charge
- negative electrons

In this model, a solid atom of positively charged matter has the negative electrons distributed throughout it.

i) What observation in Rutherford's scattering experiments led to this model being rejected?

ii) As a result of these experiments, Rutherford proposed a new model. Give two ways in which Rutherford's model differed from Thomson's model.

iii) Rutherford's model was modified to take account of the formation of line spectra.

(A) What was the modification?

(B) How does it account for the formation of line spectra?
When a crystal is placed in a beam of electrons in a vacuum tube, a diffraction pattern is observed.
What does this suggest about the nature of electrons?

SEB

11 Measurements and uncertainty

11.1 Random errors

When a physical quantity is measured, there is always some doubt about the exact value of the reading. This may be due to the person taking the measurement, the apparatus being used or some random variation which is unpredictable.

It is important to realise the limitations of any measurement and to allow for these when stating the final value for the measurement.

If a sheet of paper is passed round a group of people who are asked to find the width, there will be a variation in the answers given. Some typical examples are given in Table 1. There is a spread of results from the lowest of 208 mm to the highest of 212 mm.

person making reading	reading stated (mm)
A	209
B	210
C	210
D	211
E	212
F	210
G	209
H	208
I	210
J	211

Table 1

In general, the spread of readings in an experiment could be due to a number of factors.

1. Wrong use of equipment.

2. Mis reading of the scale, either from mistaken interpretation of scale divisions, or from a parallax error where the scale is incorrectly lined up with the pointer of the instrument or the object being measured, Figures 11.1 and 11.2.

3. Variation in the dimensions of the object being measured.

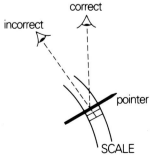

Figure 11.1

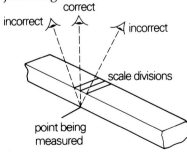

Figure 11.2

To illustrate the spread of readings, consider the count rate due to background radiation in a laboratory; a Geiger-Müller tube and a scaler are used, Figure 11.3. The scaler is started and the count recorded at the end of each minute. The results are listed in Table 2.

$$\text{mean count rate} = \frac{\text{total count}}{\text{time taken}} = \frac{563}{10}$$
$$= 56.3$$

The mean count rate is 56 counts per minute. There is a spread of values above and below this so that a random error is present.

Figure 11.3

11.2 Approximate random error

There are a number of ways of estimating the random error: computer software and programmable calculators allow this to be done using certain mathematical relationships. The final answer is achieved with the minimum of effort.

For most experimental work at this stage, a much simpler approach can be used but the random error can still be estimated reasonably well using the formula:

$$\text{approximate random error in the mean} = \frac{\text{maximum value} - \text{minimum value}}{\text{number of measurements taken}}$$

In the case of the count rate in Table 2:

$$\text{approximate random error in the mean} = \frac{64 - 46}{10} = \frac{18}{10} = 1.8$$

The approximate random error in the mean count rate is ± 2 counts. The final value of count rate would be stated: 56 ± 2 counts per minute

count	time (minutes)
0	0
60	1
50	2
61	3
46	4
47	5
61	6
64	7
57	8
55	9
62	10

Table 2

11.3 Significant figures

The way in which a value is stated is used to indicate the precision of the measurement.

A length may be given as 12.7 cm.
This indicates that the value lies between 12.65 and 12.75 cm.
In this case the result has been given to 3 significant figures.

A statement of length of 12 cm has only 2 significant figures and indicates that the length lies between 11.5 cm and 12.5 cm.

The number of significant figures used when stating experimental results will depend on the sensitivity of the instrument and the procedure used. A voltage of two volts can be expressed with different numbers of significant figures.

The range setting on the instrument allows different degrees of precision to be obtained. Although the reading is still two volts in each case, the presence of the three zeros indicates 4 significant figures in the result, Figure 11.4.

When scientific notation is used, the number of digits indicates the number of significant figures.

2.000 V

4 significant figures

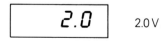

2.0 V

2 significant figures

Figure 11.4 A digital voltmeter

2 significant figures	1.2×10^5
3 significant figures	5.78×10^3
4 significant figures	3.560×10^6

Example 1

Some measurements are given in the table. State the upper and lower limits in the value indicated by the significant figures.

current	2.60 A
voltage	9.4 V
length	12.27 mm
time	3.0 s
temperature	10° C

Current is stated to two decimal places i.e. to the nearest 0.01 A
Taking half of this allows the limits to be set.
This gives $\frac{1}{2} \times 0.01 = 0.005$ A.
The lower limit is taken to be $2.60 - 0.005 = 2.595$.
By convention, the upper limit is taken to be 2.604.
This avoids the overlap with $2.61 - 0.005 = 2.605$ A.

The voltage lies between 9.35 and 9.44 V

The length lies between 12.265 and 12.274 mm

The time lies between 2.95 and 3.04 seconds

The temperature lies between 9.5 and 10.4° C

11.4   Percentage error

When taking a measurement, the absolute error does not by itself indicate how precise the stated value might be.

A more useful error is the fractional or percentage error.

A stop clock for example can measure to the nearest half second (0.5 s).

If the time is found to be 3 seconds, the 0.5 second error is of significance but if the time is 250 seconds the 0.5 s has much less importance.

The percentage error gives some indication of this.

First case: percentage error $= \dfrac{\text{absolute error}}{\text{actual measurement}} \times 100$

$$= \pm \frac{0.5}{3.0} \times 100 = \pm 17\%$$

Second case: percentage error $= \pm \dfrac{0.5}{250} \times 100 = \pm 0.2\%$

Example 2

Calculate the percentage errors in the following

    a) (5.00 ± 0.01) cm

    b) (12.5 ± 0.1) volts

    c) (85 ± 2) mA

a) percentage error $= \dfrac{0.01}{5.00} \times 100 = \pm 0.2\%$

b) percentage error $= \dfrac{0.1}{12.5} \times 100 = \pm 0.8\%$

c) percentage error $= \dfrac{2}{85} \times 100 = \pm 2.4\%$

11.5 Systematic errors

When measurements are taken in an experiment, there is often a constant factor present which affects all the results in the same direction. This error is called a **systematic error** and can arise due to several causes. There may be a zero setting error in the equipment, the procedure adopted may not be correct, or the operator may be taking the measurements wrongly.

The needle on the meter is not set at zero so that all readings will be too low, Figure 11.5.

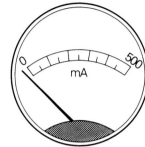

Figure 11.5

The end of the metre stick is worn so that all readings are too high, Figure 11.6.

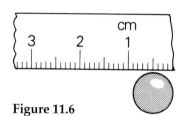

Figure 11.6

The intensity of light from a light source is measured in a room which is not darkened. Each reading will be too high because the light level of the background is added to it.

The graph in Figure 11.7 shows intensity plotted against distance from the source. The readings level off at the background level instead of tending towards zero.

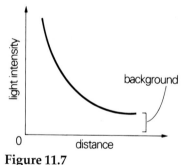

Figure 11.7

11.6 Reading errors

When only one reading is taken from an instrument, the procedure for calculating the mean and then the random error cannot be carried out.

In such cases, the error must be estimated from the scale divisions on the instrument. There is no hard and fast rule for this, but a reasonable working 'rule of thumb' is to take plus or minus half a division of the scale.

In the manometer shown, Figure 11.8,

difference in levels = 48.5 − 11.0 = 37.5 mm

Taking a random error of half a division gives a value of ± 0.5 mm

The reading lies between 37 mm and 38 mm.

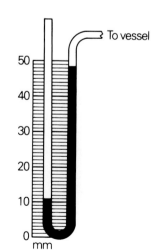

Figure 11.8

Example 3

Estimate the percentage error in the ammeter reading shown.

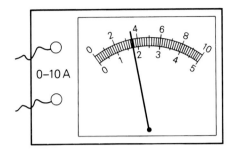

The reading is 3.5 A

absolute error = half a division

$= 0.1$ A

percentage error $= \dfrac{0.1}{3.5} \times 100$

$= \pm 2.9\%$

In some circumstances, plus or minus half a division on the scale gives an error which is much too pessimistic.

In a Bourdon gauge, for example, the divisions are widely spaced and a more realistic estimation of the error would be plus or minus one-fifth of a division.

The reading on the gauge shown is about 1.34×10^5 Pa

The error is one-fifth of a division which is $\dfrac{0.1}{5} = 0.02$

The reading would be stated as $(1.34 \pm 0.02) \times 10^5$ Pa

The percentage error is therefore $\pm \dfrac{0.02}{1.34} \times 100 = \pm 1.5\%$

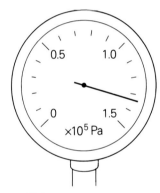

Figure 11.9

Example 4

A volume of air is trapped in a capillary tube as shown. Estimate the percentage error in the reading.

estimated reading is 2.15 cm^3

error is about quarter of a division which is ± 0.05 cm^3

percentage error $= \pm \dfrac{0.05}{2.15} \times 100$

$= \pm 2.3\%$

11.7   Digital instruments

Many instruments at present in use have a digital readout: the numbers are simply read off the output.

Digital instruments sample the quantity being measured and compare it with a standard reference. Depending on the instrument, this sampling will take a certain amount of time so that the final reading is not obtained immediately.

Once the readout is established, there is always some uncertainty in the last digit and manufacturers usually specify this as plus or minus one on the last digit.

This means that for a reading of 3.26 V the voltage will lie between 3.25 V and 3.27 V.

Figure 11.10

11.8   Error bars on a graph

When a measurement is taken and then plotted on a graph the presence of errors is indicated by error bars on the graph, Figure 11.11.

Figure 11.11

The length of the bar indicates the magnitude of the error.

A typical example is the calculation of a resistance from a graph where current is plotted against voltage. A variable voltage supply is connected to the resistor and the voltage increased in stages. The corresponding value of current is noted. If the meters shown in Figure 11.12 are used, the errors are:

ammeter ± 0.05 A   voltmeter ± 0.1 V

When the results are plotted on the graph, the error bars indicate the possible error in each reading of voltage and current, Figure 11.13.

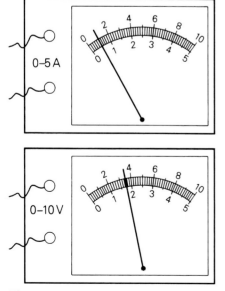

Figure 11.12

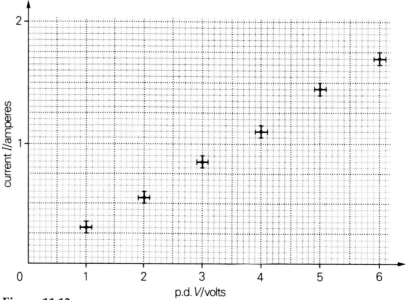

Figure 11.13

11.9 Combining errors

Often two measurements are taken and then used in a calculation to give a physical quantity, for example:

$$\text{speed} = \frac{\text{distance}}{\text{time}}$$

$$\text{power} = \text{voltage} \times \text{current}$$

The errors in each measurement contribute to the error in the final value.

There are a number of ways of combining errors, some using fairly advanced mathematics. However a reasonably good estimate of the final error can be arrived at by working out the individual percentages and taking the larger or largest one, the others being neglected.

To illustrate this, imagine the typical experiment where a card fitted to a trolley cuts a light beam which operates a timer. The speed is found by dividing the length of the card by the recorded time.

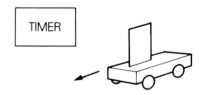

Figure 11.14

$$\text{mean time} = 0.028 \pm 0.001 \text{ second}$$
$$\text{length of card} = 120 \pm 1 \text{ mm}$$

$$\text{percentage error in time} = \frac{0.001}{0.028} \times 100 = \pm 3.6\%$$

$$\text{percentage error in length} = \frac{1}{120} \times 100 = \pm 0.8\%$$

The larger value is taken because it contributes most to the total error.

$$\text{Percentage error in speed} = \pm 3.6\%$$

The mean speed is $\dfrac{120 \times 10^{-3}}{0.028} = 4.3 \text{ m s}^{-1}$ plus or minus 3.6%

Summary

A random error is one which has an equal chance of being positive or negative compared to the true value.

Random errors are revealed by repeated observation of the quantity being measured.

The best estimate of a set of readings is given by the mean value.

$$\text{mean value} = \frac{\text{sum of all the measured values}}{\text{number of measurements taken}}$$

The approximate random error in the mean value of a set of measurements is given by

$$\frac{\text{highest value} - \text{lowest value}}{\text{number of observations made}}$$

$$\text{percentage error} = \frac{\text{absolute error}}{\text{actual value of measurement}} \times 100\%$$

Systematic errors are due to faulty equipment or incorrect experimental technique. All readings are higher or lower than the true value due to a systematic error.

Reading errors arise as a result of inadequate divisions on a scale, of incorrect reading by the operator, or of variations due to unknown fluctuations in the instrument.

In analogue instruments, the reading error is often taken as plus or minus half a division on the scale but a common sense judgement should be made to assess the error.

In digital instruments, the reading error is plus or minus one digit.

When combining errors from two or more quantities, the largest percentage error contributes most to the final value. This largest percentage error is a reasonably good estimate in the final numerical result.

Problems

1 Estimate the reading on the thermometer.
Suggest a possible error in the reading.

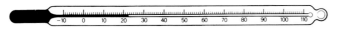

2 An experiment is carried out to find the specific heat capacity of water. Which of the following will contribute most to the final error in the specific heat capacity?

voltage   5.3 ± 0.1 V
current   1.2 ± 0.1 A
time   200 ± 1 s
temperature 5 ± 0.5 °C
mass   1 ± 0.01 kg

3 Describe clearly the difference between a systematic error and a random error.
Give one example of each.

4 An experiment is conducted to measure the mass of water flowing through a water heater per minute.
The table shows the results obtained.

Mass flowing in kg per minute

5.24	5.31	5.26	5.29	5.28	5.30
5.26	5.31	5.27	5.32	5.25	5.26

Calculate the mean value for the mass flow and also determine the approximate random error in the mean.

5 An ammeter gives the reading indicated.
State the reading and estimate the uncertainty in the reading.

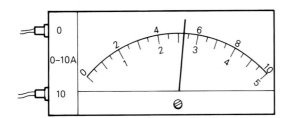

6 The ammeter and voltmeter shown are used to calculate a value for resistance.
Calculate a value for the resistance and estimate the percentage error in the value.

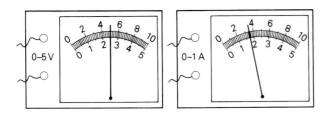

7 A section from a graph is shown.
Find the absolute errors in voltage V and in resistance R.

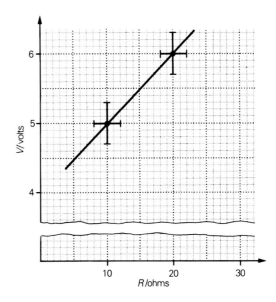

8 Estimate the percentage error in the ammeter reading shown.

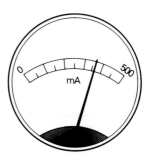

9 The density of a liquid is calculated using the formula

$$\text{density} = \frac{\text{mass}}{\text{volume}}$$

If the mass is 62.7 ± 0.1 g and the volume is 50 ± 1 cm^3, estimate the percentage error in the value of the density.

10 Part of a graph drawn to show the relationship between the force of attraction exerted by an electromagnet and the current in the coil, is shown below.

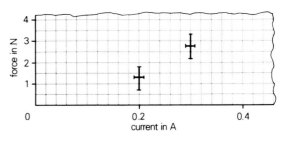

Explain why the readings have been plotted in this way.   *SEB*

11 A beam of yellow light from a single slit falls on a double slit ruled on a blackened microscope slide, which is mounted on the end of a cardboard tube as shown in Figure 1.

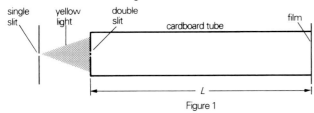

Figure 1

The interference pattern formed is recorded on a piece of photographic film placed over the end of the tube. When the film is developed a series of black lines can be seen. One such film is shown in Figure 2.

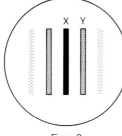

Figure 2

The separation Δx of the black lines is given by the relationship

$\Delta x = \lambda \frac{L}{d}$ where λ is the wavelength of light, d is the double slit separation and L the length of the tube.

a) In one experiment a pupil obtains an estimate Δx by measuring the separation of lines X and Y (Figure 2) and obtains (7 ± 1) mm. His measurement for d was (0.20 ± 0.01) mm and for L was (2.40 ± 0.01) m.

From these measurements, calculate

  i) the best value for the wavelength of yellow light;

  ii) the uncertainty in this value.

b) **i)** Describe one method of measuring the double slit separation to the stated degree of accuracy.

  ii) Give one way in which the uncertainty in the measurement of the separation of the black lines on the film could be reduced. *SEB*

12 In an experiment to investigate the relationship between the pressure and the volume of a gas, it is necessary to read the pressure of the gas on a Bourdon gauge and the length of a column of trapped air by a metre stick.

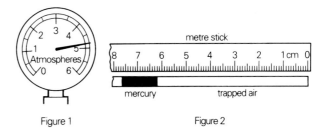

Figure 1   Figure 2

From the sketches of the Bourdon gauge in Figure 1 and the column of trapped gas and metre stick in Figure 2, estimate the values of pressure and length of gas column and the degree of uncertainty in each value.

Estimate also the upper and lower limits of the product of pressure multiplied by length of gas column. *SEB*

Numerical answers

Chapter 1 *page 19*

2   2.5 m s^{-1}, 53.1° West of North
3   3.81 m, 23° above the horizontal
4   a) 30 m s^{-1} b) 8.33 × 10^7 m s^{-1} c) 6.38 m s^{-1}
5   a) 0.12 m s^{-1}, 0.84 m s^{-1}, 1.92 m s^{-2} b) 0.48 m s^{-1}
6   a) 1.5 m s^{-2} b) 1.08 m
8   a) 3 s   b) 22.5 m
9   0.47 m s^{-1}
12   1.13 m
13   99.9 m
14   zero
16   a) 1 m s^{-1} b) 6.5 m
17   a) zero   b) 6 m s^{-2} c) –2 m s^{-2}
18   237.5 m
19   a) 22 m s^{-1} downwards   b) 21 m
22   a) 0.5 s   b) 5 m s^{-1} downwards   c) 64.4° below the horizontal   d) 1.2 m
23   a) 0.5 s   b) 2.165 m
24   a) 7.2 m   b) 14.4 m
25   a) 17.3 m s^{-1} b) 5 m above the top of the launcher
26   a) 140 m   b) 5 m   c) 40.3 m s^{-1}, 29.7° above the horizontal
28   a) C: 6.3 m s^{-1} b) 0 m, 2 m, 8 m, 16 m, 24 m
       c) i) 45.5 m from the start; he was reversing direction
            ii) he was running back to A at 3.5 m s^{-1}
29   b) 7.5 m s^{-2} c) ii) 0.55 s   iii) 9.52 m s^{-2}
30   b) 25 m s^{-1}, 53° below the horizontal
31   17.5 m s^{-1} downwards
32   270 m
33   horizontal: 40 cm, vertical: 80 cm
34   6.32 m s^{-1} at an angle of 71.6° West of North
35   b) i) 0.1 s   ii) 0.4 s   iii) 3.0 m s^{-1} iv) 5.0 m s^{-1} at 53° below the horizontal
36   a) 25.4 m s^{-1} b) 2.36 s
37   300 m

Chapter 2 *page 45*

2   a) 510 kN   b) 858 kN
3   a) 0.293 J   b) 0.71 N
4   a) 25 N   b) 6 m
7   a) 22.4 m s^{-1} b) 0.12 N
9   –0.5 m s^{-1} 1.125 J, 0.375 J
10   a) 0.8 s
12   a) 36 N s   b) 36 kg m s^{-1} c) 432 J
13   a) 287.5 m   b) 3.69 kN
14   b) 3500 m
15   a) 0.75 m s^{-1} b) 0.028 m
16   25.1 ms
17   a) 0.4 m s^{-2}, 0.2 m s^{-2}, zero, –0.6 m s^{-2} b) 70 kN   c) 360 kW
18   a) yes   b) 3 J
19   a) 12 J   b) 1.6 J   c) 5.2 N
20   a) 2 m s^{-1} c) 36 m
21   a) 0.032 N s   b) 0.71 N   c) 0.0064 J
22   b) 140 N downwards, zero, 140 N upwards
23   a) 1.0 N
24   a) i) 1.76 N   ii) 0.25 s
25   a) –10 m s^{-1} b) i) –2.5 m s^{-1} c) i) 6250 J   ii) 2400 J   d) 7.2 × 10^4 N
26   a) i) 0.7 m s^{-2} ii) 3 × 10^4 N
28   a) i)

Height h (m)	0.60	1.00	1.40	1.80
Speed at B (m s^{-1})	2.50	3.85	4.90	5.80
Potential energy at A (J)	6.0	10.0	14.0	18.0
Kinetic energy at B (J)	3.1	7.41	12.0	16.8

b) 1.30 N   c) ii) 0.34 m
29   6 kg
30   0.16 m s^{-1}

31 62.6 N, 62.6 N

32 $3 \, m \, s^{-1}$

33 3282 N

34 $F_1 = 1.09 \times 10^5$ $F_2 = 1.14 \times 10^5 \, N$

35 a) $1.5 \, m \, s^{-1}$ b) 0.195 J

36 0.24 N s, 0.96 N

37 $T_1 = 271 \, N$ $T_2 = 221 \, N$

38 $F_1 = 4396 \, N$ $F_2 = 1736 \, N$

39 $5 \, m \, s^{-2}$

40 a) BC c) 200 N

41 a) i) BC ii) CD iii) zero b) i) 3150 N c) i) $1.2 \, m \, s^{-2}$

42

	vehicle A	vehicle B	b) i) zero ii) zero
mass (kg)	0.3	0.1	
velocity ($m \, s^{-1}$)	0.2	−0.6	
momentum ($kg \, m \, s^{-1}$)	0.06	−0.06	
kinetic energy (J)	0.006	0.018	

43 11.55 N

45 a) i) $0.20 \, m \, s^{-1}$ ii) $0.125 \, m \, s^{-1}$
iii) total momentum before collision $0.02 \, kg \, m \, s^{-1}$;
total momentum after collision $0.02 \, kg \, m \, s^{-1}$

46 a) $8 \times 10^6 \, N$ b) $3.6 \, m \, s^{-2}$

47 a) $14 \, m \, s^{-2}$

48 b) ii) 30 kJ iii) 10 kJ

49 a) $1.0 \, kg \, m \, s^{-1}$

50 390 N

51 8 N

52 b) i) $2.83 \times 10^6 \, N$ at 45° to the two tow ropes
ii) $2.83 \times 10^6 \, N$ directly opposed to the resultant in i)

53 b) i) $25 \, m \, s^{-1}$

54 a) ii) $3.36 \times 10^5 \, J$ iii) $9.60 \times 10^5 \, J$ iv) 20.8 kW

55 b) 800 m c) $4.0 \, m \, s^{-2}$ d) ii) 16 667 N

Chapter 3 *page 67*

1 $6 \times 10^4 \, Pa$

2 $8 \times 10^8 \, Pa$

4 $pV = 4.5 \times 10^3$ approximately

5 $0.067 \, m^3$

6 238 kPa

9 $2.5 \times 10^5 \, Pa$

10 500 Pa

11 a) 87°C

12 a) 0 K b) 123 K c) 773 K

13 a) −273°C b) −1°C c) 227°C

14 $90 \, m^3$

15 $400 \, cm^3$

17 $1600 \, kg \, m^{-3}$, $8.08 \times 10^{-4} \, m^3$

18 Density is $1.25 \, kg \, m^{-3}$
i) Pressure reduced by factor of 0.95
ii) Density remains the same
iii) Kinetic energy is lowered by a factor of 0.95

19 a) $34.00 \, cm^3$ b) i) $21.94 \, cm^3$ ii) $12.06 \, cm^3$

23 a) $3.84 \, m^3$ b) 12.8 min

24 a) i) $pV = 0.09$ b) i) 25 kPa ii) 10.5 km

Chapter 4 *page 85*

1 0.64 C

2 $5 \times 10^3 \, A$

3 $2 \times 10^{-3} \, s$

4 6 V

6 $0.5 \, \Omega$

7 37.5 s

8 1 A

9 0.8 V

10 5 A

11 27 V, $6 \, \Omega$

12 0.1 A

13 6 V, 1.2Ω, 5 A
14 1.5 V, 0.05 Ω, 30 A
15 3.33 W
16 $\dfrac{R}{r+R}$
17 b) ii) 5 V, 2.5 Ω
18 a) 0.8 V, 1.6 V, 3.2 V, 6.4 V
   b) 0.8 V, 1.6 V, 2.4 V, 3.2 V, 4.8 V, 5.6 V, 6.4 V, 9.6 V, 11.2 V, 12.0 V
19 0–3 V
21 a) i) 9 W   ii) 3 V   b) ii) 3 Ω   iii) 6 Ω
22 4.1 Ω
24 0.63 A
25 2 Ω
27 121.5 Ω
29 b) ii) 4.1 Ω
30 b) 20 Ω, 2 Ω   c) 55 mA, 0.99 V
31 a) 102 Ω   b) $\frac{3}{20}$
32 c) 900 ± 37 Ω
33 a) i) 25 037 Ω   b) i) 16 667 Ω
34 a) i) 0.5 A   ii) 5.0 V   b) iii) (A): 4.0 A, (B): 0.25 Ω, (C): 1.0 V
35 a) 50 Ω
38 a) 108 Ω
39 48 V
40 a) 10 kΩ
41 200 Ω
42 1 A

Chapter 5   *page 93*
2 17 V
3 24 W
4 45 V

Chapter 6   *page 102*
3 60 μC
4 5×10^{-10} F
6 5×10^{-4} F
11 a) 0.1 A   b) 10 V   c) 1×10^{-3} C
12 3×10^{-2} C, 0.225 J
13 5000 μF
14 c) 0–1 μA
16 a) i) 6×10^{-3} C
18 i) 32 μF   ii) 1.44 J
19 a) 7.5 mA   b) 4.23 mC
20 a) ii) (A): 1.1×10^{-9} C   (B): 2.75×10^{-9} J
23 i) 9 mC   ii) 0.054 J

Chapter 7   *page 120*
2 $R_f/R_1 \geq 5$, 15 V approx.
3 c) zero volts
4 c) 3 V
6 input 60 kΩ, feedback 60×10^6 Ω
8 a) ii) 10.0 V
9 b) ii) –1.8 V   c) i) –5.0 V   ii) maximum zero, minimum –7 V
10 a) ii) 2.55 V   b) ii) +4.1 V   c) 0.2 V, 1 kHz
   d) i) 0°C   ii) $R_f = R_3 = 164$ kΩ

Chapter 8   *page 138*
6 a) 7×10^{-7} m   b) 2.5×10^{-5} m   c) 7×10^{-7} m   d) 4×10^{-7} m
7 a) 0.66 μ   b) 660 nm   c) 6.6×10^3 Å
10 b) 0.5°
11 a) 1.47
12 a) 1.51   c) 1.99×10^8 m s^{-1}

Chapter 9 *page 167*

1 a) 100   b) 400

5 a) 5.0×10^{14} Hz   b) i) no   ii) yes

8 a) 6   b) 1×10^{-7} m; 5×10^{-7} m

11 ii) 2.9×10^{-19} J

19 a) 5 s   b) 9.8×10^{19}

Chapter 10 *page 197*

5 9×10^{10} J

8 0.84 MeV (or 1.3×10^{-13} J)

9 20.8 MeV (or 3.3×10^{-12} J)

10 3.4 MeV (or 5.4×10^{-13} J)

11 29.3 MeV (or 4.7×10^{-12} J)

12 4.5×10^{16} J

14 3.6×10^{16}

15 91.4 MeV (or 1.46×10^{-11} J)

16 95 MeV (or 1.52×10^{-11} J), 7.9 MeV (or 1.27×10^{-12} J)

20 208.6 MeV (or 3.3×10^{-11} J)

21 17.4 MeV (or 2.8×10^{-12} J)

24 2.7 MeV (or 4.3×10^{-13} J)

25 4.3 MeV (or 6.9×10^{-13} J)

26 108×10^{-3} Sv h^{-1}, 200×10^{-6} Sv h^{-1}; 541×10^{-3} Sv

27 20.9 mSv

28 11.4×10^{-6} Sv h^{-1}

29 2.83 m

30 3 mSv

31 18 μSv h^{-1}

32 7.8 mSv h^{-1}

33 108 mm

34 $^{228}_{89}$Ac

35 $^{214}_{82}$Pb

36 $^{15}_{7}$N

37 $^{14}_{7}$C $\rightarrow$ $^{14}_{7}$N + $^{0}_{-1}$e

38 $^{234}_{92}$U

39 X is radium-228, Y is actinium-228

41 c) i) iodine-131   ii) 17 days

42 a) i) 1.2 mm   ii) 1000 counts per minute

43 b) 2.79×10^{-12} J

44 b) (A): 0.007×10^{-27} kg   (B): 6.3×10^{-13} J

45 b) i) 9×10^{-13} J   ii) (A): 1.86×10^{-13} J

Chapter 11 *page 197*

1 22.5°C ± 0.5°C

2 temperature ± 10%

4 5.28 kg min^{-1} ± 7×10^{-3} kg min^{-1}

5 5.3 A ± 0.1 A

6 7.1 Ω ± 3%

7 ± 0.3 V, ± 2 Ω

8 percentage error ± 3%

9 1250 kg m^{-3} ± 2%

11 a) i) 583 nm   ii) ± 115 nm

12 $p = 4.8 ± 0.1$ atm, $L = 6.2 ± 0.05$ cm; upper limit: 30.6, lower limit: 28.9

Index

Acknowledgements

The publisher and authors are grateful to the following for permission to reproduce previously published material:

AEA Technology, p.157 (bottom); Amstrad/Michael Joyce p.105 (middle); Associated Press p.105 (top); Bodford-Cousins/The National Meteorological Office, p.70, p.160; Paul Brierley, p.123, p.124, p.125; Camera Press p.17, p.66 (middle); J Allan Cash, p.4, p.66 (bottom); Casio p.166 (left); Coherent, p.156 (middle); Griffin & George p.92; Imperial War Museum, p.53; The John Hopkins University, p.73 (bottom); Keymed, p.156 (bottom); The Los Alamos National Laboratory, p.189; NASA, p.158; D M Nicholas, p.133; Oxford Lasers, p.156 (top); Photographs and All That, p.73, p.94, p.96, p.97, p.130; Science Photo Library, p.157, p.166; Smiths Industries, p.54; UKAEA; p.193, p.196, p.202. Additional photography by Peter Gould and Robb & Campbell Harper Studios. Special thanks to Beevers Models, Department of Chemistry, Edinburgh University.

Every reasonable effort has been made to contact copyright owners, but we apologise for any unknown errors or omissions. The list will be corrected, if necessary, in the next reprint.